DYNAMICS

FOUNDATIONS OF ENGINEERING
Series Editor: G. E. Drabble

Dynamics

G. E. Drabble

MACMILLAN

First published 1990

Published by
MACMILLAN EDUCATION LTD
Houndmills, Basingstoke, Hampshire RG21 2XS
and London
Companies and representatives
through the world

Typeset by P & R Typesetters Ltd, Salisbury, Wiltshire, UK
Printed in Hong Kong

British Library Cataloguing in Publication Data
Drabble, George E. (George Edmund), *1924–*
    Dynamics.
    1. Dynamics
    I. Title   II. Series
    531'.11

ISBN 0–333–47379–5

Series Standing Order

If you would like to receive future titles in this series as they are
published, you can make use of our standing order facility. To place a
standing order please contact your bookseller or, in case of difficulty,
write to us at the address below with your name and address and the
name of the series. Please state with which title you wish to begin your
standing order. (If you live outside the United Kingdom we may not
have the rights for your area, in which case we will forward your order
to the publisher concerned.)

Customer Services Department, Macmillan Distribution Ltd
Houndmills, Basingstoke, Hampshire, RG21 2XS, England.

CONTENTS

CONTENTS

SERIES EDITOR'S FOREWORD

This series of programmed texts has been written specifically for first year students on degree courses in engineering. Each book covers one of the core subjects required by electrical, mechanical, civil or general engineering students, and the contents have been designed to match the first year requirements of most universities and polytechnics.

The layout of the texts is based on that of the well-known text, *Engineering Mathematics* by K. Stroud (first published by Macmillan in 1970, and now in its third edition). The remarkable success of this book owes much to the skill of its author, but it also shows that students greatly appreciate a book which aims primarily to help them to learn their chosen subjects at their own pace. The authors of this present series acknowledge their debt to Mr Stroud, and hope that by adapting his style and methods to their own subjects they have produced equally helpful and popular texts.

Before publication of each text the comments of a class of first year students, of some recent engineering graduates and of some lecturers in the field have been obtained. These helped to identify any points which were particularly difficult or obscure to the average reader or which were technically inaccurate or misleading. Subsequent revisions have eliminated the difficulties which were highlighted at this stage, but it is likely that, despite these efforts, a few may have passed unnoticed. For this the authors and publishers apologise, and would welcome criticisms and suggestions from readers.

Readers should bear in mind that mastering any engineering subject requires considerable effort. The aim of these texts is to present the material as simply as possible and in a way which enables students to learn at their own pace, to gain confidence and to check their understanding. The responsibility for learning is, however, still very much their own.

G.E. Drabble

HOW TO USE THIS BOOK

This book is one of a series which has been designed to help you in learning the basic subjects of a first-year course in Engineering. You may have seen similar texts before, but if not, then you need to understand that they are all written in short sections, called frames. Each frame normally contains just one or two facts that you need to understand or to apply, before going further. So the texts are designed to be read one frame at a time, in order, without skipping. Frequently, a frame will finish with a question, or a short exercise, to test that you have understood the work up to that point. You should always attempt the appropriate response to such endings: answer the question asked; undertake the exercise; write down your version of the formula or theory asked for, and so on. When your response is incorrect, find out why as soon as you can, either by re-reading the previous work, or by getting help from someone else. If you cannot do this immediately, make a note, and do so as soon as you have the opportunity.

A note on accuracy. The margin of error of most engineering calculations is of the order of 1%, and some calculations may have a margin of error nearer to 5%. One reason for this is that the data available are often not known to greater accuracy, and it is impossible for the accuracy of a calculation to be higher than that of the data used. Normally, three-figure accuracy is sufficient for most engineering calculations. But the purpose of this text is to help you to learn engineering theory. If, in the text, a wheel reaction force on a car is given as 2127.5 N, this does not mean that the answer is accurate to that extent. But if you check the calculations yourself (as you should frequently do), you will know you are doing them correctly if you arrive at the same answer. Of course, you cannot always expect to reach exactly the same answer; the order in which the operations are performed, and even the make of calculator, may result in small variations.

Programme 1

REVISION

1

In this first programme, we deal with the simple treatment of **vectors**, the basic laws of **statics**, elementary **kinematics**, and elementary **kinetics**. You may have covered this work before, but look through the contents of it quickly, even if you do not work through all the examples and problems, so that if there are any points about which you are not sure, you have a chance to brush them up a little. Begin by writing down the definitions of vector, statics, kinematics and kinetics. Remember: always try to answer the questions asked before referring to the answers given, which are usually in the following frame.

2

A **vector**	quantity is one which possesses both magnitude and direction.
Statics	is the general study of force systems.
Kinematics	is the study of motion without regard to the forces which cause it.
Kinetics	is the study of forces, and their relation to motion.

You may have defined Statics as 'The study of bodies at rest' or something similar. You were not far wrong, but as you will see, we often have to use the techniques of Statics when dealing with moving bodies as well as stationary ones. More of this later. We shall now look at Vectors. Write down four physical quantities which must be expressed as vectors. If you can't think of four, write down as many as you can.

3

Displacement is a vector.
Velocity is a vector.
Acceleration is a vector.
Force is a vector.

You may have thought of several not on the list, particularly if you are keener on electrical theory than on mechanical. But these are the four that we shall be most concerned with in this book. We shall eventually need to add vectors together—forces, velocities, and accelerations. This will not be difficult, but we have to stick to the rules. What is the principle to be observed when we add vectors?

4

Vectors must be added **graphically**

The vectors must be drawn, end-to-end, correct as to length and direction, the arrows on them all running the same way. This, of course, is to take account of the *direction* of the vector as well as its magnitude. What would be the result of adding a displacement of 3 km north to a displacement of 4 km west?

5

5 km in direction 53.1 deg. west of north

The solution is shown below; both diagrams (a) and (b) are correct; the vectors may be taken in either order. The resultant vector is shown as a chain-line, to distinguish it from the component vectors, and the arrow on this vector opposes the direction of those on the components. Diagram (c) shows how *not* to add the two vectors; the arrows are not running the same way.

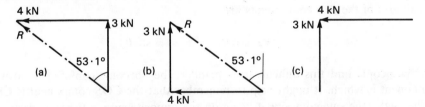

When the diagram is very simple, as here, we obtain the result by calculation. We need only to sketch the diagram, and not to draw it accurately. We used the words 'resultant' and 'component' above. When a number of vectors are added together, the answer is called the **resultant**: each of the vectors is called a **component** of the result.

6

We now turn to **Statics** and recall how to find the resultant of forces acting at a point. Here is a simple problem. Try to solve it before turning over.

> *Example.* A body is subjected to two forces, both of magnitude 10 N and the second at 45 deg. to the first. What is the magnitude and direction of the resultant force?

The answer to the first part (the magnitude) can be calculated. Just sketch the vector diagram, and do not try to draw it accurately.

3

7

> 18.48 N midway between the two forces

Here is the sketch. (a) shows the two forces, and (b) is the vector diagram.

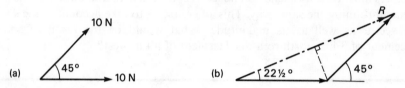

(a)   (b)

If we draw the perpendicular from the apex of the isosceles triangle, it is then easy to see that $R = 2 \times 10 \cos 22\frac{1}{2}° = 18.48$ N. (Or you can use the Cosine formula. We shall look at this in Frame 14.)

8

It is always more accurate to calculate than to draw and measure. This brings us to force **resolution**. This consists of replacing a single force by two components, acting in two directions mutually at right-angles. In the figure below, the single force F is expressed as the two components F_x and F_y in the x and y directions shown. The magnitudes of the two components are:

$$F_x = F \cos \theta; \qquad F_y = F \sin \theta$$

Some people find this difficult to remember; they become confused as to which component is which. It might help to remember that the **COS** component is **ClOSe** to the angle (the sine component being on the opposite side of the triangle).

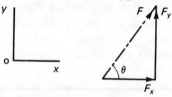

So, to find the resultant of a number of forces acting at a point, we choose an arbitrary set of x- and y-axes, calculate the x and y components of every force, add all the x components, add all the y components, and finally, calculate the resultant of the two final components. For practice, solve the problem of Frame 6 again, using this technique of resolution. The answer is, of course, the same as before: 18.48 N at $22\frac{1}{2}°$. You can choose any set of x- and y-axes you want, of course, but it is clearly simpler to choose directions which will make for the easiest calculation. This means that you choose either horizontal and vertical axes or axes at $45°$ to the horizontal and vertical. In the solution following, we have chosen horizontal and vertical axes.

9

Here is the diagram: (a) shows the two forces; (b) shows x- and y-axes, arbitrarily horizontal and vertical; (c) shows the x and y components; and (d) the vector diagram.

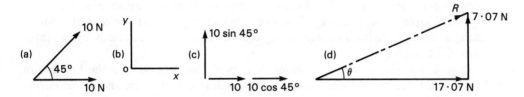

The resultant x and y components, F_x and F_y are given by:

$$F_x = 10 + 10\cos 45° = 17.07 \text{ N}; \qquad F_y = 10\sin 45° = 7.07 \text{ N}$$

The resultant, R, of these components is calculated from the triangle in (d):

$$R = \sqrt{\{(17.07)^2 + (7.07)^2\}} = \mathbf{18.48 \text{ N}}$$

and angle θ from:

$$\theta = \tan^{-1}(7.07/17.07) = \mathbf{22.50°}$$

10

Here are three statements concerning the **Polygon of Forces.**

1. If a number of co-planar forces acting at a point are in equilibrium, they may be represented, in magnitude and direction, by the sides of a closed polygon.
2. If a number of co-planar forces acting at a point are not in equilibrium, the single extra force required to produce equilibrium (the **equilibrant**) may be found from the single vector needed to close the polygon.
3. If a number of co-planar forces acting at a point are not in equilibrium, the **resultant** force is the force which is equal in magnitude to the equilibrant but opposite in direction.

The example solved in Frame 7 makes use of the third statement. Any system of co-planar forces acting at a point may be solved by means of a force polygon. But drawing is time-consuming, and can be inaccurate, and it is usually preferable to use the technique of force resolution. There are some occasions, however, where a force polygon solution is preferable. You will find one in the problems which follow in Frame 16.

11

The principle of the **Parallelogram of Forces** establishes that the resultant of two forces acting at a point may be represented vectorially by the diagonal of the parallelogram of which the two forces are represented by two adjacent sides.

The principle of the **Triangle of Forces** established that when three co-planar forces acting at a point are in equilibrium, they can be represented vectorially by the three sides of a triangle.

But you don't need to bother about these two principles, because the Polygon of Forces is a more general statement which includes both of them, and which covers any number of co-planar forces acting at point, whether in equilibrium or not. Force resolution is a method of mathematically analysing the geometry of a force polygon. Sometimes, although rarely, it may be desirable to draw the polygon accurately. and solve by actual measurement.

12

Solution of Statics problems, and indeed, of all problems in engineering theory, requires a certain fluency in mathematics. You have probably discovered yourself that if you fail to get the 'book' answer to a problem, the reason is often a mathematical slip. The only final answer to this is, practice, and more practice, but the following suggestions may be of some help.

1. Keep work *neat*, even if working a problem in 'rough'. Experience shows a high correlation between untidy scribbling and mathematical slips. Perform your procedures steadily and carefully, and set down your work neatly and clearly.
2. If you fail to obtain the correct answer, begin the solution again, on a fresh sheet, not referring to your first attempt at all. If possible, look for an alternative way of solving. (If you come up again with the same answer, there is always the possibility that the 'book' answer may be wrong.).
3. Fractions are traps for the careless worker. Example: A car travels at 15.6 m s^{-1}. To travel 12 m takes $(15.6/12) = 1.3$ seconds! If you used this calculation to determine the time to travel 1 metre, the incorrect answer of 15.6 seconds would most probably be obvious, but in this case, it could easily be overlooked.

We mentioned the Cosine formula in Frame 7. This, with the Sine formula, is valuable in solving triangles, that is, determining the lengths of all sides and values of all angles. Frames 13 and 14 are devoted to a statement of the trigonometric formulae you are most likely to encounter in this book.

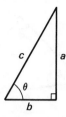

$$\sin \theta = a/c; \cos \theta = b/c; \tan \theta = a/b$$

This may seem rather basic, but many students get them wrong. It may help to think that **COS** θ is calculated by taking side b of the triangle **ClOS**e to the angle, while $\sin \theta$ uses the side which i**S IN** front of θ.

It is easily seen from the triangle that:

$$\sin \theta = \cos(90° - \theta); \cos \theta = \sin(90° - \theta); \tan \theta = \sin \theta / \cos \theta$$

Some special values (found by analysing 30–60–90 and 45–45–90 triangles):

$$\sin 30° = \cos 60° = \tfrac{1}{2}; \sin 60° = \cos 30° = \tfrac{1}{2}\sqrt{3} = 0.866$$
$$\tan 30° = \tfrac{1}{3}\sqrt{3} = 0.5774; \tan 60° = \sqrt{3} = 1.732$$
$$\sin 45° = \cos 45° = \tfrac{1}{2}\sqrt{2} = 0.707; \tan 45° = 1$$

Other special values:

$$\sin 0° = 0; \quad \cos 0° = 1; \ \tan 0° = 0$$
$$\sin 90° = 1; \ \cos 90° = 0; \tan 90° = \infty \text{ (infinity)}$$
$$\sin 180° = 0; \cos 180° = -1$$

$$\sin(180° - \theta) = \sin \theta; \cos(180° - \theta) = -\cos \theta$$

The angle-summation identities:

$$\sin(A + B) = \sin A \cos B + \cos A \sin B$$
$$\sin(A - B) = \sin A \cos B - \cos A \sin B$$

$$\cos(A + B) = \cos A \cos B - \sin A \sin B$$
$$\cos(A - B) = \cos A \cos B + \sin A \sin B$$

$$\tan(A + B) = \frac{\tan A + \tan B}{1 - \tan A \tan B}; \qquad \tan(A - B) = \frac{\tan A - \tan B}{1 + \tan A \tan B}$$

The sine and cosine formulae are given in the following frame, but try and write them down yourself first.

14

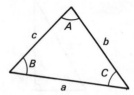

We use a special notation of the triangle for the sine and cosine formulae. The sine formula:

$$\frac{a}{\sin A} = \frac{b}{\sin B} = \frac{c}{\sin C}$$

The cosine formula:

$$a^2 = b^2 + c^2 - 2bc \cos A$$
$$b^2 = c^2 + a^2 - 2ca \cos B$$
$$c^2 = a^2 + b^2 - 2ab \cos C$$

15

Here is a summary of the work so far.

1. Force is a vector quantity, having magnitude and direction.
2. Most systems of co-planar forces acting at a point may be analysed by the method of resolution:

   (a) Choose a set of x- and y-axes at right-angles.
   (b) Calculate the x and y components of all forces.
   (c) Calculate the algebraic sum of the x and y components, F_x and F_y.
   (d) For a system in equilibrium, both these will be zero.
   (e) For a non-equilibrium system, the sums of (c) will be the components of the resultant, R, directed at an angle θ to the x-axis. Then:

   $$R = \sqrt{(F_x^2 + F_y^2)}; \qquad \theta = \tan^{-1}(F_y/F_x)$$

3. When resolution does not give a ready solution, the geometry of the polygon may provide an alternative analytical solution. The Sine and Cosine formulae may be found helpful.

PROBLEMS

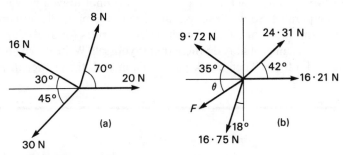

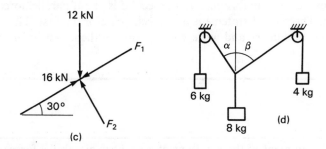

1. Diagram (a) shows forces of 20 N, 8 N, 16 N and 30 N acting at a single point in relative directions of 0°, 70°, 150° and 225°. Calculate the magnitude and direction of the resultant of the four forces. [*Ans. 13.59 N at 204.8°.*]

2. Five forces acting at the same point are shown in diagram (b) above. Given that the forces are in equilibrium, determine the magnitude of the force F, and the value of the angle θ. [*Ans. 21.95 N; 15.63°.*]
   Hint: write equilibrium equations along horizontal and vertical, giving $F \cos \theta$ and $F \sin \theta$. Divide one by the other to get $\tan \theta$ and hence θ. Substitute in either equation to find F.

3. Diagram (c) shows a joint of a roof member, with a vertical load of 12 kN acting on it. The force in the lower inclined member is 16 kN compressive. Evaluate the magnitudes of the two forces F_1 and F_2. [*Ans. 10.0 kN, 10.39 kN.*]
   Hints: the forces at the joint are in equilibrium. Do *not* resolve along horizontal and vertical directions, but along, and perpendicular to the slope. One equation will give F_1, and the second, F_2.

4. Three hanging weights are connected by strings so that two strings pass over pulleys, while the third hangs free as shown in diagram (d) above. The masses of the weights are shown. Assuming the pulleys frictionless, determine the inclinations, α and β, of the strings to the vertical. [*Ans. 28.96°, 46.57°.*]
   Hint: sketch the polygon of the three forces acting at the string junction, and use the cosine rule to determine the angles. (See Frame 14.)

17

If you have a system of forces, all of which are parallel, you cannot use the methods we have set down for forces acting at a point; you cannot draw a polygon with lines all of which are parallel. So we have to make use of the principle of **moments**. First, we define the term 'moment'. Then we set down the rules for analysing a system of parallel forces. You can probably do these things yourself. Write down your definition of the moment of a force. Then check your version with the answer in Frame 18.

18

> The moment of a force about a point is the product of the force, and the perpendicular distance from the point to the line of action of the force.

The moment of a force is an indication of its **turning effect**; a given force acting at a greater distance will produce a greater turning effect. Pushing a door open at the edge is easier than pushing it at a point close to the hinges. The principle of moments allows us to make two statements about parallel forces. The first is about parallel forces which are not in equilibrium, and the second is about parallel forces which are in equilibrium. The second statement is a special case of the first. These statements follow in Frame 19, but try and write your version of them first before reading on.

19

> The moment of the resultant of a number of parallel forces with respect to a point is the same as the algebraic sum of the moments of the individual forces.
>
> When a number of parallel forces are in equilibrium, the total moment of the forces about any point will be zero.

The word 'algebraic' is a reminder that moments, like forces, must be accorded a sign when writing a moment equation. Some forces will tend to turn one way, and others the other way. One may choose the point about which moments are taken. It is often convenient, with a system of parallel forces, to let the point lie on the line of action of one of the unknown forces.

20

Here is a revision example. When solving it, read the final sentence of the previous frame.

Example. A light horizontal beam rests on a rigid support at B and is also supported by a vertical wire at E. Various vertical loads are carried at A, C, D and F, as indicated in the figure. Calculate the support reaction force at B and the wire tension force at E.

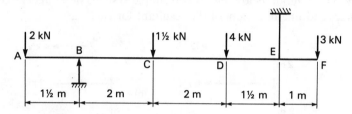

This is a simple problem, so you should be able to solve it without further help. If you have trouble, the solution follows.

21

The force system is of course in equilibrium. We write a moment equilibrium equation, taking point E as our reference point. The reaction force at B is designated by *R*. The equation is:

$$(2 \times 7) - (R \times 5\tfrac{1}{2}) + (1\tfrac{1}{2} \times 3\tfrac{1}{2}) + (4 \times 1\tfrac{1}{2}) - (3 \times 1) = 0$$

In the equation, an anti-clockwise moment about E has been taken as positive. The equation can be arranged and simplified:

$$R \times 5\tfrac{1}{2} = 14 + 5\tfrac{1}{4} + 6 - 3 = 22\tfrac{1}{4}$$
$$\therefore \qquad R = \textbf{4.045 kN}$$

A similar moment equilibrium equation is now written with B as the reference point. Call the wire tension force *T*; it clearly acts upwards.

$$(2 \times 1\tfrac{1}{2}) - (1\tfrac{1}{2} \times 2) - (4 \times 4) + (T \times 5\tfrac{1}{2}) - (3 \times 6\tfrac{1}{2}) = 0$$

which simplifies to

$$T \times 5\tfrac{1}{2} = 19\tfrac{1}{2} + 16 + 3 - 3 = 35\tfrac{1}{2}$$
$$\therefore \qquad T = \textbf{6.455 kN}$$

The sum of *R* and *T* is seen to be $10\tfrac{1}{2}$ kN which is the sum of the external loads.

22

When parallel forces are not in equilibrium, two things are needed to define the resultant force: the **magnitude**, and the **line of action**. The magnitude of the resultant is determined by algebraically adding the forces in one direction—the term 'algebraically' reminding us that some forces may be directed one way and some another, and a sign convention will be needed. The line of action is determined by applying the first of the two statements of Frame 19.

Example. The diagram below shows two simple systems of parallel forces. Find the magnitude, and line of action, of the resultant for each case.

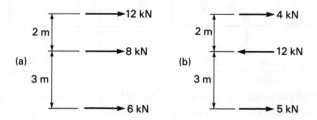

When a force system is in equilibrium, and one or more of the forces is unknown, we usually choose a point on the line of action of one of the unknown forces about which to take moments, as in Frame 21. But in these examples, there is no guide pointing to a suitable fulcrum, so any point may be chosen. In order that you can check your working, choose in each case a point 2 m below the lowest force; this will agree with the solutions which follow in Frame 23.

Your answers should be, for (a), 26 kN on a line 0.23 m above the 8 kN force; and for (b), 3 kN to left, on a line 0.333 m above the 4 kN force.

23

Example (a) $R = 12 + 8 + 6 = $ **26 kN to the right**

Height above datum, h is given by:

$$R \times h = (6 \times 2) + (8 \times 5) + (12 \times 7) = 136$$
$$\therefore \quad h = 136/26 = \textbf{5.23 m}$$

Example (b) $R = 12 - 4 - 5 = $ **3 kN to the left** (taking left as $+$ve)

Height h above datum (taking anti-clockwise moments as $+$ve):

$$R \times h = (12 \times 5) - (5 \times 2) - (4 \times 7) = 22$$
$$\therefore \quad h = 22/3 = \textbf{7.333 m}$$

24

In solving the example of the previous frame, there is, of course, no obligation to choose the reference point stated for moments; the working would indeed be slightly simpler by choosing, say, a line through the lowest force, and you can solve the problems alternatively this way if you prefer. There will be a few more problems to practise on in Frame 29.

The example also shows that you don't have to adopt a rigid and arbitrary sign convention for directions of forces or moments. In part (a), we chose 'left-to-right is positive' simply because all the forces are in that direction; in part (b) we chose the opposite convention, i.e. 'right-to-left is positive', because a very quick check shows that the resultant will be in that direction. In regard to moments, since we take moments about a point below all forces, the convention 'clockwise is positive' is obvious for part (a), but in part (b), because the force of 12 kN has an anti-clockwise moment about the chosen point, we have arbitrarily chosen to use 'anti-clockwise is positive'. But part (b) can be solved just as simply using the first moment convention. Each of the four moment terms will simply change sign, resulting in the same answer.

25

When dealing with systems of parallel forces, sometimes a system reduces to two equal forces, acting in opposite directions, but not in the same line. Such a system is called a **couple**. The magnitude of the couple is the resultant moment of the force system about any point, and this will be found to be constant. Its 'sense' (i.e. clockwise or anti-clockwise) must also be stated. As an example, let us take part b of the example of Frame 22, just completed, but replace the 12 kN force by a force of 9 kN. The solution now will be:

$$R = 9 - 4 - 5 = 0$$

Taking moments of the three forces about the same point as before, 2 m below the lowest force, and again taking anti-clockwise moments as +ve:

$$\text{Moment} = (9 \times 5) - (4 \times 7) - (5 \times 2) = +7 \text{ kN m (i.e. anti-clockwise)}$$

and you can show for yourself that you will always get this answer, whichever point you choose to take moments about.

Problem 2 of Frame 29 offers another example of a couple.

26

A common case of parallel forces is that of the weights of a system of masses. If you imagine a number of small concentrated masses arranged along a horizontal bar, the weights of all masses will act vertically and will thus be all parallel. The resultant of these weights will pass through a point which is called the **centre of gravity** of the system.

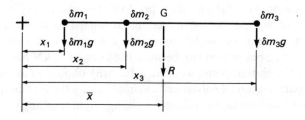

In the diagram above, we can say:

$$R = \delta m_1 g + \delta m_2 g + \delta m_3 g \qquad \text{etc.}$$
$$R \times \bar{x} = \delta m_1 g x_1 + \delta m_2 g x_2 + \delta m_3 g x_3 \qquad \text{etc.}$$

So, in general, the x co-ordinate of the centre of gravity of a system of masses is given by the expression:

$$\bar{x} = \frac{\Sigma(\delta m g x)}{\Sigma(\delta m g)} = \frac{\Sigma(\delta m x)}{\Sigma(\delta m)}$$

where δm is a 'mass element' (δm_1, δm_2, etc.). In the above expression, g is seen to cancel out; the location of the point G is thus seen to be independent of actual weight. The term **centre of mass** or **mass centre**, is therefore preferable to 'centre of gravity'. For two-dimensional bodies, such as flat non-symmetrical sheets, two co-ordinates $\bar{x}$ and $\bar{y}$, are necessary to locate G, and for three-dimensional bodies, three co-ordinates, $\bar{x}$, $\bar{y}$ and $\bar{z}$.

When the mass of a body is distributed non-uniformly and *continuously*, the Σ (sigma) terms are replaced by integral signs, the δm is replaced by the differential dm, and we have to determine $\bar{x}$ by integration, instead of a simple arithmetical calculation. An example is given in Frame 28.

We shall work through two examples before the next set of problems. The first is an application of the formula of Frame 26, comprising simple arithmetical work, while the second shows the use of the calculus. Here is the first example.

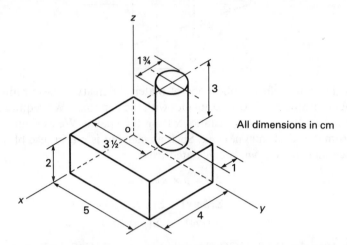

Example. The figure shows a composite solid body comprising a cuboid 4 cm by 5 cm by 2 cm with a cylindrical projecting column $1\frac{3}{4}$ cm diameter. Calculate the co-ordinates of the mass centre G with respect to the $x-y-z$ co-ordinate framework shown.

We use the formula of Frame 26. There are two mass 'elements' with mass centres at their respective geometric centres. We call the material density, ρ.

$$\bar{x} = \frac{\rho(4 \times 5 \times 2) \times 2 + \rho((\pi/4)(1\frac{3}{4})^2 \times 3) \times 1}{\rho(4 \times 5 \times 2) + \rho((\pi/4)(1\frac{3}{4}^2 \times 3)} = \frac{80 + 7.216}{40 + 7.216} = \textbf{1.847 cm}$$

$$\bar{y} = \frac{\rho(4 \times 5 \times 2) \times 2\frac{1}{2} + \rho((\pi/4)(1\frac{3}{4})^2 \times 3) \times 3\frac{1}{2}}{\rho(4 \times 5 \times 2) + \rho((\pi/4)(1\frac{3}{4})^2 \times 3)} = \frac{100 + 25.255}{40 + 7.216} = \textbf{2.653 cm}$$

$$\bar{z} = \frac{\rho(4 \times 5 \times 2) \times 1 + \rho((\pi/4)(1\frac{3}{4})^2 \times 3) \times 3\frac{1}{2}}{\rho(4 \times 5 \times 2) + \rho((\pi/4)(1\frac{3}{4})^2 \times 3)} = \frac{40 + 25.255}{40 + 7.216} = \textbf{1.382 cm}$$

You see that ρ cancels out. This simple arithmetical method can be used for any body which can be divided into regular symmetrical 'elements'. In the case of such a body with a hole in it, you treat the hole as a negative mass. Observe that the bottom line in every instance is the same as the top line with the co-ordinates of the mass centres of the elements excluded.

In Frame 28 we shall determine the location of the mass centre of a regular cone by the use of calculus.

28

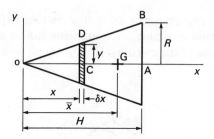

The figure shows a uniform solid cone of material density ρ, base radius R, length of axis H. A co-ordinate axis o–x coincides with the cone axis. We require the location of G, the mass centre, shown a distance $\bar{x}$ from the apex o. We examine an 'element' distant x from o and of thickness δx. Such an element is a thin disc of radius y. The mass of such an element, δm, is calculated from:

$$\delta m = \rho \times \pi y^2 \times \delta x$$

Then
$$\bar{x} = \frac{\Sigma(\delta m x)}{\Sigma(\delta m)} = \frac{\Sigma(\rho \pi y^2 \delta x)x}{\Sigma(\rho \pi y^2 \delta x)}$$

The similar triangles OAB, OCD show that $y = x \times R/H$. Substituting:

$$\bar{x} = \frac{\Sigma(\rho \pi x^2 (R/H)^2 \delta x)x}{\Sigma(\rho \pi x^2 (R/H)^2 \delta x)}$$

which reduces on cancelling to:

$$\bar{x} = \frac{\Sigma(x^3 \delta x)}{\Sigma(x^2 \delta x)}$$

Expressed as an integral, with limits of x from 0 to H:

$$\bar{x} = \frac{\displaystyle\int_0^H (x^3\,dx)}{\displaystyle\int_0^H (x^2\,dx)} = \frac{[\frac{1}{4}x^4]_0^H}{[\frac{1}{3}x^3]_0^H} = \frac{\frac{1}{4}H^4}{\frac{1}{3}H^3} = \tfrac{3}{4}H$$

We can use this result to locate the mass centre of a truncated cone—a tapered shaft, for example—without having to have recourse to integration again. We just treat the truncated cone as a combination of two whole cones, one of them being 'negative'. (See Problem 4 in Frame 29.)

A summary of work on parallel forces before the next set of problems:

1. The magnitude of the resultant of a number of parallel forces is the algebraic sum of the forces.
2. The moment of the resultant of a number of parallel forces about a point is the algebraic sum of the moments of the individual forces about the same point.

PROBLEMS

1.

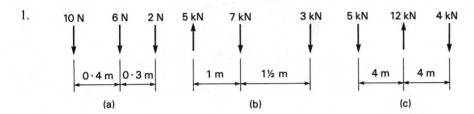

(a)   (b)   (c)

Calculate the magnitude of the resultants of the three force systems shown. Find also the location of the lines of action. [*Ans. (a) 18 N ; 0.211 m from left. (b) 5 kN ; 2.9 m from left. (c) 3 kN ; 5.333 m from left.*]

2.

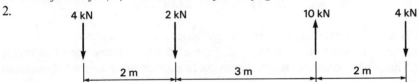

Evaluate the resultant of the system of parallel forces shown. [*Ans. A couple, 18 kN m anti-clockwise.*]

3.

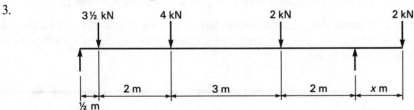

A loaded horizontal beam rests on two supports and carries four loads, as shown. Determine the value of distance x, i.e. the overhang of the right-hand load of 2 kN so that the two support reaction forces should be equal. [*Ans. 2.6875 m.*] *Hint*: each reaction force will be half the total downward load. Take moments about left-hand end.

4. A solid steel shaft is 1.8 m long and tapers uniformly from 10 cm diameter at one end to 5 cm diameter at the other end. Locate the mass centre. [*Ans. 70.71 cm. from end.*] *Hint*: see Frame 28. Treat as two complete cones, one negative.

30

We must define the term **centroid.**

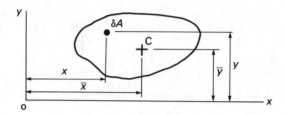

The figure above shows any closed area, set in a co-ordinate frame of reference o−x−y. The point C is defined as the **centroid** of the area. It is located by the co-ordinates $\bar{x}$ and $\bar{y}$, which in turn are *defined* by the expressions:

$$\bar{x} = \frac{\Sigma(\delta Ax)}{\Sigma(\delta A)}; \qquad \bar{y} = \frac{\Sigma(\delta Ay)}{\Sigma(\delta A)}$$

where δA is any element of area having co-ordinates x and y as shown.

These expressions are similar to those of Frame 26 which define the mass centre of a body. This is why 'centroid' is sometimes confused with 'mass centre'. Remember the following:

1. Mass centre is an indication of the distribution of *mass* of a *solid body*. Centroid is an indication of the distribution of *area* of a *shape*, or *enclosed figure*.
2. $\Sigma(\delta mx)$ is the product of a mass and a length: dimensions are thus ML.
   $\Sigma(\delta ax)$ is the product of an area and a length: dimensions are thus L^3.

For symmetrical figures, the centroid always lies on an axis of symmetry. You should be able to recall how to locate the centroid of a triangle. Try to do so, and then read the answer in the next frame.

31

> The centroid of a triangle lies on the intersection of the **medians**; i.e. the lines joining an apex to the mid-point of the opposite side.

The centroid of a figure consisting of a composite of regular figures, such as rectangles, circles, triangles, etc. is located by taking 'moments' of each sub-area about appropriate axes; thus, the formulae above may be modified to:

$$A\bar{x} = A_1\bar{x}_1 + A_2\bar{x}_2 + A_3\bar{x}_3 + \text{etc.}; \qquad A\bar{y} = A_1\bar{y}_1 + A_2\bar{y}_2 + A_3\bar{y}_3 + \text{etc.}$$

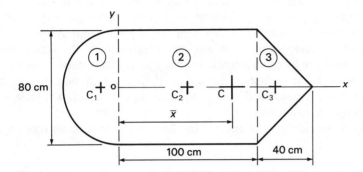

Example. Determine $\bar{x}$, the location of the centroid C of the composite figure shown.

Use the formula at the end of Frame 31. The figure is already divided into three 'sub-areas', and the co-ordinate axes shown. Take care with the following.

1. Remember that the medians of a triangle intersect at one-third their length.
2. The centroid of a semi-circle is $4R/3\pi$ from the centre, where R is the radius.
3. Because the semi-circle is on the opposite side of the y-axis, $\Sigma(\delta Ax)$ will be negative.

You should get 44.47 cm for your answer. The solution follows.

33

Adapting the formula of Frame 31:

$$\bar{x} = \frac{A_1\bar{x}_1 + A_2\bar{x}_2 + A_3\bar{x}_3}{A_1 + A_2 + A_3}$$

$$= \frac{(\frac{1}{2}\pi(40)^2)(-4 \times 40/3\pi) + (80 \times 100)50 + (\frac{1}{2} \times 80 \times 40)(100 + 40/3)}{\frac{1}{2}\pi(40)^2 + (80 \times 100) + (\frac{1}{2} \times 80 \times 40)}$$

$$= \frac{-42\,666.7 + 400\,000 + 18\,133.3}{2513.3 + 8000 + 1600}$$

$$= \frac{538\,666.6}{12\,113.3} = \textbf{44.47 cm}$$

Identify your mistakes, if any. Notice that although $\Sigma(\delta Ax)$ for the semi-circle was negative, the actual *area* $(\Sigma(\delta A))$ is positive. You can, if you prefer, re-calculate the problem, using another y-axis. For example, the y-axis could be a tangent to the top of the semi-circle. Then all the figure would be to the right of the axis, and all the $\Sigma(\delta Ax)$ terms would then be positive.

34

Friction is a phenomenon which crops up in Statics, and also in kinetics. It is a term which is frequently misused. A friction force occurs when one surface slides across another, or tends to slide. When this happens, slight roughnesses and irregularities on the surfaces in contact interfere, and cause resistance to the sliding motion.

Friction can be reduced by attention to the contacting surfaces; a smooth polished surface will offer less resistance to sliding than a rough one. Much engineering production work is concerned with producing surfaces which will slide across each other with minimum friction.

Think of a few examples of engineering devices where surfaces slide together.

35

> A piston in a cylinder.
> A shaft in a bearing.

These two are probably the commonest of many possible examples.

Now if two metal surfaces slide together, and there is a resisting force, work will be done, and this will produce heat. In the early days of industrial machinery, this was not such a serious problem as it is now, because speeds of machines were then much slower, and the heat generated by friction forces often could be dissipated. But as speeds increased, friction became much more serious; a shaft running in a bearing could get so hot that the bearing surface actually melted, and the bearing and shaft fused together, or 'seized up'.

What is done to try to prevent seizing up when surfaces slide together?

36

> The surfaces are **lubricated**

Oil is fed to the surfaces, which has the effect of reducing the friction force.

In fact, oil or grease has the function of *separating* the surfaces. When a shaft runs in a bearing, the surfaces are, for the most part, separated by a very thin film of oil. Oil has another function. What is this?

37

It dissipates heat

Although oil reduces friction force, and thus reduces heat, some heat is produced, and in a modern engine, oil is pumped through the system, so that heat is conducted away as it is produced. The oil is then cooled before being re-circulated.

38

When unlubricated surfaces slide together, the friction force may be determined approximately according to certain laws which are called the Laws of Dry Friction. These are:

1. The friction force opposes, or tends to oppose, the relative motion.
2. The friction force is proportional to the normal reaction force between the two surfaces. ('Normal' means, perpendicular to the surface.)
3. The friction force is independent of the surface area in contact.
4. Friction force is independent of speed of sliding.

You should understand that these laws are based on experiment only, and cannot be proved. They are what are called **empirical** laws. For this reason, calculation of friction forces is always approximate only. Let us look at some of the implications of the three laws.

The first law is clear. Whichever way you move, or try to move one surface across another, the friction force will act against you. It is a **reaction** force.

The second law may be considered invariable for our purposes, but in practice, two surfaces could be pressed together with such force that one of them could be damaged: a steel block on a wooden surface could cut through the surface, for example, and this law would then cease to be valid.

The third law also has a limitation. You may have performed an experiment with a wood block on a wood surface, showing that changing the surface area does not change the friction force. But if you were to place spiked feet on the block, these could cut the surface, and again, the law would not be valid.

Engineers have found by experience that certain materials in surface contact exhibit less friction force than others. For example, it was found that a steel shaft would run in a brass bearing with low friction. This friction would become even less when the bearing had been 'run in' for some time, so that the surface became polished by the continuous rubbing.

39

Experimental work based on the second Law of Dry Friction allows us to define the coefficient of friction. This is defined as the ratio of friction force to normal reaction force. For a friction force F, and a normal reaction force N:

$$F = \mu N$$

and μ (Greek mu) is called the **coefficient of friction**, or **friction coefficient** for the two surfaces in contact. Values of μ taken from textbooks and data books must be treated with caution, as it is not possible to define accurately either the materials or the states of the surfaces. A friction force can be determined accurately only by performing a test on the actual components.

This formula should be used with care. The force F is the resisting force offered by the surfaces *when they are actually sliding across each other*. But the friction force can be *less* than this value. If a body is at rest on a surface, and is subjected to a sideways force, and does not move, then the friction force will be exactly equal to the force, whatever value this has. Only when the force reaches the limiting value, determined by the formula above, will the body begin to move. So remember that the friction formula applies only when there is actual sliding between surfaces, or when sliding is just about to take place.

There is a further complication. It is found experimentally that if the sideways force is steadily increased until motion begins, the limiting force is greater than the resisting friction force when the body is actually sliding. Thus, you have to exert a greater pull to get the body moving than you need to keep it moving. Thus, **static friction** (sometimes abbreviated engagingly to 'sticktion') is greater than **dynamic**, or **sliding friction**. But whenever friction forces are referred to without qualification, it may be assumed that sliding friction is referred to.

40

Here is an example. You should be able to solve this yourself.

Example. A block of weight 150 N rests on a slope of 20° to the horizontal. The coefficient of friction between block and plane is 0.45. Calculate the least force, directed along the plane, to move the block (a) up the plane; (b) down the plane.

The two answers are 114.73 N and 12.13 N. The working follows in the next frame.

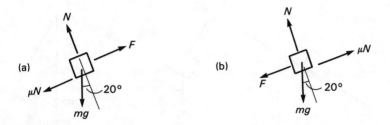

The diagrams show the four forces acting on the block in each of the two cases. These are called free-body diagrams; they show the body and the forces and nothing else. Note that the friction force acts down the plane for the first part, and up the plane for the second, that is, in each case, opposite to the direction of motion. Both cases are examples of equilibrium; although the block will just begin to move, there will be no acceleration.

Resultant force perpendicular to plane $= 0$ (both cases)

$$\therefore \qquad N - 150 \cos 20° = 0$$
$$\therefore \qquad N = 150 \cos 20°$$

Parallel to plane: Part (a):

$$F = \mu N + 150 \sin 20°$$
$$\therefore \quad F = 0.45 \times 150 \cos 20° + 150 \sin 20°$$
$$= 63.43 + 51.30$$
$$= \mathbf{114.73 \ N}$$

Parallel to plane: Part (b):

$$F + 150 \sin 20° = \mu N$$
$$\therefore \qquad F = 0.45 \times 150 \cos 20° - 150 \sin 20°$$
$$= 63.43 - 51.30$$
$$= \mathbf{12.13 \ N}$$

A second example.

>   *Example.* A body is at rest on an inclined plane the angle of which can be varied. If the plane is set at an angle θ such that the body just begins to slide down, determine θ in terms of the mass of the body, m, and the friction coefficient, μ.

You might already know the answer to this simple question. In this case, rather than writing equations, it may help just to sketch the triangle of forces.

42

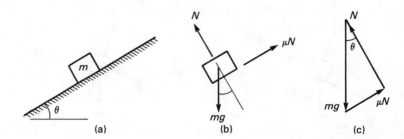

(a)   (b)   (c)

(a), (b) and (c) show the mass on the plane at angle θ, the free-body diagram showing three forces, and the triangle of forces, which is seen to be a right-angled triangle. From this last, it is immediately seen that:

$$\tan \theta = \mu N / N = \mu$$

Thus the required angle θ is given by:

$$\theta = \tan^{-1} \mu$$

This particular value of θ is called the **angle of friction**.

43

The term friction is used somewhat loosely. When dealing with the motion of bodies through the air, or through water, or other fluids, it is common to speak of the friction of the air, or of the water. While it is true that such fluids offer resistance to motion, the nature of the resisting force is quite different, and does not conform to the same laws. Air or fluid resistance is *not* independent of velocity. The resistance to the motion of a vehicle offered by the air increases to very high values at high speed. When dealing with such forces, they should be called resistance forces, and not friction forces.

Friction has tended to gain a reputation as an 'enemy', because it offers resistance to motion, and efforts have to be made to minimise its effects. There are cases, however, where friction is an asset, rather than a liability. In a car, there are three components where friction is necessary for correct and efficient functioning. Can you think what these components are?

44

The tyres: the brakes: the clutch

We shall discuss these components in the following frame.

45

The actual driving force on a powered wheeled vehicle is the friction force between wheels and track: the driven wheels thrust backwards on to the track, which reacts with an equal forward force. This is called the **tractive force**. No matter how powerful the engine, this force can never exceed the maximum friction force between wheels and road. Beyond this limit, the wheels just skid. Tyres have a high friction coefficient, so that the maximum tractive force is much greater than would be possible with wheels without tyres. Vehicles designed for arduous conditions, such as slippery roads, are equipped with four-wheel drive; this enables the tractive force to be considerably increased.

Brakes are used to stop motion. They consist essentially of friction pads which press on part of the wheels of the vehicle—the rims, in the case of an old-style bicycle, or the inside of a drum, or a disc, in the case of a car. If you have ever examined a brake disc, you may have been surprised to see how smooth it is. While it is true that a rough surface would produce a greater braking torque, such a surface would also cause the friction pad (the shoe) to wear out very quickly. Brake design is a compromise between good braking force and long brake life. Like tractive force, the *real* braking force on a vehicle is the friction force between wheels and road. No matter how efficient your brakes are, you can never retard a car with a force greater than this friction force. Thus, when driving along icy roads, application of the brakes may result in the car proceeding forwards at the same rate, with the four wheels locked.

The clutch is the connection between a car engine and the driving wheels. It is somewhat like a disc brake in reverse: the gearbox (or driven) shaft, which connects to the car driving wheels, carries a circular plate on which pads of friction material are fixed. This plate can be gripped between a pair of plates attached to the driving shaft, which connects to the engine. Depressing the clutch pedal releases these plates from the friction plate, thus isolating the engine from the drive.

It is significant that these three components are those which usually suffer the greatest wear, and are the most frequent in needing attention and replacement.

46

Now some revision work on **kinematics**. Write definitions of **velocity**, **speed** and **acceleration**, and also the calculus versions of velocity and acceleration.

47

> **Velocity** is the rate of change of displacement
> **Speed** is the magnitude of velocity
> **Acceleration** is the rate of change of velocity
> $$v = \frac{dx}{dt} \qquad a = \frac{dv}{dt} = \frac{d^2x}{dt^2}$$

We know that displacement, velocity and acceleration are all vector quantities. Speed is just the magnitude of velocity, and as such, is not a vector. In mathematical terms, speed is the **modulus** of velocity.

If we consider motion in a straight line, and with a constant acceleration, we can derive four equations which relate time, t, displacement, x, acceleration, a, initial velocity, v_0, and final velocity v. Write down as many of these four equations as you can remember. You have probably used u and s in place of v_0 and x in your earlier work.

48

> $$x = \tfrac{1}{2}(v_0 + v)t \qquad (1)$$
> $$v = v_0 + at \qquad (2)$$
> $$x = v_0 t + \tfrac{1}{2}at^2 \qquad (3)$$
> $$v^2 = v_0^2 + 2ax \qquad (4)$$

The first equation simply states, mathematically, that displacement is average velocity × time, while the second tells us that the increase of velocity is acceleration × time. The remaining two can be derived from these first two. You should notice that of the five variables listed in the previous frame, each equation leaves out one of these variables. Thus:

> Equation (1) does not include a
> Equation (2) does not include x
> Equation (3) does not include v
> Equation (4) does not include t

49

Note these points when using the four equations in Frame 48.

1. Before using any of the equations, ALWAYS make sure that you are dealing with CONSTANT acceleration.
2. Adopt a **sign convention**.
3. List the data given, and the data required, and find the equation which relates these.
4. Sketching a velocity–time graph is frequently helpful.
5. The area under such a graph = displacement.
6. For simple problems of bodies falling under gravity, the acceleration will always be g (9.81 m s^{-2}) and will always be directed downwards.

Here is an example to illustrate the application of the equations.

Example. A body has an initial velocity of 80 m s^{-1} and suffers a constant retardation of 4.5 m s^{-2}. Determine (a) the displacement in 10 s; (b) the time to travel 400 m; (c) the time to come to rest; (d) the distance covered in coming to rest.

This is of course four problems, not one. Point 1 on the list above is verified; the retardation is constant. Point 2: the acceleration is actually a retardation, i.e. a negative acceleration. So we shall assume that the initial velocity is positive. The acceleration is thus negative.

Part (a) Go through check-point 3 yourself; list the data given and required, and select the appropriate equation.

50

We are given: v_0 ($+80$ m s^{-1}); a (-4.5 m s^{-2}); t (10 s)
We require: x
So the required equation is (3).

Substitute the data in the equation, and solve for x.

51

$$x = v_0 t + \tfrac{1}{2} a t^2 = 80 \times 10 + \tfrac{1}{2}(-4.5)(10)^2 = \textbf{575 m}$$

Part (b): Check-point 3 again: the equation to use is ...

52

Equation (3) again

(We are given: v_0 ($+80$ m s^{-1}); a (-4.5 m s^{-2}); x (400 m) and we require: t.)

Substitute the data in the equation again. Notice that you finish with a quadratic, which means two answers. Calculate these, and at the same time, ask yourself why there are two answers to this equation. If you can't think of the reason straight away, it might help to refer to check-point 4 in Frame 49.

53

$$x = v_0 t + \tfrac{1}{2}at^2$$
$$400 = 80t + \tfrac{1}{2}(-4.5)t^2$$

Re-arrange, and divide throughout by the coefficient of t^2:

$$t^2 - 35.56t + 177.78 = 0$$

$$t = (1/2a)(-b \pm \sqrt{\{(b^2 - 4ac)\}} = \tfrac{1}{2}(35.56 \pm \sqrt{\{(35.56)^2 - 4 \times 177.78\}}$$

$$= 17.78 \pm \tfrac{1}{2}\sqrt{\{(1264.5 - 711.1)\}}$$

$$= 17.78 \pm \tfrac{1}{2} \times 23.52$$

$$= 17.78 \pm 11.76$$

$$= \mathbf{6.02 \text{ s}} \text{ and } \mathbf{29.54 \text{ s}}$$

Because the body has a constant retardation, it is slowing down all the time. This means that it will eventually come to rest, and *start moving backwards*. If you sketched the velocity–time graph, you can see that the velocity falls uniformly to zero and then goes negative. So that eventually, it must return to the displacement of 400 mm from the starting-point. This explains the two answers; it takes 29.54 seconds to shoot past the 400 m point, slow down and stop, and return to the same point.

Part (c) The equation you need this time is ...

54

Equation (2)

(v_0, a and v are given ($v = 0$); t is required.) Solve for t.

55

$$
\begin{aligned}
& v = v_0 + at \\
\therefore\quad & 0 = 80 + (-4.5)t \\
\therefore\quad & t = 80/4.5 = \mathbf{17.78\ s}
\end{aligned}
$$

This answer is incidentally seen to be the first part of the solution of the quadratic in Frame 53.

Part (d) Which equation this time?

56

Equation (4)

(Given: v_0, a, v. Required: x.)

Now you could argue that equation (1) or equation (3) could be used for this part, because we have now calculated t in part (c). This is true, but both of the equations require the value of $t = 17.78$ s calculated in part (c), and if a mistake had been made in the calculation, then the answer to part (d) would also be wrong. It is good practice, therefore, to calculate your answers from the data given when possible, rather than from answers you have calculated. So complete the exercise by using equation (4).

57

$$
\begin{aligned}
& v^2 = v_0^2 + 2ax \\
& 0 = (80)^2 + 2(-4.5)x \\
\therefore\quad & x = 6400/9 = \mathbf{711.1\ m}
\end{aligned}
$$

Things are not quite so easy when the motion consists of more than one part.

Example. A vehicle is capable of a maximum acceleration of 5.2 m s^{-2} and a maximum retardation of 7.2 m s^{-2}. Calculate the maximum distance it can travel in 10 seconds, starting from rest, and finishing at rest, assuming there is no upper limit to its speed.

Begin with a velocity–time graph. (Point 5 in the list in Frame 49.) The vehicle accelerates at 5.2 m s^{-2} up to a maximum velocity which we don't know: call it v_{max}. It will take an unknown time to reach this speed; call this time t_1. It will then take another unknown time to come to rest: call this t_2.

58

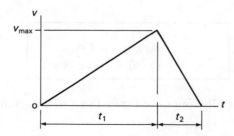

Now we need some equations relating the three unknown quantities v_{max}, t_1 and t_2. Two of these come from equation (2) of Frame 48. And a third comes from the fact that we know the *total* time taken. Write the three equations, and check in the next frame.

59

$$v = v_0 + at \qquad \therefore \qquad v_{max} = 0 + 5.2t_1 \qquad (1)$$
$$\text{and} \qquad 0 = v_{max} + (-7.2)t_2 \qquad (2)$$
$$t_1 + t_2 = 10 \qquad (3)$$

We can use the first two equations to obtain t_1 and t_2 in terms of v_{max}, and substitute these into the third equation.

From (1): $t_1 = v_{max}/5.2$;   From (2): $t_2 = v_{max}/7.2$

Substituting in (3): $v_{max}/5.2 + v_{max}/7.2 = 10$
$$v_{max}(0.1923 + 0.1389) = 10$$
$$\therefore \qquad v_{max} = \frac{10}{0.3312} = 30.19 \text{ m s}^{-1}$$

which gives: $t_1 = 30.19/5.2 = 5.806$ s; $t_2 = 30.19/7.2 = 4.193$ s

and from these times, the two distances are calculated. We use equation (1) of Frame 48. It can be seen that in doing so, we are also calculating the triangular areas under the graph.

$$x = \tfrac{1}{2}(v_0 + v)t \qquad \therefore \qquad x_1 = \tfrac{1}{2}(0 + 30.19)5.806 = 87.64 \text{ m}$$
$$\text{and } x_2 = \tfrac{1}{2}(30.19 + 0)4.193 = 63.29 \text{ m}$$

The total distance travelled is the sum of these: $\therefore$ $x = \textbf{150.93 m}$.

The following frame contains some problems on this topic. Do not be discouraged if you don't find them all simple; the example above shows that frequently, a lot of thought is necessary. Never look for 'standard' solutions to problems of this type, and almost always, sketch the velocity–time graph.

Here is a summary of the work from Frame 46.

1. For straight-line motion *with constant acceleration*, the equations are:

$$x = \tfrac{1}{2}(v_0 + v)t: \; v = v_0 + at: \; x = v_0 t + \tfrac{1}{2}at^2: \; v^2 = v_0^2 + 2ax$$

2. A sign convention should be used.
3. Displacement = area under the velocity–time graph.

PROBLEMS

1. A body is projected vertically upwards with an initial velocity of 60 m s^{-1}. Determine (a) the time to reach a height of 100 m; (b) the velocity at this height; (c) the height after 5 s; (d) the maximum height; (e) the time to reach maximum height. Neglect air resistance and assume g to be 9.81 m s^{-2}. [*Ans. 1.991 s and 10.241 s. ± 40.47 m s^{-1}. 177.4 m. 183.5 m. 6.116 s.*]
   Hint: similar to exercise of Frame 49 *et seq.*
2. A missile is projected in a straight line from a point with an initial velocity of 40 m s^{-1} and a retardation of 5 m s^{-2}. Exactly 1 second later, a second missile is projected along the same path with initial velocity of 50 m s^{-1} and the same retardation. Calculate the distance travelled when the second one catches up with the first, and the time taken for this to happen. [*Ans. 109.38 m; 3.5 s.*]
   Hints: call distance x, and times t and $(t-1)$. Use equation (3) (Frame 48) twice, eliminate x and solve for t.
3. Two vehicles, A and B, are 5000 m apart on a straight track. They start from rest at the same instant and travel towards each other, A with constant acceleration 1.2 m s^{-2} and B with constant acceleration 1.6 m s^{-2}. At what point do they meet, and after what time? [*Ans. 2143 m (2857 m); 59.76 s.*]
   Hints: use equation (3) (Frame 48) for two displacements x_1, x_2. Sum of these is 5000 m. This gives an equation in t.
4. A vehicle travels with constant retardation along a straight level track. It passes three points, A, B and C. AB = BC = 100 m. The time to travel from A to B is 4 s and from B to C, $5\tfrac{1}{2}$s. Calculate the retardation, and the speeds at A, B and C. [*Ans. 1.44 m s^{-2}; 27.88 m s^{-1}, 22.12 m s^{-1}, 14.24 m s^{-1}.*]
   Hints: sketch the v–t graph. Obtain two equations in v_A, v_B and v_C by equating areas to distances travelled. (See Frame 49, point 5.) Use Equation (2) (Frame 48) twice; eliminate a, thus getting another equation in v_A, v_B, v_C. Use the first two equations to substitute for v_A and v_C; hence find v_B.

61

Do not be disheartened if you found some of the problems rather difficult. And do not fall into the error of assuming, because of the hints given, that there is only one way of solving these problems. There may be several ways, and any method which leads to the correct answer is the 'right' method. Of course, the shortest way is the best, and only practice will enable you to learn how to find this. One way of getting practice is to try other ways of solving these problems.

Now to deal with **angular motion**. What is the unit of angular displacement? And how is it defined?

62

> The unit of angular displacement is the **radian**
>
> 1 radian is the angular displacement subtending an arc equal to the radius
>
> Or: 1 radian $= \dfrac{1 \text{ revolution}}{2\pi} \simeq 57.3$ degrees

It follows that angular velocity is measured in radians per second, and angular acceleration is measured in radians per second per second.

We normally use the Greek letters θ (theta), ω (omega) and α (alpha) for angular displacement, velocity and acceleration. Thus:

$\theta =$ angular displacement in radians   (rad)
$\omega =$ angular velocity in radians per second   (rad s^{-1})
$\alpha =$ angular acceleration in radians per second per second (rad s^{-2})

When bodies move in a circular path, there is a relation between the linear distance travelled along the path, and the corresponding angular displacement. There is a similar relation between linear and angular velocity, and linear and angular acceleration. State these three relationships.

63

> For a body moving along a circular path of radius R with tangential displacement x, velocity v and acceleration a:
>
> $$x = \theta R$$
> $$v = \omega R$$
> $$a = \alpha R$$

and you should not need to be reminded that these three equations are valid *only when all angular quantities are expressed in terms of radians and derivatives*. Since the radian is fundamental to kinematics, but less common in practice, write down the connection between angular velocity ω in radians per second, and angular velocity N in revolutions per minute (rev/min).

64

> $$\omega = \frac{2\pi}{60} \times N$$

Problems of angular kinematics can be treated with four equations exactly analogous to the four equations of Frame 48. You don't have to remember these: just re-write the equations, substituting the angular terms for the linear in each case. The four equations are:

$$\theta = \tfrac{1}{2}(\omega_0 + \omega)t \qquad (1)$$
$$\omega = \omega_0 + \alpha t \qquad (2)$$
$$\theta = \omega_0 t + \tfrac{1}{2}\alpha t^2 \qquad (3)$$
$$\omega^2 = \omega_0^2 + 2\alpha\theta \qquad (4)$$

There is one thing that you must be sure of before using any of these four equations. What is this? If you have difficulty recalling it, look back to Frame 49, check-point 1.

65

> Before using any of the equations, ALWAYS make sure that the angular acceleration is CONSTANT.

Problems of angular motion are usually simpler than those of linear motion, which as we have seen, can be quite difficult. A single example will be sufficient. This is set out in the next frame.

66

Example. A rotor can be accelerated from rest at a maximum rate of 15 rad s^{-2}, and can be brought to rest at a rate of 24 rad s^{-2}. It has a maximum permissible speed of 1950 rev/min. Calculate the maximum number of revolutions it can make in 30 s, starting, and finishing at rest.

A sketch of angular velocity against time will be helpful.

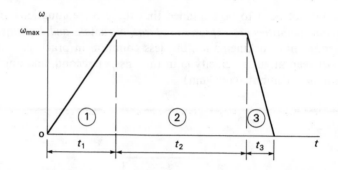

Begin by using equation (2) of the previous frame to calculate the time t_1 for the acceleration phase and t_3, the time for retardation. You should find $t_1 = 13.6$ s and $t_3 = 8.51$ s. Check in the following frame.

67

$$\omega_{max} = 1950 \times 2\pi/60 = 204.2 \text{ rad s}^{-1}$$

$$\omega = \omega_0 + \alpha t; \qquad \therefore \qquad 204.2 = 0 + 15t_1$$
$$\therefore \qquad t_1 = 13.6 \text{ s}$$

$$\text{and } 0 = 204.2 + (-24)t_3$$
$$\therefore \qquad t_3 = 8.51 \text{ s}$$

Since total time is given, t_2 is simply calculated. The three angular displacements must then be calculated. To find θ_1 and θ_3 you *could* use equation (1) or equation (3) of Frame 64. But this would mean using the values of t_1 and t_3 just calculated. Remember the warning in Frame 56. It is better to use equation (4). The displacement during phase 2 is simply calculated as the product of ω and t_2. The calculations are completed in Frame 68.

$$\omega^2 = \omega_0^2 + 2\alpha\theta \qquad \therefore \qquad (204.2)^2 = 0 + 2 \times 15\theta_1$$
$$\therefore \qquad \theta_1 = 1389.9 \text{ rad}$$

$$\text{and} \qquad 0 = (204.2)^2 + 2 \times (-24)\theta_3$$
$$\therefore \qquad \theta_3 = 868.7 \text{ rad}$$

$$\theta_2 = \omega t_2 = 204.2(30 - 13.6 - 8.51)$$
$$= 1611.1 \text{ rad}$$

$$\therefore \qquad \text{Total displacement} = 3869.7 \text{ rad}$$
$$= \textbf{615.9 rev}$$

It is sound practice, where possible, to have checks on your calculations. One check, which is left for you to make, is to calculate the values of θ using the times calculated. This has the additional advantage of checking that the values of t_1 and t_3 must then also be correct.

We now consider the acceleration of a point moving along a circular path. You are reminded that such a point, even though it is moving along the path at constant speed, will nevertheless be accelerating. Acceleration means change of velocity, and this is true for change of direction as well as change of magnitude. There are three things to be said about this acceleration.

1. What is it called?
2. In which direction does it act?
3. What is its magnitude.

The answers to these follow in Frame 69 but try and answer them yourself.

The acceleration is called **centripetal** acceleration.
It is always directed **towards the centre** of the circular path.
It is calculated from either of the formulae:

$$a_c = \omega^2 R \qquad \text{or} \qquad a_c = v^2/R$$

where ω is the angular velocity of the circular motion,
v is the linear velocity along the circular path,
R is the radius of the path.

70

Here is a simple example of the use of the first formula.

Example. The crank of an automobile engine has a radius of 5.4 cm. Calculate the magnitude of the centripetal acceleration of the crankpin when the engine is turning at 5600 rev/min.

We require a direct substitution in the formula, remembering to convert angular speed to radians per second, and radius to metres.

$$\omega = \frac{2\pi}{60} \times N = \frac{2\pi}{60} \times 5600 = 586.43 \text{ rad s}^{-1}$$

$$a_c = \omega^2 R = (586.43)^2 \times 0.054 = \mathbf{18\,571 \text{ m s}^{-2}}$$

from which it is easily seen that high-speed rotating machinery is sometimes subjected to very high accelerations, with corresponding forces.

71

An example of the use of the second formula:

Example. The maximum permissible centripetal acceleration of a car travelling round a circular bend is 5.6 m s^{-2}. Calculate its maximum permissible speed, if the radius of the bend is 35 m.

Re-arranging the second formula of Frame 69:

$$v^2 = a_c R$$

$$\therefore \quad v = \sqrt{(a_c R)} = \sqrt{(5.6 \times 35)} = \mathbf{14 \text{ m s}^{-1}}$$

or approximately 50 km per hour, a modest speed. But attempts to take bends at high speed may result in side-slipping, or more likely, turning the car over.

Do this next example yourself. You will need to refer to the formulae of Frame 63. Be careful not to confuse track radius with wheel radius.

Example. A vehicle having wheels of radius 0.35 m travels at a steady speed of 65 km per hour around a curved track of radius 90 m. Determine the value of the centripetal acceleration of the vehicle, and also the centripetal acceleration of a point on the rim of one of the wheels, relative to the wheel centre.

The solution follows, but try it yourself first.

$$v = 65\,000/(60)^2 = 18.06 \text{ m s}^{-1}$$

$$a_c = \frac{v^2}{R} = \frac{(18.06)^2}{90} = \textbf{3.624 m s}^{-2}$$

For wheel: $$\omega = \frac{v}{R_{\text{wheel}}} = \frac{18.06}{0.35} = 51.6 \text{ m s}^{-2}$$

$$\therefore \quad a_c = \omega^2 R_{\text{wheel}} = (51.6)^2 \times 0.35 = \textbf{931.9 m s}^{-2}$$

Here is a summary of work on angular motion and motion in a circle.

1. The unit of angular displacement is the radian, i.e. $(1/2\pi)$ revolution.
2. When a point moves along a circular path, the linear displacement, velocity and acceleration, x, v and a, are related to corresponding angular displacement, velocity and acceleration, θ, ω and α by:

$$x = \theta R; \; v = \omega R; \; a = \alpha R$$

   where R is the path radius.
3. Angular speed, ω, in radians per second, and angular speed, N, in revolutions per minute, are related by the formula:

$$\omega = \frac{2\pi}{60} \times N$$

4. For angular motion with constant angular acceleration, the following equations apply.

$$\theta = \tfrac{1}{2}(\omega_0 + \omega)t \qquad \omega = \omega_0 + \alpha t$$

$$\theta = \omega_0 t + \tfrac{1}{2}\alpha t^2 \qquad \omega^2 = \omega_0^2 + 2\alpha\theta$$

5. A point moving along a circular path of radius R with linear velocity v and angular velocity ω has a centripetal acceleration a_c given by:

$$a_c = v^2/R = \omega^2 R$$

Centripetal acceleration is always directed towards the centre of the circular path.

74

PROBLEMS

1. A car has a wheel radius of 0.32 m. The wheel speed increases uniformly from 15 rad s^{-1} to 60 rad s^{-1} in 5 seconds. Calculate the initial and final speeds of the car, its linear acceleration, and the distance travelled during the 5-second period. Assume a straight level track and no wheel slip. [*Ans. 4.8 m s^{-1}, 19.2 m s^{-1}, 2.88 m s^{-2}, 60 m.*]

   Hints: find θ and α from equations (1) and (2) Frame (64). Then use equations of Frame 63 to find x, a, v_1 and v_2.

2. A motor takes $7\frac{1}{2}$ seconds to reach full speed of 1450 rev/min starting from rest with constant acceleration. What is its acceleration? How many revolutions does it make? A brake is then applied, bringing it uniformly to rest in 285 revolutions. Calculate the retardation and the time to come to rest. [*Ans. 20.246 rad s^{-2}; 90.625 rev. 6.438 rad s^{-2}; 23.59 s.*]

   Hints: calculate ω (Frame 64). Use equations (1) and (2) (Frame 64) for α and θ. For braking, use equations (1) and (4) to find t and α.

3. A winding drum of a hoist has a diameter of 1.3 m. It can accelerate at a maximum rate of 1.8 rad s^{-2} and has a maximum permissible speed of 40 rev/min. Calculate the least time for it to raise a load through a vertical distance of 6 m. [*Ans. 3.367 s (2.327 s + 1.040 s).*]

   Hints: see Frame 64. Use equations (2) and (4) to find time t_1 to reach maximum speed, and corresponding θ_1. Total $\theta = x/R$. Hence find θ_2. Time t_2 at maximum speed $= \theta_2/\omega$.

75

Now we turn our attention to **kinetics**. We can elaborate slightly on that earlier definition, which we gave in Frame 2, and state that kinetics is the application of Newton's Laws of Motion to moving bodies.

As we did with kinematics, we shall begin by considering the motion of bodies along straight paths. Later, we consider rotating bodies. We shall also examine the concepts of work, energy and power, and the principle of momentum.

In the following frame will be found a statement of Newton's three Laws of Motion. There is no single absolutely correct way of stating the laws (which were in any case, originally formulated in Latin). There is no merit in just remembering the laws. To understand kinetics, and to be competent at solving problems, it is necessary that you understand them. So following a statement of them, we shall discuss them in some detail.

76

The first law:

Bodies continue in a state of rest, or uniform motion in a straight line except when acted upon by a force.

The second law:

Acceleration of a body is proportional to the resultant force acting upon it, and is in the same direction.

And the third:

A force on any one body is always accompanied by an equal and opposite reaction on another body.

The first law defines force, as that which causes, or tends to cause, acceleration. The second law can be written as an equation of motion; thus:

$$\Sigma(F) = ma$$

and you must be clear as to the meanings of all the terms in it—including the Σ. So give this some thought before reading on.

77

The Σ reminds us that when using the Second Law, we must consider *all* the forces acting on a body: that is to say, the **resultant** force. This may appear simple, but many mistakes in applying this formula arise from failure to take all forces into account, or from inclusion of a force which has no existence in fact.

To establish a strict discipline in considering all forces acting on a body, we make use of the device called the **free-body diagram.** We draw a diagram of the body, isolated in space (hence the word 'free'). For example, if the body is a vehicle on a road, we do not include the road. We then indicate on the diagram all the forces which we know to be acting on the body, from the data provided. If we know the line of action of the acceleration, this also is included. For example, we know that the acceleration of a car on a road must be parallel to the road. If we also know its direction, we include this. If this is not known, we assume it, and if the assumption is incorrect, the subsequent calculation will produce a negative answer.

78

To emphasise this matter of the free-body diagram, here is a simple example for you to try. There is a small catch in it, so think carefully.

Example. A bullet fired vertically upwards from a gun has a mass of 0.1 kg. When in the barrel of the gun, it is subjected to an average propelling force of 32 kN. Determine the acceleration of the bullet just after it leaves the gun barrel. Neglect resistance of the air.

Follow the method outlined in the previous frame. Draw a sketch of the bullet, showing all the forces which must be acting on it, and then apply the equation.

79

mg

The *only* force acting on the bullet is its weight, and this acts downwards. So the resulting acceleration is 9.81 m s^{-2} downwards. The mass of the bullet, and the propelling force are not required. This was the catch.

Do not confuse velocity with acceleration. It is a mistake to assume that because something is moving very fast, it must have a forward acceleration.

Here is a check-list of forces which might be acting on a body.

1. Weight—always acts vertically downwards.
2. Pull of a flexible rope or chain attached to the body.
3. Pull or push of a stiff bar attached to the body.
4. Normal reaction force of surface on which body stands. ('Normal' means perpendicular to the surface.)
5. Sideways friction force of surface on which body stands.
6. Tractive force of a powered vehicle.
7. Fluid resisting force, or fluid pressure.

Regarding points 2 and 3, the only effect of a flexible rope on a body can be a pull. You can pull a boat towards you with a rope, but you can't push it away. With a boat-hook, though, you can do either.

A reminder about units. State the units in which F, m and a must be expressed.

> Force must always be expressed in **newtons**
> Mass must always be expressed in **kilograms**
> Acceleration must always be expressed in **metres per second per second**

The second law is used to *define* the newton, which is the force to accelerate a mass of 1 kg at 1 m s^{-2}.

The third law is vital to the full understanding of forces. Remember this very important principle: **forces always exist in pairs**. A force cannot exist in abstract: it is always a reaction between two bodies. Think of the following.

Your body presses downward on the ground; the ground pushes upwards with equal force. If you step on a tack, it is driven *upwards* into your foot.

A locomotive pulls a train forwards; the train pulls backwards on the locomotive. (Imagine yourself as the connection between the two, in place of the steel draw-bar. What will you be doing?)

The earth attracts the moon with a gravitational pull; the moon pulls at the earth with an equal force.

A magnet attracts a block of iron; the iron pulls the magnet with equal force.

A car is propelled *forwards* along the road because its driving wheels exert a *backward* frictional force upon the road surface.

Many mistakes in dynamics arise because of an imperfect understanding of this principle. The problem is, that we apply the second law to a *single body*, and therefore have to consider only the force acting on the body, and not its equal and opposite reaction. This is why a free-body diagram is so important. It forces your attention on the actual body you are analysing. Consider, for example, a crate on the floor of a truck.

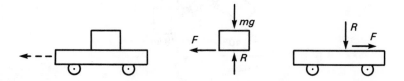

If you draw truck and crate together, you are likely to be confused about the reaction force and the friction force between truck and crate. But if you draw them separately, it becomes much clearer what is happening.

81

The first diagram at the end of Frame 80 shows the two bodies together. But when you separate them, as in the second diagram, it becomes clear that the truck is pushing the crate upwards, and the friction force is driving it forwards. When you consider the truck, the opposite is true: the reaction force pushes downwards, and the friction exerts a retarding force on the truck. Note particularly that the downward force on the truck is *not* the weight of the crate, but the reaction force between crate and truck (although, of course, it might have the same value as the weight).

When drawing a free-body diagram, never include a force that cannot be justified in terms of an actual physical force on the body—a pull or push from a rod or string; a reaction or friction force from a surface, or a weight. This may appear obvious, but it is sometimes tempting to include a force 'because of the acceleration'. The commonest instance of this occurs in motion in a circular path, when learners sometimes have an irresistible urge to include a force pulling outwards from the centre. Now it must be said that this is not actually wrong, but it is an alternative method of approach, and an example of what is called d'Alembert's Principle, concerning which we shall have more to say later. Being an alternative approach, it must NOT be used when applying the second law in the form we have stated it in Frame 76.

82

Example. Two masses are connected by a string. The mass of 24 kg lies on a rough plane of slope 40° and the mass of 18 kg hangs freely. The friction coefficient between mass and plane is 0.2. The 24 kg mass is moving down the plane. Calculate the acceleration of the two masses.

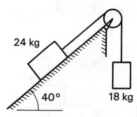

Begin by drawing the two free-body diagrams. You should identify four forces on the 24 kg mass and two on the other. The direction of acceleration is not stated. Assume that the 24 kg mass accelerates down the plane. This determines which way the other mass must be assumed to accelerate. Both accelerations have the same value.

83

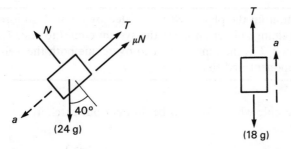

(24 g)

(18 g)

The string tension is shown as *T*. This is the same force on both bodies, because the pulley is assumed to have negligible mass. A common error is to assume that this tension is equal to the value of the hanging weight. This could be so only if there were no acceleration. Note that the friction force must act up the plane if the mass is moving downwards, as stated.

Now write the two equations of motion. For each one, take the direction of the acceleration as positive.

84

$$24g \sin 40° - \mu N - T = 24a \qquad (1)$$
$$N = 24g \cos 40° \qquad (2)$$
$$T - 18g = 18a \qquad (3)$$

The second equation is an equilibrium equation of the 24 kg mass, in the direction perpendicular to that of the acceleration.

Check any mistakes carefully, and try and make sure you know where you went wrong. Then complete the solution by solving the three equations. Use (2) and (3) to substitute for *R* and *T* in (1).

85

$$24g \sin 40° - 0.2(24g \cos 40°) - (18a + 18g) = 24a$$
$$24g \sin 40° - 0.2(24g \cos 40°) - 18g = a(24 + 18)$$
$$151.3 - 36.1 - 176.6 = 42a$$
$$\therefore \quad a = -\mathbf{1.462 \ m \ s^{-2}}$$

The negative answer means that the acceleration is directed up the plane instead of downwards, as assumed. Thus, although the 24 kg mass is moving down the plane, it is being slowed down, and will eventually come to rest. It will *not* then begin to move the other way. Why not?

86

Motion up the plane will be resisted by the friction force, which will change direction when the system comes to rest. The string tension T is then insufficient to overcome both the weight component and the friction.

Here is an example which needs to be thought out carefully.

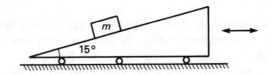

Example. A rough inclined plane of slope 15° is arranged so that it can move horizontally. A block of mass $m = 2$ kg rests on the plane, and the coefficient of friction between block and plane is 0.3. Determine the required linear acceleration of the inclined plane (a) to the right, just sufficient to cause the block to move down the plane; (b) to the left, just sufficient to cause it to move up the plane.

We shall draw the free-body diagram of the block only. Try and answer these questions before reading on.

1. How many forces act on the block?
2. What are they?
3. What will be the direction of acceleration of the block?

And be particularly careful with question 3.

87

There will be **three** forces: weight, friction, normal reaction. The block acceleration will be **horizontal**.

Actually, friction and normal reaction are two *components* of a *single force*. Regarding the second statement, remember the condition is that the block is just about to move: therefore, it will have the same acceleration as the plane. It is about to begin slipping down, but is not actually moving relative to the plane.

The free-body diagrams for the two cases appear in the following frame.

(a) shows the block about to slide down the plane as the plane moves from left to right. (b) shows it about to slide up, as the plane moves right to left. Note particularly the direction of the friction force in each case. It acts opposite to the direction the block is trying to move.

Now write the two equations for case (a) first. One is the equation of motion $(\Sigma(F) = ma)$ taking the direction of acceleration as positive, and the second will be an equation of equilibrium in the direction perpendicular to the acceleration. Check your equations in the next frame before continuing.

In direction of a: $\qquad\qquad \mu N \cos \theta - N \sin \theta = ma$
and perpendicular to plane: $\quad \mu N \sin \theta + N \cos \theta = mg$

Eliminate N by dividing one equation by the other.

$$\frac{\mu N \cos \theta - N \sin \theta}{\mu N \sin \theta + N \cos \theta} = \frac{ma}{mg}$$

Cancel:

$$\frac{\mu \cos \theta - \sin \theta}{\mu \sin \theta + \cos \theta} = \frac{a}{g}$$

$$\therefore \quad a = g\left(\frac{0.3 \cos 15° - \sin 15°}{0.3 \sin 15° + \cos 15°}\right)$$

$$\therefore \quad a = 9.81 \times \frac{0.2898 - 0.2588}{0.0776 + 0.9659}$$

$$= \textbf{0.291 m s}^{-2}$$

The important feature of this example is to resist the temptation always to write equations parallel to, and perpendicular to the line of the plane. Always choose the two directions, parallel to, and perpendicular to the acceleration. You *can* choose other directions, but this would mean resolving the acceleration as well, and the algebra would be more difficult.

90

The calculations for part (b) are similar.

In direction of a: $\qquad\qquad \mu N \cos\theta + N \sin\theta = ma$

and perpendicular to plane: $\qquad N \cos\theta - \mu N \sin\theta = mg$

The treatment is the same, leading to:

$$a = g\left(\frac{\sin 15° + 0.3 \cos 15°}{\cos 15° - 0.3 \sin 15°}\right)$$

$$= 9.81 \times \frac{0.2588 + 0.2898}{0.9659 - 0.0776}$$

$$= \mathbf{6.059\ m\ s^{-2}}$$

Frame 91 contains a few problems.

91

PROBLEMS

1. A body of mass 45 kg rests on a horizontal flat surface, the coefficient of friction between body and surface being 0.15. It is pulled along by a rope inclined at an angle of 35° above the horizontal. What tensile force in the rope will cause the body to have an acceleration of 2 m s^{-2}? [*Ans. 172.58 N.*]

2. A mass of 4 kg rests on an inclined plane of angle 32°. A light string is attached to the mass, and passes over a light frictionless pulley at the top of the plane. A second mass m attached to the other end of the string hangs freely. Determine what value of m will cause the first mass to accelerate up the plane at 1.4 m s^{-2}: (a) if the plane is smooth; (b) if the coefficient of friction is 0.12. [*Ans. (a) 3.138 kg. (b) 3.613 kg.*]

   Hint: solve algebraically, and solve part (b) first. (See example in Frame 82.) For part (a), let $\mu = 0$.

3. A crate rests on the flat floor of a truck. The coefficient of friction between crate and floor is 0.4. Calculate the maximum forward acceleration for the truck when it ascends a slope of 8° in order that the crate shall not slip backwards. [*Ans. 2.521 m s^{-2}.*]

   Hint: the problem is similar to the example in Frame 86 part (a) except that the direction of acceleration of the block will be at 8° upwards, i.e. the same as the truck.

92

The kinetic analysis of a body moving in a circular path is simple, provided you remember the characteristics of centripetal acceleration. These were set down in Frame 69; you should be able to recall them without looking back. They are repeated in the next frame, but try and write down (a) the formulae for the acceleration (there are two of them), and (b) its direction.

93

> Centripetal acceleration $a_c = v^2/R = \omega^2 R$
>
> where v and ω are the linear and angular velocities of motion, and R is the path radius.
> The acceleration is directed towards the centre of curvature of the path.

94

Here are some rules for the solution of kinetic problems.

1. Examine the body to be analysed, and draw a **free-body diagram**, i.e. a diagram showing the body 'in space', with all the forces shown that can be deduced to be acting on it. In seeking these, refer to the list in Frame 79.
2. Include on the diagram, the direction of the acceleration, if known. If the direction is not known, assume it. Indicate the acceleration by an arrow different from the arrows used to indicate force.
3. Resolve all forces along two directions, one of which is that of the acceleration (known or assumed), the other perpendicular to this.
4. Write an **equation of motion**, i.e. $\Sigma(F) = ma$, taking the direction of the acceleration, known or assumed, as positive.
5. Write an **equation of equilibrium** in the direction perpendicular to that of 4.
6. Solve these equations for unknown terms.

There are occasions where acceleration may exist in two directions. In such a case, rule 5 would require modification. We shall deal with such cases as they arise. For the examples that follow, these rules will suffice.

95

Let us see how to apply the rules of Frame 94 in this example.

Example. A car having a mass of 1150 kg travels around a curved track of mean radius 45 m at a speed of 75 km per hour. Calculate the sideways friction force between wheels and road if the track is inclined at 12° inwards towards the centre of the turn.

Now for the free-body diagram. We are concerned with sideways motion, not forward. Our diagram will therefore show a rear view of the car, turning to the right as it rounds the bend.

List all the forces that you think must be acting on it. The list in Frame 79 may help. It is repeated here, in abbreviated form.

(1) Weight. (2) Pull of rope or chain. (3) Pull or push of bar.
(4) Surface reaction force. (5) Sideways friction force.
(6) Tractive force. (7) Fluid resistance or pressure.

You should identify three forces.

96

> The forces are: weight; surface reaction; friction.

Tractive force acts on the car but does not affect its sideways motion. Air resistance also acts, but no details are given, so assume this to be negligible.

The free-body diagram also includes the acceleration. Here is the diagram.

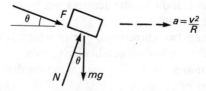

All the data are shown as symbols rather than figures. The reaction force is shown as N. The friction force F is shown acting down the slope. We do not know this to be correct. For a track banked at a very steep angle, friction could act the other way. Wherever the direction of a force is uncertain, assume it. If wrong, this will appear as a negative answer.

Applying rule 4 (Frame 94), we write $\Sigma(F) = ma$ taking direction left to right as positive (because this is the direction of the acceleration):

$$F \cos \theta + N \sin \theta = ma = mv^2/R \qquad (1)$$

Rule 5 gives us:

$$F \sin \theta + mg = N \cos \theta \qquad (2)$$

All values are given except F and N. Since F is required, we can eliminate N from these two equations. Re-arranging and dividing (1) by (2):

$$\frac{N \sin \theta}{N \cos \theta} = \tan \theta = \frac{mv^2/R - F \cos \theta}{F \sin \theta + mg}$$

$\therefore \qquad F \sin \theta \tan \theta + mg \tan \theta = mv^2/R - F \cos \theta$
$\therefore \qquad F \sin \theta \tan \theta + F \cos \theta = mv^2/R - mg \tan \theta$

$$v = \frac{75\,000}{(60)^2} = 20.83 \text{ m s}^{-1}$$

$$\therefore \qquad \frac{v^2}{R} = \frac{(20.83)^2}{45} = 9.642 \text{ m s}^{-2}$$

Substituting:

$$F(\sin 12° \tan 12° + \cos 12°) = 1150(9.642 - 9.81 \tan 12°)$$
$$\therefore \qquad 1.022F = 1150(9.642 - 2.085)$$
$$\therefore \qquad F = \textbf{8503.5 N}$$

Try this next example. The working is given later, if you need it.

Example. The friction coefficient between wheels and road for the car of the example of Frame 95 is 0.55. Calculate the maximum speed at which it may travel round the curved track without slipping.

The free-body diagram will be as before, except that the friction force can now be written as μN. Eliminating N from the two equations will yield v.

99

A new free-body diagram is unnecessary. We re-write equations (1) and (2) from the last frame, replacing F by μN:

$$\mu N \cos \theta + N \sin \theta = mv^2/R$$
$$\mu N \sin \theta + mg = N \cos \theta$$

Collecting the N-terms to one side and dividing the equations:

$$\frac{N(\mu \cos \theta + \sin \theta)}{N(\cos \theta - \mu \sin \theta)} = \frac{mv^2}{mgR}$$

Substituting values and cancelling:

$$\frac{0.55 \cos 12° + \sin 12°}{\cos 12° - 0.55 \sin 12°} = \frac{v^2}{45g}$$

$$\therefore \quad v^2 = 45 \times 9.81 \times 0.8635$$
$$\therefore \quad v = \textbf{19.52 m s}^{-1} = \textbf{70.27 km per hour}$$

100

PROBLEMS

1. A small weight of mass 0.4 kg is attached to the end of a rod of negligible mass of length 1.6 m. The other end of the rod is connected to a shaft which turns at 30 rev/min so that rod and weight move in a vertical plane. Calculate the tension force in the rod when the weight is (a) at the top of its path; (b) at the bottom of its path. [Ans. (a) 2.3925 N, (b) 10.2405 N.]

2. A small weight of mass 0.3 kg is attached to a light string of length 0.95 m. The upper end of the string is attached to a fixed point. The weight can then move at constant angular speed in a horizontal circular path, the string then tracing out the slant side of a cone, the apex of which is the fixed point. Such a device is called a conical pendulum. Find the circle radius, and the tension in the string when the weight moves at 35 rev/min. [Ans. 0.6076 m. 3.829 N.]

101

Here are a few revision notes on work, energy and power.

Work is said to be done when a force moves its point of application along the direction of the force. When motion is in any direction other than that of the force, only the component along the force line must be considered.

When a force acts on a body and motion of the body is in the direction of the applied force, work is done **on** the body. When motion is in the opposite direction, work is done **by** the body.

Work is defined quantitatively as the product of force (in newtons) and distance moved (in metres). The unit of work is the **joule**, which is the work done by a force of 1 newton moving a distance of 1 metre.
So for a force F moving a distance of x:

$$\text{work done} = (F \times x) \text{ joules}$$

Energy is what is gained or lost by a body or a system when work is done.
When work is done **on** a body or system, energy is **gained**.
When work is done **by** a body or system, energy is **lost**.
Energy is measured in the same unit as work, i.e. in joules.
In Engineering Dynamics, we are concerned with mechanical energy. This can be manifested in three forms. List these if you can. If you have difficulty, it might help to think of a hydro-electric power station, a wind-driven generator, and a bow and arrow. These are examples of the three types of energy.

102

Potential energy; kinetic energy; strain energy

Potential energy:	energy by virtue of height above a datum
Kinetic energy:	energy by virtue of acquired velocity
Strain energy:	energy by virtue of work done in straining a body

Write down expressions for (a) the potential energy of a mass m at height h above a datum; (b) the kinetic energy of a mass m moving at velocity v.

103

$$E_{pot} = mgh; \qquad E_{kin} = \tfrac{1}{2}mv^2$$

Remember that h is the vertical height above a datum. A generating station may be four kilometres from the dam supplying it, but the vertical height of the dam above the station may be only 100 metres.

Example. A dam is situated a vertical height above a generating station of 100 m. Water passes down to the station at a rate of 56 cubic metres per second. Calculate the energy available per second.

Complete this simple calculation for potential energy. By way of a reminder, the density of water is 1000 kg per cubic metre. The solution is in Frame 104.

104

$$\text{mass of water/s} = \text{volume} \times \text{density} = 56\,000 \text{ kg s}^{-1}$$

$$\therefore \quad \text{potential energy/s} = m \times g \times h$$

$$= 56\,000 \times 9.81 \times 100$$

$$= \textbf{54.9} \times \textbf{10}^{\textbf{6}} \textbf{ joules per second}$$

Now a calculation of kinetic energy.

Example. A locomotive and train has a total mass of 265 tonnes. How much work must be done to bring the train up to a speed of 120 kilometres per hour from rest?

This is again a simple calculation with no catch. The solution follows. You may need reminding that 1 tonne = 1000 kg.

105

$$E_{kin} = \tfrac{1}{2}mv^2 = \tfrac{1}{2} \times 265 \times 10^3 \left(\frac{120 \times 1000}{60 \times 60} \right)^2 = \textbf{147.2} \times \textbf{10}^{\textbf{6}} \textbf{ J}$$

This is the kinetic energy possessed by the train, and therefore this is the work that must be done to impart this energy to the train.

Rotating bodies also possess energy. We shall develop the expression for kinetic energy of rotation later in this programme. The calculation of strain energy will be left until Programme 7.

The principle of Conservation of Energy states that energy is neither created nor destroyed. It is always accountable. Thus, if energy is known to be lost from some part of a system, it must be gained by some other part—it cannot just disappear. It may be 'lost' to the part of the system that you are particularly interested in. If you leave a door open in winter, heat may be 'lost' from your house. But the air outside must be warmer by the amount lost.

This principle offers a useful alternative approach to the solution of some problems of kinetics. Take this simple example.

Example. A simple pendulum consists of a mass m of negligible size at the end of a string of length 0.75 m. It swings through a half-angle of 24°. What will be the maximum speed of the mass? Neglect air resistance.

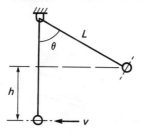

The figure shows the mass at the extreme of swing, where it has maximum potential energy, and at the lowest point, where it has maximum kinetic energy. Because it is not being pushed, and because it loses no energy due to air resistance, we can say that the total kinetic energy at the bottom is the total potential energy at the top. If we call the vertical height h:

$$mgh = \tfrac{1}{2}mv^2$$

From the simple geometry of the figure:

$$h = L - L \cos \theta = 0.75(1 - \cos 24°) = 0.0648 \text{ m}$$
$$\therefore \quad v = \sqrt{(2gh)} = \sqrt{(2 \times 9.81 \times 0.0648)} = \textbf{1.128 m s}^{-1}$$

The example is interesting because a calculation of the velocity by applying the equation of motion and determining the acceleration would be extremely complex. On the other hand, the analysis using an energy equation cannot reveal the time required for the mass to travel the quarter-swing.

107

A general energy equation for a system may be written:

Initial energy + work done on system − energy loss = final energy

The example following is an application of this.

Example. A truck having a mass of 2400 kg is driven up a slope of 5° by a tractive force of 2250 N. There is a wind resistance equivalent to a constant force of 350 N. If the speed at the beginning of the slope is 25 m per second, what will be the speed after it has moved 100 m up the slope?

Do this yourself. Always draw a diagram when using an energy equation. The initial energy will be kinetic. Work is done on the system by the tractive force, and energy is lost because of work done against friction. There is a gain of potential energy.

108

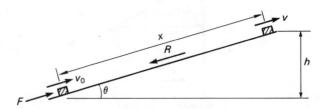

Calling the initial speed v_0, the final speed v, the tractive force F, the wind resistance R, the distance travelled x, and the vertical height h:

Initial E_{kin} + W.D. by tractive force − W.D. against friction = final $E_{kin} + E_{pot}$

$$\therefore \quad \tfrac{1}{2}mv_0^2 + Fx - Rx = \tfrac{1}{2}mv^2 + mgh$$

h is seen to be $x \sin \theta = 100 \sin 5° = 8.716$ m.
Re-arranging and substituting values:

$$\tfrac{1}{2} \times 2400v^2 = \tfrac{1}{2} \times 2400(25)^2 + 100(2250 - 350) - 2400 \times 9.81 \times 8.716$$
$$= 750\,000 + 190\,000 - 205\,210$$
$$= 734\,790$$
$$\therefore \quad v = \sqrt{612.33} = \textbf{24.75 m s}^{-1}$$

Unlike the first example, this could also be solved relatively simply by writing the equation of motion, calculating the acceleration (actually, a retardation) and using the kinematic equations to determine the final velocity. If you need practice, do it this way, and compare the two solutions.

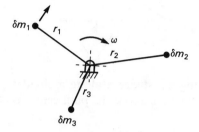

Imagine a body comprising three small concentrated masses, δm_1, δm_2 and δm_3 attached to light rods of different radii, r_1, etc. all rotating about a fixed centre O, at angular speed ω as shown. The system will have kinetic energy. The linear velocity of mass δm_1 is given by:

$$v_1 = \omega r_1$$

The kinetic energy of the mass is $\frac{1}{2}\delta m_1 v_1^2 = \frac{1}{2}\delta m_1 \omega^2 r_1^2$.
The energy of the other masses is similarly calculated. So the total kinetic energy of the system is given by:

$$E_{\text{kin}} = \frac{1}{2}\omega^2(\delta m_1 r_1^2 + \delta m_2 r_2^2 + \delta m_3 r_3^2)$$

and, more generally, for any system consisting of a number of rotating 'elements':

$$E_{\text{kin}} = \frac{1}{2}\omega^2 \Sigma(\delta m r^2)$$

The 'Σ' term at the end is called the **moment of inertia** of the rotating system, and is given the symbol I. The expression for kinetic energy is seen to be analogous to that for a mass m moving at speed v. Angular velocity ω takes the place of linear velocity v, and mass is replaced by moment of inertia, I. I is seen to be a rotating equivalent of mass, i.e. that which resists acceleration. We can write the above equation:

$$E_{\text{kin}} = \frac{1}{2}I\omega^2$$

The next stage is to obtain an equation of motion for a rotating body, in terms of force and acceleration. When accelerating a rotating body, although force is applied, another factor to be considered is the *radius* at which the force acts. A force at a large radius has a greater accelerating effect than the same force at a small radius. It is not just the force, therefore, but the *moment* of the force, M, which is to be taken into account. First, we require an expression for the work done by a moment. This we derive in the next frame.

110

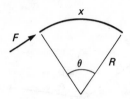

A force F is shown, moving a distance x along a circular path. The work done is (Fx). The moment M of the force about the path centre is (FR). Also, we can say:

$$x = \theta R$$

$$\therefore \quad \text{work done} = Fx = (M/R)(\theta R) = M\theta$$

and this is seen to be analogous to linear work, moment taking the place of force. Thus:

work done = moment × angular displacement

111

A **torque** is a moment acting on a rotating body. Consider a torque M acting on a rotating body of moment of inertia I. From energy conservation:

$$\text{work done} = \text{gain of kinetic energy}$$

$$\therefore \quad M\theta = \tfrac{1}{2}I(\omega^2 - \omega_0^2)$$

where ω_0 and ω are the angular speeds before and after M acts. But θ, ω and ω_0 are kinematically related (see Frame 64):

$$\omega^2 = \omega_0^2 + 2\alpha\theta$$

Substituting:

$$M\theta = \tfrac{1}{2}I(2\alpha\theta)$$

$$\therefore \quad M = I\alpha$$

and this is our fundamental equation of angular motion—Newton's Second Law applied to a rotating body. Again, it is analogous to the linear law, $\Sigma(F) = ma$, force being replaced by torque, mass by moment of inertia, and linear acceleration by angular acceleration. We add a sigma to the left-hand side to remind us that the *total* torque is required for the law to apply.

$$\mathbf{\Sigma(M) = I\alpha}$$

Example. A wheel is mounted on a horizontal shaft of diameter 45 mm. A string is wound round the shaft and a constant force of 5 N is applied to the string. The wheel reaches a speed of 2.5 rev s^{-1} in 6 seconds. What is the moment of inertia of the wheel? Neglect any frictional resistance.

The equation $\Sigma(M) = I\alpha$ applies. The force of 5 N acts at a radius of $22\frac{1}{2}$ mm.

$$M = 5 \times 22.5 \times 10^{-3} = 0.1125 \text{ N m}$$

$$\omega = \omega_0 + \alpha t$$

$$\therefore \quad 2.5 \times 2\pi = 0 + \alpha \times 6$$

$$\therefore \quad \alpha = 2.618 \text{ rad s}^{-2}$$

$$\Sigma(M) = I\alpha$$

$$0.1125 = I \times 2.618$$

$$\therefore \quad I = \textbf{0.043 kg m}^2$$

Moment of inertia is sometimes expressed in terms of **radius of gyration**, k. This is the radius at which all the mass of the rotating body would have to be concentrated for the rotor to have the same moment of inertia. k, is an equivalent, or effective radius. From the definition:

$$I = mk^2$$

The **Parallel Axis theorem** is useful for calculating moments of inertia of bodies about one axis when given its value about another.

Theorem. If I_G is the moment of inertia of a rotating body of mass m about an axis through the mass centre, and I_x is the moment of inertia with respect to any other axis parallel to the axis through the mass centre, then:

$$I_x = I_G + mh^2$$

where h is the perpendicular distance between the two axes.

Example. For a thin uniform rod rotating about one end, $I = \frac{1}{3}mL^2$, Show that I about a transverse axis through the rod centre is $\frac{1}{12}mL^2$.

The distance between the two axes is $\frac{1}{2}L$. Substituting values:

$$\tfrac{1}{3}mL^2 = I_G + m(\tfrac{1}{2}L)^2$$

$$\therefore \quad I_G = m(\tfrac{1}{3}L^2 - (\tfrac{1}{2}L)^2) = mL^2(\tfrac{1}{3} - \tfrac{1}{4}) = \tfrac{1}{12}mL^2$$

114

Power is the rate of doing work, or the rate of release of energy. It is therefore energy per unit time. The unit is the watt:

$$1 \text{ watt} = 1 \text{ joule per second}$$

Power is also measured in multiples of watts:

$$1 \text{ kilowatt} = 10^3 \text{ watts} \qquad 1 \text{ megawatt} = 10^6 \text{ watts}$$

For a force F, power = force × distance moved per second
$\qquad\qquad\qquad\quad$ = force × velocity
$\qquad\qquad\qquad\quad$ = Fv.

For a torque M, power = torque × angular displacement per second
$\qquad\qquad\qquad\qquad$ = torque × angular velocity
$\qquad\qquad\qquad\qquad$ = $M\omega$.

115

PROBLEMS

1. A body of mass 16 kg is projected vertically upwards with initial velocity of 200 m s^{-1}. Calculate the maximum height it ascends, and the velocity with which it strikes the ground on return. Assume a constant resisting force due to the air of 30 N. [*1711.6 m; 164.81 m s^{-1}.*]
   Hint: for second part, loss of K.E. = resistance × 2 × maximum height.
2. A flywheel is mounted on a horizontal shaft of diameter 50 mm. A string is attached to the shaft, and wound round it, and a weight of 20 N hangs vertically on the other end of the string. The weight is released from rest, and after it has descended 4 m, the wheel is turning at 3.35 revolutions per second. Calculate the moment of inertia of the wheel. Neglect friction and air resistance. [*Ans. 0.3598 kg m^2.*]
   Hint: loss of P.E. of weight = gain of K.E. of wheel *plus K.E. of weight.*
3. A wheel has a mass of 450 kg, an outside diameter of 1.25 m and a radius of gyration of 0.54 m. It rolls without slip along a horizontal rail, at a speed of 15 m s^{-1}. Calculate its kinetic energy. [*Ans. 88.416 kJ.*]
   Hint: the wheel has kinetic energy due to rotation (about its own axis) and translation (i.e. it moves with linear velocity along the rail). $v = \omega R$.

Momentum is defined as (mass × velocity). It has also been defined, with less precision, as 'quantity of motion'. We may state Newton's Second Law in an alternative form in terms of momentum. Thus:

$$F = m \times a$$

But

$$a = \frac{v - v_0}{t}$$

$$\therefore \quad F = m\left(\frac{v - v_0}{t}\right) = \frac{mv - mv_0}{t}$$

This means that force may be defined as **rate of change of momentum**. This alternative form is useful when dealing with problems of dynamics where the mass cannot be clearly defined, such as the force exerted by a fluid jet on a surface.

The **Conservation of Momentum** follows directly from Newton's Second Law. It states that the total momentum of a body or of a system of bodies may be altered only by the application of an external force. An internal force may alter the momentum of parts of the system, but not the whole. For example, a shell fired from a gun is a system. The force firing the sheel is an internal force, and therefore cannot change the momentum of (shell + gun). So any momentum in one direction gained by the shell must be balanced by equal momentum gained by the gun in the opposite direction. Momentum, being a function of velocity, is a vector quantity.

Conservation of Momentum is not to be confused with Conservation of Energy. In dealing with the dynamics of colliding bodies, energy will be found frequently to be lost *to the system*, although we know that it is not lost absolutely. For example, if a bullet is fired into a sandbag hanging by a cord, the Conservation of Momentum will reveal the combined velocity of bullet + sandbag. But much of the initial energy of the bullet will be expended in ploughing through the sand, and thus heating it. So the final kinetic energy of the system will be very much less than the initial kinetic energy of the bullet.

A bullet hitting a sandbag is a useful example to demonstrate momentum conservation, as this device can actually be used, to determine the speed of a bullet. Such a device is called a **ballistic pendulum**. Assuming that the sandbag retains the bullet (i.e. that the bullet does not go right through it and out the other side), the sideways movement of the sandbag may be measured, and used to calculate the bullet speed. An example follows in the next frame.

117

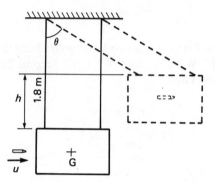

Example. A box full of sand has a mass of 40 kg. It hangs by four equal strings of length 1.8 m, so that when displaced sideways, the box is raised but does not turn, as shown dotted in the diagram. A bullet of mass 0.025 kg is fired horizontally into the box and remains within it. The impact causes the box to swing sideways so that the strings make a maximum angle to the vertical of 19°. Estimate the speed of the bullet, and the loss of kinetic energy.

In fact, the box begins to move the instant the bullet strikes, and has actually moved some distance by the time the bullet comes to rest (relative to the box) inside. A strictly accurate analysis of the situation is difficult, and we simplify the situation considerably, without any noticeable sacrifice of accuracy, by assuming the change of speed of the box to take place instantaneously.

The force exerted on the box by the bullet causes the box to suffer an increase of forward momentum. The reaction force of box on bullet causes a decrease of the forward momentum of the bullet. Since the two forces are equal, the momentum gain of the box equals the momentum loss of the bullet. Thus, the total momentum of box and bullet is conserved. Calling the masses of bullet and box m_1 and m_2, the initial velocities u_1 and u_2, and the final velocities v_1 and v_2, write your version of the equation of conservation of momentum.

118

$$m_1 u_1 + m_2 u_2 = m_1 v_1 + m_2 v_2$$

Given (a) that the box is initially at rest, and (b) that the final velocity of the bullet equals that of the box, first simplify this equation accordingly, and then substitute the values given for the masses.

$$m_1 u_1 = (m_1 + m_2)v_1$$
$$\therefore \quad 0.025\, u_1 = 40.025\, v_1$$

To determine v_1, we use an energy balance equation. Notice that we may do this *after* the impact. (We may assume resistance of the air to be negligible, as we are not given information about it.) Write the simple energy equation in words.

loss of E_{kin} of bullet + box = gain of E_{pot} of bullet + box

$$\tfrac{1}{2}(m_1 + m_2)v_1^2 = (m_1 + m_2)gh$$
$$\therefore \quad v_1 = \sqrt{(2gh)}$$

The diagram in Frame 117 clearly shows that h is given by:

$$h = 1.8 - 1.8 \cos 19°$$
$$= 0.0981 \text{ m}$$
$$\therefore \quad v_1 = \sqrt{(2 \times 9.81 \times 0.0981)}$$
$$= 1.387 \text{ m s}^{-1}$$

Substituting in the momentum equation in Frame 119:

$$u_1 = (40.025 \times 1.387)/0.025$$
$$= 2220.6 \text{ m s}^{-1}$$

The loss of kinetic energy is simply calculated.

loss of E_{kin} = initial E_{kin} of bullet $-$ final E_{kin} of bullet and box
$$= \tfrac{1}{2}(0.025)(2220.6)^2 - \tfrac{1}{2}(40.025)(1.387)^2$$
$$= 61\,638.3 - 38.5$$
$$= \mathbf{61\,599.8 \text{ J}}$$

and the discrepancy between initial and final values of energy demonstrates how wrong it would be to write an energy balance equation for the impact itself. It is seen that practically all of the initial kinetic energy of the bullet has disappeared. Where has it gone to?

121

Mostly converted to heat energy in the sand

Try to complete this next example yourself.

Example. A fence post standing vertically in the ground has a mass of 12 kg. It is struck by a 'beetle' (a large wooden hammer) which has a mass of 5 kg. When the beetle strikes, its velocity is 5 m s^{-1}. Assuming the blow drives the post 4 mm into the ground, estimate the average resistance of the ground to the post, and calculate the loss of kinetic energy on impact. Assume that the beetle head does not rebound on striking.

The calculations will be similar to the previous example. Here are a few points to guide you.

1. If the beetle head does not rebound, it will have the same final velocity after impact as the post; hence $v_1 = v_2$ as before.
2. When applying the energy balance equation after impact, don't forget that there will also be a *loss of potential energy*.

You should find that the common velocity after impact is 1.471 m s^{-1}, the energy loss is 44.1 J and the average ground resistance is 4765 N. A short version of the solution follows in Frame 122.

122

$$m_1 u_1 + 0 = (m_1 + m_2)v$$

$$\therefore \quad 5 \times 5 = 17v$$

$$\therefore \quad v = 1.471 \text{ m s}^{-1}$$

$$\text{Loss of } E_{\text{kin}} = \tfrac{1}{2} \times 5 \times 5^2 - \tfrac{1}{2} \times 17 \times (1.471)^2$$

$$= \mathbf{44.1 \text{ J}}$$

$$\text{Initial } E_{\text{kin}} + E_{\text{pot}} = \text{work done against resistance}$$

$$\therefore \quad \tfrac{1}{2} \times 17 \times (1.471)^2 + 17g \times 0.004 = R \times 0.004$$

$$\therefore \quad \mathbf{R = 4765 \text{ N}}$$

123

You should appreciate that specifying the condition that two bodies remain in contact after colliding, or impacting, makes for the simplest solution to the problem. This is not to say that problems are just invented, for easy solution by students. It is a fact that when a hammer is used to strike a body, the rebound of the hammer-head is usually negligible. Even when a heavy weight is dropped on to a steel 'pile', there is very little rebound. This device is called a pile driver, and you may have seen it in operation on large building-sites. Piles are long steel rods or plates which are driven vertically into the ground, usually to support a building to be constructed above them, when the ground itself would be insufficiently hard to support the weight.

When bodies separate after impact, a momentum equation is insufficient to predict the result, as there are two unknown velocities. We require some information about the energy lost, or concerning how the bodies rebound from each other. This will be examined in Programme 8, although one example will be found in the following frame of three problems. A final frame of eight problems covering the work of the whole programme brings this programme to an end.

124

PROBLEMS

1. Bullets are fired horizontally from a machine-gun into a coal-truck of mass 1500 kg which is on a horizontal frictionless rail. If a bullet has a mass of 0.022 kg, and its speed is 1450 m s^{-1}, how many bullets would be needed to start the truck moving at 0.5 m s^{-1}? [*Ans. 24.*]

2. A pile-driver has a mass of 1200 kg. It falls from rest through a height of 4 m on to the top of a pile of mass 450 kg which stands vertically in the ground. Assuming the resistance of the ground to be a constant force of 1.75 MN, determine how far into the ground this pile is driven by one blow. Calculate the energy lost to the system by the blow. Assume the pile-driver does not rebound on striking. [*Ans. 19.75 mm.*]

   Hint: solve as Frame 122.

3. Two wagons move on a single horizontal rail. A moves towards B at 4 m s^{-1} and B towards A at 3 m s^{-1}. The mass of A is 1200 kg and that of B, 600 kg. If they collide without loss of kinetic energy, determine the two final velocities. [*Ans. $-\frac{2}{3}$ m s^{-1} (i.e. reversed) and $+6\frac{1}{3}$ m s^{-1}.*]

   Hint: write an *energy* conservation equation as well as a momentum conservation equation. The two simultaneous equations result in a quadratic. Use the formula, and reject the solution which obviously cannot apply.

125

FURTHER PROBLEMS

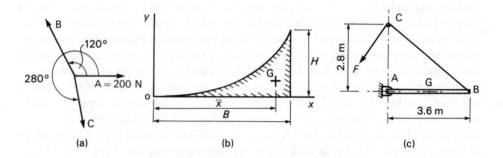

(a)   (b)   (c)

1. Three forces, A, B and C act at a point at respective angles of 0°, 120° and 280° as shown in (a) above. The magnitude of A is 200 N. Determine the magnitudes of B and C. [*Ans. B = 575.9 N ; C = 506.4 N.*]
   Hint: sketch the force triangle and use the sine formula (Frame 14).

2. A steel bar has a constant thickness throughout, and tapers uniformly in width from 40 mm at one end to 80 mm at the other end. The bar is 1.2 m long. Locate the mass centre of the bar. [*Ans. 0.667 m from 40 mm end.*]
   Hint: as problem 4, Frame 29, except treat as +ve and −ve triangles, instead of cones. Or treat as two triangles, 40 mm base and 80 mm base.

3. The figure at (b) above shows an area enclosed by a parabola, a vertical ordinate and the x-axis. The vertex of the parabola is o, the origin, and the axis coincides with the y-axis. Show (a) that the area of the enclosed figure is $\frac{1}{3}BH$, and (b) that the centroid is distance $\frac{3}{4}B$ from the origin o.
   Hints: use expression of Frame 30 except use integral instead of Σ. The parabola is defined by $y = kx^2$ for the conditions stated. Find k by substituting $x = B$ and $y = H$ in expression.

4. A large trapdoor is 3.6 m long and weights 2400 N. It is hinged at one end and is raised by a force F on a cable which is attached to the end of the door and passes over a pulley 2.8 m vertically above the hinge, as shown in the diagram at (c) above. Calculate the force F to raise the door (a) in the position shown, and (b) when the door has been raised 30°. [*Ans. (a) 1954.6 N ; (b) 1403 N.*]
   Hints: (b) Solve triangle ABC using sine and cosine formulae. You should get angle at B = 47.79°. Take moments about hinge of component of F perpendicular to door.

5. Vehicle A starts from rest from a point on a straight level track with a constant acceleration of 0.75 m s^{-2}, reaching a maximum speed of 24 m s^{-1}. Vehicle B starts from the same point at the same instant with constant acceleration of 0.6 m s^{-2}, reaching a maximum speed of 31 m s^{-1}. How long does it take for B to catch up on A, and how far have they travelled? [*Ans. 59.57 s; 1045.7 m.*]
   Hints: calculate times (t_A, t_B) and distances for A and B to attain maximum speed. Sketch $v-t$ graphs; areas are the same (i.e. distances travelled), giving one equation in t_A, t_B. Total times are the same, giving a second equation.

6. A wheel of rim diameter 0.42 m starts from rest and accelerates uniformly to a maximum speed of 1440 rev/min in 8 seconds. Calculate (a) the angular acceleration; (b) the rim velocity at maximum speed; (c) the centripetal acceleration of a point on the rim at maximum speed; (d) the total revolutions turned through in reaching maximum speed; (e) the revolutions turned through in successive 2-second intervals from rest. [*Ans. (a) 18.85 rad s^{-2}, (b) 31.67 m s^{-1}, (c) 4775.3 m s^{-2}, (d) 96 rev, (e) 6, 18, 30 and 42 rev.*]
   Hints: equations of Frames 63 and 64.

7.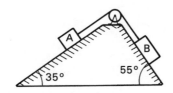

   Two bodies resting on two inclined planes are connected by a light string as shown. Body A has a mass of 4 kg and B a mass of 7 kg. μ between body and plane is 0.2 for both bodies. Calculate the acceleration of the two masses. Assume A to move up the plane. [*Ans. 1.767 m s^{-2}.*]
   Hint: both bodies have same acceleration. The string tension T will be the same on both bodies.

8. A horizontal shaft of diameter 36 mm running in bearings which may be assumed frictionless carries a large rotor. (A rotor is anything designed to be rotated on a shaft—for example, an electric motor armature.) A string is attached to the shaft, and wound round it several times. A weight of mass 2 kg attached to the other end of the string hangs vertically. The weight is released from rest, and takes 3.5 seconds to descend 1 metre. Use an energy equation to estimate the moment of inertia of the rotor. [*Ans. 0.0383 kg m^2.*]
   Hints: Frame 48, equation (1) to find final velocity of weight, v. Frame 63 to calculate ω. Then loss of P.E. = gain of K.E. of wheel (Frame 109) + gain of K.E. of weight (Frame 103).

Programme 2

KINEMATICS OF MECHANISMS:
VELOCITY DIAGRAMS

1

This programme describes a graphical method of analysing mechanical devices, in order to determine the velocities of the various parts. Such analysis might be needed by the designer of a machine tool, who may need to know how the speed of the cutting-tool varies during its stroke, when the driving motor turns at a certain speed. Graphical methods have the disadvantage that they are slow, and not always very accurate. For some simple devices it is possible to determine velocity by calculation, and this is the subject of Programme 4. In recent times, velocity analysis of more complex machines has become possible by the use of computers. But engineers are still required to know the principles of the graphical analysis of machines.

A graphical method clearly requires accuracy of drawing if an accurate result is to be obtained. The programme therefore begins with some suggestions to help you towards developing a good drawing technique. Then, because velocity, along with displacement and acceleration, is a vector, we discuss the properties of vectors, and establish a system of notation. We then discuss the concept of Relative Velocity. By Frame 10, we shall then be able to attempt an actual problem.

2

You will need the following things to see you through this programme:

1. A4 paper, preferably unlined.   5. A fairly large set-square.
2. A good hard pencil, well-sharpened.   6. Compasses.
3. A ruler, or draughtsman's scale   7. Dividers.
4. A protractor.

A small drawing-board is an asset, but not essential.

In drawing ruled lines, remember that the ruler, scale or set-square is not always infinitely thin at the edge. So you should cultivate the technique of tucking the point of the pencil up to the bottom of the edge—the part touching the paper—if you want to be sure of a line that is truly straight.

When you have to draw a line through a point on the paper, it is more accurate to put the pencil on the point and move the edge of the ruler or set-square up to the pencil than to set the edge to the point on the paper.

To measure the distance between two points on the paper, it is more accurate to set the dividers to the points and transfer the dividers to the scale, than to measure directly from the paper with the scale.

You will need frequently to draw lines parallel to, and perpendicular to, other lines, and this is described in Frame 3.

3

The following is a method for drawing parallel and perpendicular lines.

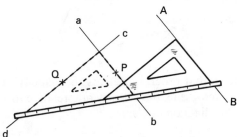

   If you require lines parallel to, or perpendicular to the line AB on the paper, set one edge of the set-square to the line; set the ruler to the edge of the set-square, and then, holding the ruler firmly on the paper, slide the set-square along the ruler until the appropriate edge coincides with the point through which the line must pass (P or Q in the figure). The line ab is parallel to AB; the line cd is perpendicular to AB.

4

A vector needs both magnitude and direction to define it. To state that Birmingham is 110 miles from London does not completely locate Birmingham; you must also state the direction. A line, drawn in the correct direction and to a suitable scale, is a **displacement vector**.

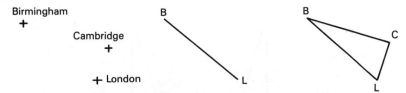

   The vector L–B 'read' in that order, represents the displacement of Birmingham relative to London. If we 'read' the vector in the reverse order, B–L, this is the displacement of London relative to Birmingham. Vectors frequently have arrows on them, indicating the direction of the quantity—particularly force vectors. You will have found examples in Programme 1. But vectors representing relative velocity, which can be 'read' in either direction, should not have arrows on them.

   Vectors may be added. We may, if we wish, travel to Birmingham via Cambridge. This is shown on the third diagram above. The vector LB is then said to be the **resultant** of the two component vectors LC and CB. This may be written:

$$\overline{LB} = \overline{LC} + \overline{CB}$$

The lines across the tops are important. They indicate that the quantities are vectors, and therefore must be added vectorially, in other words, graphically.

5

The rules for velocity vectors are the same as for displacement.

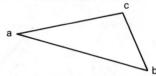

The vector a–c, read in that order, represents the velocity of a point c relative to a point a; a–b similarly represents the velocity of b relative to a. We can actually write six equations from this diagram:

$$\overline{ab} = \overline{ac} + \overline{cb}; \quad \overline{bc} = \overline{ba} + \overline{ac}; \quad \overline{ca} = \overline{cb} + \overline{ba}$$
$$\overline{ba} = \overline{bc} + \overline{ca}; \quad \overline{cb} = \overline{ca} + \overline{ab}; \quad \overline{ac} = \overline{ab} + \overline{bc}$$

and these equations serve to emphasise that vector addition is definitely not the same as algebraic addition. The above diagram illustrates three vectors, but of course the same rules continue to apply for as many vectors as are needed.

Example. A light aircraft capable of an air speed of 90 km/h travels in a wind blowing at 30 km/h from East to West. (a) If the plane is directed due North, what will be its actual direction of flight, and its speed relative to earth? (b) To what direction should the plane be directed in order to travel due North, and what then will its speed be relative to earth?

We adopt the letters e, a and p to indicate earth, air and plane. The vector diagrams are shown.

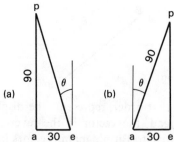

(a) Diagram (a) shows that the direction of the plane relative to earth (ep) will be at an angle of $\theta = \tan^{-1}(30/90) = $ **18.43 degrees West of North**. The true speed, relative to earth, will be $\sqrt{(30^2 + 90^2)} = $ **94.87 km/h**.

(b) Diagram (b) shows the true speed of the plane relative to earth to be due North. The required direction is that of vector ap, the plane velocity relative to air. The magnitude of this is, of course, still 90 km/h. The required heading is at an angle of $\theta = \sin^{-1}(30/90) = $ **19.47 degrees East of North**, and the speed relative to earth now is $\sqrt{(90^2 - 30^2)} = $ **84.85 km/h**.

We have used the term 'relative' several times in this exercise. We shall discuss it in more detail in the next frame.

6

Relative velocity is simply, the velocity of a point relative to some other point. It is not difficult to see that all velocity must be relative; velocity ceases to have meaning if you have no datum by which to measure it. In this programme, you should think of relative velocity as the velocity of one point, relative to some other point, which is assumed to be fixed, even though the second point may clearly be moving. The plane in part (b) of the example of Frame 5 travels due North relative to earth, and an observer on the earth would see the plane moving away to the North. But the pilot would see the observer disappearing away to the South at 84.85 km per hour, and this would be the velocity of the earth relative to the plane. In this programme, we shall frequently refer to 'fixed points'. There are actually no such things; the earth moves beneath us as it rotates; the earth also moves around the sun, which itself moves within the galaxy. But from the point of view of engineering analysis, we may assume the earth to be a fixed point. This really means that the movement of the earth is not relevant to the problem. When engineers design machines such as motor cars, lathes, electrical generators, typewriters, pumps, tractors and so on, the movement of the earth has a negligible effect on calculations of stress, dynamics, fluid or aerodynamics, thermodynamics, and other engineering disciplines which may be relevant to the design and operation of such devices. Of course, the design of a rocket launcher aiming to land a body on the moon would need to take earth movement into account. But in the problems we shall solve in this book, we may assume that the earth is fixed.

7

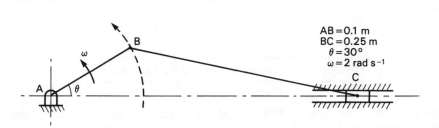

AB = 0.1 m
BC = 0.25 m
$\theta = 30°$
$\omega = 2$ rad s^{-1}

Here is a diagram of a crank, connecting-rod, cylinder and piston mechanism, called the **slider–crank mechanism**. It is used in car engines and many other devices. All bars, cranks and levers are shown just as lines; they are called **links**. Cross-hatching indicates points or surfaces which are assumed to be fixed; thus, the crankshaft turns about the fixed point A, and the cylinder wall, or slider, is also fixed. It is assumed that links do not deform, and that pin-joints between links such as A, B and C, permit turning only, and no lateral movement. In the language of engineering, the system has no **backlash**. These assumptions mean that we can now define a mechanism as a **system of links so arranged that the motion of any one point defines the motions of all other points in the mechanism**.

We shall construct the velocity vector diagram for this mechanism.

8

The drawing of velocity vector diagrams for mechanisms is made easier when you understand one basic principle. This concerns the relative velocities of two points on as single link. In diagram (a) below is a single link with two points A and B on it.

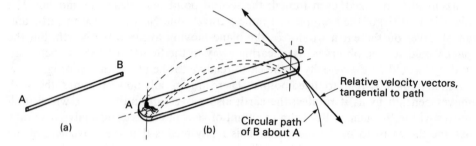

(a)   (b)   Circular path of B about A

Relative velocity vectors, tangential to path

Suppose we need to know the velocity of B *relative to point A*. (We may assume that the link is restricted to motion in the plane of the paper.)

When considering the motion of one point relative to another, you will find it helpful to imagine yourself attached to the second point. So imagine the link to be very large, moving randomly through space, with a seat bolted to the end A, in which you are firmly strapped. This is shown in diagram (b). Now no matter what the link as a *whole* is doing, there is one definite statement that you can make about the point B. Can you think what it is?

9

> It must always remain the same distance from A (you)

This must be so, because the link is rigid: thus, AB is always a constant length. It follows that the motion of B *relative to A* is restricted to a circular path about A. If a point moves in a circular path, the direction of its velocity at any instant must be along the tangent to the circular path. And because a tangent is perpendicular to the radius at that point, this means that the velocity of B relative to A must be perpendicular to the line AB. So the principle you need to understand can be stated:

The velocity of a point on a rigid link at any instant relative to any other point on the link is perpendicular to the straight line joining the two points at that instant

and you will find that you need to apply this to all the problems in this programme. Notice that the argument applies even if the link is not straight. The link could be curved, as shown by the broken lines in diagram (b).

10

To draw the velocity diagram for the mechanism shown in Frame 7, we first calculate the velocity of the crank-pin, B. The magnitude is given by:

$$v = \omega R = 2 \times 0.1 = 0.2 \text{ m s}^{-1}$$

The direction of the velocity must be tangential to the circular path along which B moves around A, that is, it must be perpendicular to AB, and in an 'up-left' direction. But in order to draw a perpendicular to AB, we need an accurate drawing of the mechanism itself. This is called the **configuration diagram**.

Begin your solution of this problem by drawing the configuration diagram of the mechanism on a sheet of A4 paper. Adopt a scale of 4 cm $\equiv$ 0.1 m. Begin with a horizontal line about 5 cm from the top of the paper, and mark point A on it. When you have completed the drawing, draw the vector ab, in the middle of the space below the configuration diagram. Use the method described in Frame 3 to ensure that ab is perpendicular to AB. Adopt a scale of 5 cm $\equiv$ 0.1 m s^{-1}.

11

Your sheet should look something like this, although the diagram here is not to the scale suggested above.

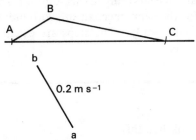

The steps in drawing the configuration diagram are:
1. Draw horizontal line and mark point A.
2. Draw line through A at 30°.
3. Measure 0.1 m along this line to locate B.
4. Centre B, draw arc, radius 0.25 m to intersect horizontal, to locate C.
As a check on your drawing, the angle ACB should be approximately $11\frac{1}{2}°$.

Now consider the velocity of C relative to B. At any instant, the direction of the velocity of C must be perpendicular to the path radius, BC. If this is not immediately obvious to you, re-read Frames 8 and 9.

So draw a line of indefinite length through b, perpendicular to line BC, again using the method of Frame 3; c must lie somewhere on this line.

Finally, the point C is constrained to move along the horizontal slider. So relative to A, C must move horizontally. Complete the diagram by drawing a line through a parallel to AC. It intersects the second vector at c.

12

Your completed solution should look like this.

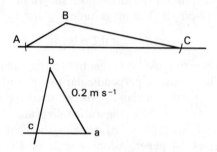

Scaling from the velocity diagram, you should find that ac scales 0.135 m s^{-1} and that bc scales 0.177 m s^{-1}. Do not be too concerned if your figures are slightly different from these; drawing must always involve some error. However, your error in this example should not be more than about 3%.

The vector bc is the velocity of C relative to B. Knowing this enables us to calculate the angular velocity of the link BC. Thus:

$$\omega_{BC} = v/R = v_{BC}/\text{BC} = 0.177/0.25 = \textbf{0.708 rad s}^{-1}$$

Be sure you are clear about everything in this solution. Then draw the configuration and velocity diagrams for the same mechanism, with crank AB moving at the same speed, but now with angle $\theta = 135°$. The steps are exactly as before, but of course the diagrams will be different.

13

Your diagrams should look like this.

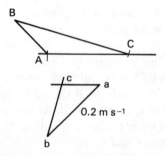

As a check on your configuration diagram, the angle ACB should be approximately $16\frac{1}{2}°$. On the velocity diagram, ac should scale 0.100 m s^{-1} and bc should scale 0.147 m s^{-1}.

Now draw the corresponding diagrams for (a) $\theta = 90°$ and (b) $\theta = 180°$.

Here are the two sets of diagrams.

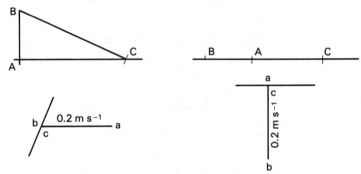

For $\theta = 90°$, draw ab as usual, 0.2 m s^{-1} in length. The velocity of C relative to B is perpendicular to BC; so draw a line through b perpendicular to BC. But relative to A, the velocity of C is horizontal. This means that c is concurrent with b, so (b,c) is one point. So vector bc is of zero length, which means that the angular velocity of link BC at this particular configuration is zero. The slider velocity is the length of vector ac which is 2 m s^{-1}.

Following the same procedure for diagram (b) when $\theta = 180°$, you find that c must lie on a line through b perpendicular to BC, and also on a horizontal through a; thus, point a is concurrent with c. So (a,c) is a single point, or a vector of zero length, and the slider velocity at this instant is zero.

It is not unusual for two points on a velocity diagram to be concurrent; it means simply that the relative velocity of the two points is zero.

15

Example. Draw the velocity diagram for the four-bar chain shown. AB = 0.1 m; BC = 0.16 ,m; CD = 0.2 m; AD = 0.3 m. Angle θ is 60° and link AB is turning clockwise at 5 rad s^{-1}.

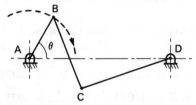

A system of three links connected to two fixed points is called a **four-bar chain**. The fourth 'bar' is the link AB, which is a fixed link.

Begin by drawing the configuration diagram, at the top of an A4 sheet, using a scale of 4 cm $\equiv$ 0.1 m as for the last example. As a check, you should find that CD is 18° below the horizontal. Draw the velocity diagram if you can, but if you have trouble, the solution follows.

16

Your solution should look like this.

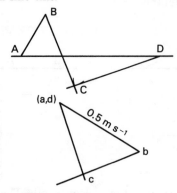

The steps in drawing the configuration diagram are:

(1) Draw horizontal, mark A, and mark D (AD = 0.3 m).
(2) Draw line through A at 60°.
(3) Mark off AB = 0.1 m along this line.
(4) With centre B, draw an arc of radius BC = 0.16 m.
(5) With centre D, draw an arc of radius DC = 0.2 m to intersect the first arc at C.

(You may notice that the two arcs could intersect at two points. But it is clear from the original diagram that C is below the line AB.)

The velocity of B relative to A is calculated

$$v = \omega R = \omega(\text{AB}) = 5 \times 0.1 = 0.5 \text{ m s}^{-1}$$

Vector ab is perpendicular to AB (see Frames 8 and 9). AB rotates clockwise; the direction of ab is therefore 'down-right' as shown. Vector bc must be perpendicular to link BC, so a line is drawn through b of indefinite length.

To locate the point d, we recognise that relative to A, point D has zero velocity, because they are both fixed points. Thus, (a,d) is a single point on the velocity diagram. The rest is simple. Vector dc must be perpendicular to DC; this intersects the other vector at c.

If your drawing was correct, you will find that ac scales 0.395 m s^{-1} and bc scales 0.335 m s^{-1}. The angular velocities of BC and CD are then:

$$\omega_{\text{BC}} = v/R = \text{bc}/\text{BC} = 0.335/0.16 = \textbf{2.094 rad s}^{-1}$$

$$\omega_{\text{CD}} = v/R = \text{cd}/\text{CD} = 0.395/0.2 = \textbf{1.975 rad s}^{-1}$$

The diagram shows that relative to B, C is moving left; thus, ω_{BC} is clockwise. Similarly, ω_{CD} is anti-clockwise.

Now, for this same mechanism, and with the same configuration, i.e. AB at 60° to the horizontal, determine the angular velocities of links BC and CD if the speed of AB is (a) 250 rev/min clockwise; (b) 8 rad s^{-1} anti-clockwise.

17

(a) First convert 250 rev/min to rad s^{-1}:

$$\omega = 2\pi N/60 = 2\pi \times 250/60 = 26.18 \text{ rad s}^{-1}$$

If you take the trouble to go through the whole procedure again, you will of course have the same configuration diagram, but the velocity diagram will be bigger (or perhaps smaller, if you change the scale). But it will be *geometrically similar to the first one*. So there is no need to draw another diagram. All velocities will be *directly proportional to the angular speed of AB*; you can use the same velocity diagram, and in effect, just change the scale. The calculations follow.

$$\omega_{BC} = 2.094 \times 26.18/5 = \textbf{10.96 rad s}^{-1} \textbf{ clockwise}$$

$$\omega_{CD} = 1.975 \times 26.18/5 = \textbf{10.34 rad s}^{-1} \textbf{ anti-clockwise}$$

If the direction of rotation is changed, it is true that the velocity diagram will then be different, but the lengths of the vectors will be the same, if the speed of AB remains the same. So it is still not necessary to re-draw the diagram. The magnitude is again proportional to the angular speed of AB, and reversing direction reverses direction of all the vectors, and the angular velocities of all the links. So for (b):

$$\omega_{BC} = 2.094 \times 8/5 = \textbf{3.35 rad s}^{-1} \textbf{ anti-clockwise}$$

$$\omega_{CD} = 1.975 \times 8/5 = \textbf{3.16 rad s}^{-1} \textbf{ clockwise}$$

So remember: **only ONE velocity diagram is necessary for a given configuration of a mechanism, for all values of speed and for either direction of motion.**

18

The figure below shows the dimensions of a single link. It turns about a pivot at the point A at 1 rad s^{-1}. Draw the velocity diagram for the whole link. Begin with the vector ab; then draw the vector ac, and finally, draw ad, remembering that ad must be perpendicular to AD—even though there is no actual direct link AD. This must be so, because D moves in a circular path around A.

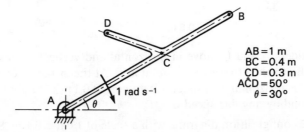

AB = 1 m
BC = 0.4 m
CD = 0.3 m
A$\hat{C}$D = 50°
θ = 30°

1 rad s^{-1}

19

The velocity of B relative to A is given by:

$$v = \omega R = 1 \times 1 = 1 \text{ m s}^{-1}$$

The configuration and velocity diagrams should look like this.

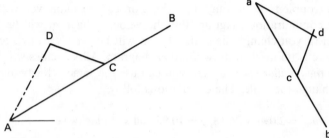

ab is perpendicular to AB and its length is 1 m s^{-1}. To draw ac, we know that ac must be perpendicular to link AC because C turns about A. And because C is at a smaller radius than B, its velocity is reduced in proportion. So ac = ab(AC/AB). Because D turns in a circular path about A, ad is perpendicular to AD, and because D turns about C, cd is perpendicular to CD; thus d is located.

Because all the vectors are perpendicular to the corresponding links, the resulting vector diagram is *geometrically similar in all respects to the configuration diagram.* Such a vector diagram representing various points on a single link is called the **velocity image** of the link. Once we have obtained a velocity vector relating two points on a link, we can extend the vector to include any other points, by drawing the velocity image of the link. This will be found to result in some saving of time in some of the examples following.

This next example makes use of the velocity image principle.

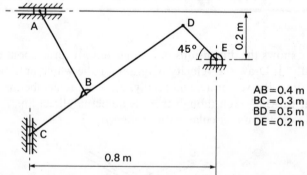

AB = 0.4 m
BC = 0.3 m
BD = 0.5 m
DE = 0.2 m

Example. Sliders A and C move in horizontal and vertical guides. CD is a single link with AB attached to it by a pin-joint at B. At the instant shown, the crank DE is at 45° to the horizontal, and slider A is moving at 0.1 m s^{-1} right to left. Determine the corresponding angular speed of DE.

Begin with the configuration diagram, with a scale of 1 cm ≡ 0.1 m. Start by locating point E, and the horizontal and vertical lines for the slider guides.

20

Do not be misled by the lettering of a diagram. The correct order of drawing the configuration diagram is to begin with the crank DE. The complete procedure follows.

1. Locate E.
2. Draw the horizontal line 0.2 m above E.
3. Draw the vertical line 0.8 m to the left of E.
4. Draw a line through E at 45°.
5. Step off ED = 0.2 m along this line to locate D.
6. With centre D, draw an arc of radius DC = 0.8 m to intersect the vertical line; thus locate C.
7. Step off CD = 0.3 m along CD to locate B.
8. With centre B, draw an arc of radius BA = 0.4 m to intersect the horizontal line; thus locate A.

Check that your diagram is correct. AB and CD should make angles of approximately 59° and 35° with the horizontal.

Now try to draw the velocity diagram.

21

Because the velocity of the slider at A is given, you might well expect to begin the velocity diagram by drawing this vector. Point E is a fixed point, and so this vector would be labelled ea from right to left, scaled proportionately to a length of 0.1 m s^{-1}. You can then draw a line through a perpendicular to the link AB; point b must lie along this line somewhere.

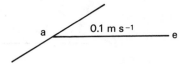

But from here on, you are in trouble; you can go no further. The correct procedure is to begin with vector ed. Because the magnitude of the velocity of D is unknown, you make this vector any convenient length. You do not even know whether ED rotates clockwise or anti-clockwise. So assume that it turns clockwise, and make the vector ed a length of 2 cm. You can then draw dc, knowing that C moves vertically relative to the fixed point E. Then draw the velocity image of line DBC; just divide dc in the ratio 5:3. This may be done either by measuring dc, or by a simple geometrical subdivision. Finally, ba can be drawn.

The procedure is set out in detail in Frame 22, with completed diagrams. It is interesting to note that you actually draw the complete velocity diagram without using any stated value of velocity.

22

The steps in drawing the velocity diagram follow.

1. Fix the starting-point, e.
2. Draw ed = 2 cm perpendicular to ED, in an 'up-right' direction, i.e. assuming a clockwise rotation of ED.
3. Draw a vector through d perpendicular to DC of indefinite length; point c must lie on this line.
4. Draw a vertical through e to locate point c. (The velocity of C relative to E is vertical.)
5. Divide the vector dc at b such that the ratio db:bc is the same as the ratio DB:BC which is 5:3.
6. Draw a vector through b perpendicular to BA of indefinite length; point a must lie on this line.
7. Draw a horizontal through e to locate point a. (The velocity of A relative to E is horizontal.)

This completes the diagram, which is reproduced below. You should find that the vector ea scales approximately 4.03 cm.

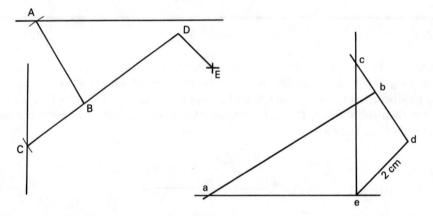

The information given in the question can now be used. The length of the vector ea must represent a velocity of 0.1 m s^{-1}. With this information, we can now establish a scale for the diagram, and then calculate any other velocities required. The question asks for the angular velocity of ED, which requires the linear velocity ed. This was drawn 2 cm long. Taking the length of ea as 4.03 cm, we can say:

$$\text{velocity of D} = 2 \times (0.1/4.03) = 0.0496 \text{ m s}^{-1}$$

$$\therefore \quad \omega_{ED} = v/R = 0.0496/0.2 = \mathbf{0.248 \text{ rad s}^{-1}}$$

The direction of vector ea indicates that slider A moves right-to-left. Therefore, the rotation of ED was correctly assumed to be clockwise.

Here are a few suggestions which might be helpful.

1. Do not draw diagrams too small, because they will not be very accurate.
2. But do not draw them too large, because you might find yourself running out of paper half-way through your solution!
3. Use a complete sheet of A4 paper for each problem, and arrange for the configuration to occupy about one-third to one-half of the sheet. This should leave adequate space for a velocity diagram of reasonable size.
4. Make a rough preliminary sketch of the velocity diagram on a separate sheet. This can be done quite quickly, will give you good practice, and will also help you to choose a convenient scale, and to determine whereabouts in the available space to begin the diagram.
5. Finally, do not decide on a complicated scale simply in order to fill your paper. A scale for a configuration diagram of $13\frac{1}{2}$ cm to 1 m will be no more accurate than, say, 10 cm to 1 m, and will be less simple to draw.

24

PROBLEMS

1.

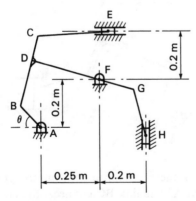

The figure illustrates a double-pump mechanism. The crank AB turns clockwise at 45 revolutions per minute and operates the two pump pistons at E and H. BC and DG are both single links, with pin-joints at intermediate points D and F. Lengths are: AB = 0.12 m; BC = 0.3 m; BD = 0.2 m; DG = 0.45 m; DF = 0.3 m; CE = 0.3 m; GH = 0.2 m. Dimensions relating fixed pivots and sliders are shown. Determine the speeds of the two sliders when AB is at angle $\theta = 45°$ to the horizontal. [*Ans. E: 0.032 m s^{-1}; H: 0.21 m s^{-1}.*]

Hints: begin velocity diagram with 'fixed' point (a,f). Construct in the order ab, bd/fd; image d–f–g; gh; image b–d–c; ce.

2.

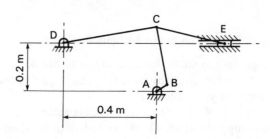

The diagram shows details of a simple press. A and D are fixed pivots, about which crank AB and link DC turn. The slider at E is the actual press. The lengths of the links are: AB = 0.05 m; BC = 0.25 m; DC = 0.4 m; CE = 0.3 m.
(a) For the configuration shown, AB is at 30° to the horizontal. Determine the angular speed of AB when the slider E is moving at 0.02 m s^{-1}.
(b) Determine the speed of the slider at E, assuming the same angular speed of AB, after it has turned 120° clockwise from the position shown.
[*Ans. (a) 1.067 rad s^{-1}; (b) 0.*]
Hints: for (a), begin the velocity diagram with vector ab; see Frame 21. For (b) it is necessary only to sketch the velocity diagram.

3.

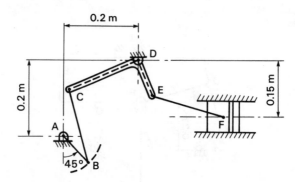

The figure above shows the mechanism of a pump. Crank AB turns clockwise about the fixed pivot at A. The link BC connects the crank to a single link CDE which is right-angled, and which pivots about the fixed point D. The connecting-rod EF connects this link to the pump plunger at F which is constrained to move along the fixed horizontal cylinder. Dimensions of the links are: AB = 0.1 m; BC = 0.2 m; CD = 0.2 m; DE = 0.1 m; EF = 0.2 m. Other dimensions are shown in the figure.
(a) With the crank AB in the position shown, determine the crank speed corresponding to a plunger speed of 0.05 m s^{-1}.
(b) Assuming the same crank speed, what will be the speed of the plunger when the crank has turned through an additional 45° from the position shown?
[*Ans. (a) 2.5 rad s^{-1}; (b) 0.0175 m s^{-1}.*]
Hints: begin with vector ab. The velocity image of link CDE will be required.

25

Sometimes, links are connected so that one link slides along another.

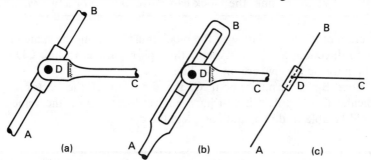

(a)   (b)   (c)

In diagram (a), a block is fitted to slide easily along the link AB. The end of the other link CD is forked and fits on two pins attached to the sliding block. Diagram (b) is similar, except that the sliding block is smaller, and link AB is made with a slot in which the block slides. Diagram (c) shows how this arrangement is normally illustrated.

This calls for a particular treatment when a velocity diagram is required.

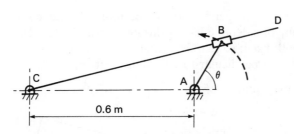

26

0.6 m

Example. In the diagram, crank AB, 0.2 m long, turns anti-clockwise at 8 rad s^{-1} about the fixed point A. End B is attached by a pin to a block which slides freely along the link CD which pivots about the fixed point C, so that as the crank rotates, the link oscillates up and down. Calculate the angular speed of the link CD when angle θ is (a) 60°; (b) 0°; (c) 120°.

Begin your solution by drawing the configuration diagram for $\theta = 60°$, adopting a scale of 1 cm $\equiv$ 0.1 m. You should find that CD is at 13.9° to the horizontal.

Now calculate the velocity of B relative to A. Draw the vector ab, perpendicular to AB.

At this point we must recognise that B is the block at the end of crank AB. Link CD passes through this block and we need a letter to define the point on CD corresponding to the position of the block at this instant. Call this point B_L (B_{LINK}). What is the direction of the velocity of B relative to B_L?

27

Relative to the link, the block can move *only up or down the link*.

The direction of the link relative to the block must be along the same line, although opposite in direction. So draw a vector through b parallel to link CD of indefinite length: b_L must lie somewhere on this line.

Now since B_L is turning about C, the direction of the vector cb_L must be perpendicular to CB_L. And if you have not yet located c on the velocity diagram, you should be able to do so, and complete the diagram.

28

For the configuration diagram:

1. Draw CA = 0.6 m.
2. Draw AB = 0.2 m at 60°.
3. Join CB and extend.

Velocity of B relative to A = $\omega R = 8 \times 0.2 = 1.6$ m s^{-1}.

Steps for the velocity diagram:

1. Draw ab = 1.6 m s^{-1} perpendicular to AB, 'up-left' (for a/c rotation).
2. Draw vector bb_L of indefinite length through b parallel to CD.
3. A and C are both fixed; so (a,c) is a single point on the velocity diagram.
4. Draw vector cb_L perpendicular to CD; thus locate b_L.

And here are the diagrams.

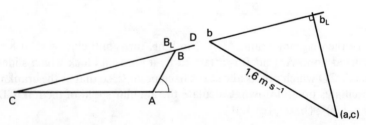

From the velocity diagram, cb_L scales 1.109 m s^{-1} and $b_L b$ scales 1.153 m s^{-1}. For link CD, angular velocity $\omega = v/R = cb_L/CB_L$. From the configuration diagram, CB scales 0.721 m.

$$\therefore \quad \omega_{CD} = 1.109/0.721 = \textbf{1.538 rad s}^{-1}$$

Vector $b_L b$, the sliding velocity of block relative to link, is **1.153 m s^{-1}**.

Now solve part (b) of the exercise (i.e. when $\theta = 0°$).

29

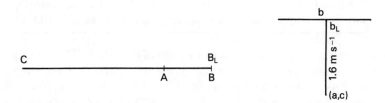

For the case when $\theta = 0°$, the configuration diagram is a straight line. Vector ab is 1.6 m s^{-1} as before but now vertically upwards. Point b$_L$ lies on the intersection of the line through b parallel to CB$_L$ and the line through c perpendicular to CB$_L$. This means that bb$_L$ is a single point. The length of CB$_L$ is seen to be $(0.6 + 0.2) = 0.8$ m.

$$\therefore \qquad \omega_{CD} = cb_L/CB_L = 1.6/0.8 = \textbf{2 rad s}^{-1}$$

The sliding velocity of the block along the link is seen to be zero.

Now complete the exercise by drawing the diagrams for case (c), with $\theta = 120°$. Avoid referring to the solution following if you can. The answer should be $\omega_{CD} = 0.571$ rad s^{-1}.

30

The configuration diagram and the velocity diagram for $\theta = 120°$ are below.

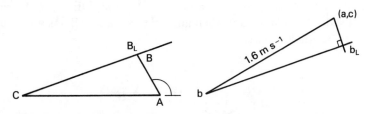

The steps in drawing are the same as listed in Frame 28, allowing for the different angle. As a check on your work, the angle ACB on the configuration diagram should be approximately 19°, the length of CB should be approximately 0.529 m and the length of velocity vector cb$_L$ should be approximately 0.302 m s^{-1}, giving:

$$\omega_{CD} = cb_L/CB_L = 0.302/0.529 = \textbf{0.571 rad s}^{-1}$$

You should note that in this case, the direction of vector cb$_L$ has now reversed; the swinging link CD is now moving back towards the centre. Can you deduce the necessary condition for the angular velocity of the link to be zero?

31

> The link CD will be instantaneously at rest, at the outermost part of its travel, when AB is at right-angles to the link CD

It is easy to show that this corresponds to an angle of $\theta = 109.5°$. The velocity diagram then becomes a single line. Point b_L will coincide with point (ac) and the block will slide along the link at the maximum speed of 1.6 m s^{-1}.

So as the crank turns from $\theta = 0°$ to 180°, link CD moves one way for 109.5° and moves the other way for the remaining 70.5°. For a whole cycle of motion from 0° to 360°, it can be seen that for 219 degrees of crank travel, link CD will move one way, while for the remaining 141 degrees, it moves the other way. This means that the time to travel in one direction is approximately two-thirds the time it takes to travel back again. For this reason, the mechanism is called the 'quick-return mechanism'.

Notice that on the velocity diagrams for both cases (a) and (c), the angle $bb_L c$ is a right-angle. This is a frequent feature of diagrams of mechanisms involving slider-blocks on links.

32

Example. Details of part of a mechanism are shown below. A crank AB turns about a fixed pivot A. A block pinned to end B is arranged to slide along a second link CD which pivots about the fixed point C. Link DE is pinned to D and end E carries a slider which is constrained to move in the horizontal guide. A and C lie on the centre-line of the guide. AB = 1.2 m; CD = 3 m; DE = 2 m. Determine the velocity of slider E at an instant when angle θ is 30° and AB has an angular speed of 10 rad s^{-1} anti-clockwise.

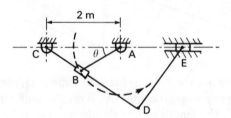

Links AB and CD form the same mechanism as the previous example. A scale of 2 cm ≡ 1 m is satisfactory for the configuration diagram. As a guide, you should find that DE makes an angle of 52.6° with the horizontal. After completing the velocity diagram for AB and CB_L, you then need to draw the velocity image of link $CB_L D$. For this, you will need to measure CB_L accurately from the configuration diagram. It should be approximately 1.13 m. Adopt a scale of 1 cm ≡ 2 m s^{-1} for the velocity diagram.

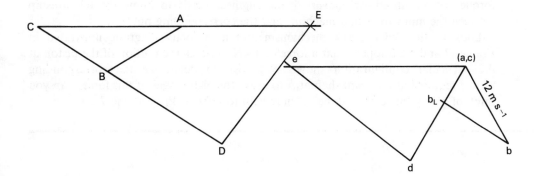

Steps for the configuration diagram:

1. Locate point C. Draw horizontal through C.
2. Measure CA = 2 m to locate A.
3. Draw line at 30° at A.
4. Measure AB = 1.2 m to locate B.
5. Join CB and extend to D (CD = 3 m).
6. Centre D, radius DE = 2 m, draw arc to intersect horizontal at E.
7. Define point B_L on CD coincident with B.

Velocity of B relative to $A = \omega R = 10 \times 1.2 = 12$ m s^{-1}.
  Steps for the velocity diagram:

1. Draw ab = 12 m s^{-1} perpendicular to AB: 'down right' (corresponding to anti-clockwise rotation).
2. Draw 'sliding velocity' vector bb_L through b parallel to CD of indefinite length.
3. Draw tangential velocity vector cb_L perpendicular to CB_L to intersect sliding vector at b_L (points a and c are one point on diagram).
4. Measure CB on configuration diagram.
5. Extend cb_L to d in ratio cb_L:cd::CB_L:CD (velocity image).
6. Draw vector de of indefinite length perpendicular to DE.
7. Draw horizontal through (a,c) to intersect vector at e (velocity of e relative to A, C is horizontal).

From the diagram the velocity of E (vector ae) scales **24.5 m s^{-1}**.

34

Although this programme is titled Kinematics, we shall introduce kinetics at this point, because an understanding of mechanisms must include their function as machines. Regarding a mechanism as an actual machine, through which force or torque is transmitted, or converted, the engineer needs to know the relationship between the input to such a machine, and the corresponding output.

Look at the slider–crank mechanism and its velocity diagram, illustrated in Frames 7 and 12. Suppose that a force of 4 kN opposes the motion of the piston at the particular configuration shown. We wish to determine the corresponding torque required at the crankshaft at A to move the piston against this force. Can you think of a way this can be done? It may help to refer to Programme 7.

35

We make use of the principle of Conservation of Energy.

During a given time, we argue that the work put into the machine (at the crankshaft) must be equal to the work done by the machine (at the piston).

Work per unit time is called **power**. For a shaft turning at angular speed ω, with torque M, the power input is $(M\omega)$. For a piston moving with linear velocity v against a force F, the power is (Fv). Assuming no energy loss in the machine:

$$Fv = M\omega$$

v is found from the velocity diagram (Frame 12). So go ahead and calculate M.

36

From Frame 12, $v = 0.135$ m s^{-1}

$$Fv = M\omega$$

$$\therefore \quad M = Fv/\omega = 4000 \times 0.135/2 = \textbf{270 N m}$$

This calculation assumes no loss of energy. No real machine delivers the same power at the output as the power input; there is always loss due to friction, heat dissipation, and other causes. The ratio of output power to input power is called **efficiency**. It is usually given the Greek letter η (eta):

$$\eta = \text{output power/input power}$$

Look at the diagram in Frame 19. If the piston at A is opposed by a force of $2\frac{1}{2}$ kN and the one at C by 3 kN, what input torque will be required at the shaft at E if the mechanism has an efficiency of 65%?

37

Output power = input power $\times$ 0.65

Here, there are two power output points. From the velocity diagram in Frame 22, the vector ec scales 3.45 cm. Vector ea, which scaled 4.03 cm, represents a velocity of slider A of 0.1 m s^{-1}. To this scale, ec represents a velocity of 0.856 m s^{-1}. The angular velocity of ED was found in Frame 22 to be 0.248 rad s^{-1}. Substituting values in the power equation:

$$2500 \times 0.1 + 3000 \times 0.0856 = M\omega = M \times 0.248 \times 0.65$$

giving:
$$M = \textbf{3142.7 N m}$$

38

This completes the programme except for a summary and problems.

It has to be said that the graphical solution to a kinematic problem has disadvantages. It is relatively slow, and can be inaccurate, particularly in cases where the value of velocity required is very small in comparison with other velocities. For example, if you were to evaluate the piston velocity for the slider–crank mechanism of Frame 7, for a crank angle of 178°, adopting the same scale of 5 cm $\equiv$ 0.1 m s^{-1}, a careful drawing would probably give a sliding velocity vector 2 mm long, indicating a piston velocity of 0.004 m s^{-1}. An accurate *calculation* of the velocity gives a value of 0.004 198 m s^{-1}. Thus, even a very careful drawing results in an error of about 4.7%.

A second disadvantage is that considerable work is required to obtain values for a single configuration. Again referring to the slider–crank mechanism, if we were required to produce a graph of slider velocity against the crank angle θ, we should have to draw complete graphical solutions for at least six different configurations of the mechanism. At the present state of technology this would be impractical, as simple computer methods could be devised for such a project. Moreover, simple mechanisms can be analysed mathematically, as we shall see in Programme 4.

Yet another disadvantage of this method of analysis is that we have to assume rigid links and perfect joints for the graphical work to be valid. There are many examples of quite complex link mechanisms in, for example, printing and textile machinery, in which the actual rods, bars, slides, pin-joints, etc. do allow movement which is not taken into account in the analysis of a theoretically perfect mechanism.

You will have more chances to practise drawing velocity diagrams in the following programme on Acceleration Diagrams.

39

There follows a summary of the procedure for drawing velocity diagrams.

1. Draw a configuration diagram to a suitable scale.
2. Make a rough sketch of the velocity diagram to ascertain the approximate shape and size. (See Frame 23, item 4.)
3. Use the rough sketch to decide on a suitable scale for the velocity diagram.
4. Draw the velocity diagram accurately.
   (a) The velocity of one point on a link relative to another point on the same link is a vector perpendicular to the line joining the two points.
   (b) All 'fixed' points on the configuration diagram are represented on the velocity diagram by a single point.
   (c) The velocity of a slider moving in a fixed guide, relative to fixed points, is a vector parallel to the direction of the guide.
   (d) When a block slides on a moving link, define a point on the link coincident with the position of the block at the instant. The sliding velocity of the block relative to the point on the link will be a vector parallel to the direction of the link at the instant.
   (e) When a velocity vector is defined for any two points on a single link, the vector for any other points on the same link can be determined by extending the vector in geometric ratio to the corresponding points on the link. The resulting extended vector is called the velocity image of the link.
   (f) When necessary, begin the velocity diagram with a vector of arbitrary length. When the diagram is complete, define the scale by reference to the information given.
5. Do not draw more than one velocity diagram for any one configuration. Values of velocity for other conditions vary in proportion to the velocity of any one element, both as to magnitude and direction.
6. Scale all velocities required from the diagram. Calculate any angular velocities required. For a single link defined by any two points, A and B, with a corresponding velocity vector ab, the angular velocity of the link, ω_{AB} is given by:

$$\omega_{AB} = ab/AB$$

7. Calculate all forces and torques required.

$$\text{Output power} = \text{input power} \times \text{efficiency}$$

$$\text{Power} = \text{force} \times \text{velocity}$$

$$\text{Power} = \text{torque} \times \text{angular velocity}$$

When force opposes the motion of a point, the work done *by* the machine is positive. When force acts in the same direction as the motion, the work done *by* the machine is negative, i.e. work is *being* done *on* the machine.

PROBLEMS

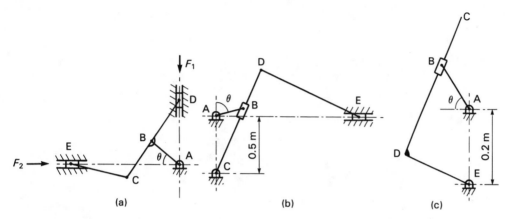

(a) (b) (c)

1. In diagram (a) above, AB, 100 mm long, is pinned at B to CD, D moving in a vertical slideway. CD is 250 mm and BC is 120 mm. CE is 150 mm long and E moves in the horizontal slideway. When θ is 40°, E is moving to the left at 0.2 m s^{-1}. Find the angular speed of AB, and the velocity of D. Find the torque at crank AB assuming no energy loss, if forces $F_1 = 2$ kN and $F_2 = 3\frac{1}{2}$ kN act in the directions shown. [*Ans. 1.734 rad s^{-1}; 0.214 m s^{-1}; 157.7 N m.*]
   Hints: begin with vector ab; see Frame 21. Work at D will be *negative* (see Frame 39, item 7).

2. Diagram (b) above shows a quick-return mechanism. AB = 0.25 m; CD = 1 m; DE = 1 m. Pivot A lies on the horizontal line of the slideway at E, and pivot C is vertically below pivot A. At the instant shown, angle θ is 75° and the crank AB is turning clockwise at 30 rev/min. Determine the sliding velocity of the slider at E, and the angular velocities of links CD and DE. If the motion of E is opposed by a force of 450 N, calculate the torque required at the crank AB, if the machine efficiency is 85%. [*Ans. 0.86 m s^{-1}; 0.783 rad s^{-1} clock.; 0.345 rad s^{-1} anti-clock.; 144.9 N m.*]

3. The mechanism shown at (c) above comprises a crank AB, a sliding swivel-block at B and a single link CDE which has a right-angled bend at D. AB = 0.14 m; CD = 0.4 m; DE = 0.2 m. E is vertically below A. At the instant shown, the angle θ is 55° and AB is turning anti-clockwise at 2 rad s^{-1}. Determine the angular velocity of the bent link CDE and the linear velocity of point C. [*Ans. 0.579 rad s^{-1}; 0.258 m s^{-1}.*]
   Hints: Conf. diag.: locate points A and E and draw AB. Draw semi-circle on BE as diameter and draw arc radius ED centre E to intersect (the angle in a semi-circle is a right-angle). Vel. diag.: B_L relative to B is parallel to CD; B_L relative to E is perpendicular to the line BE. $\omega_{CDE} = eb_L/EB_L$. Construct the image of E–C–D.

Programme 3

KINEMATICS OF MECHANISMS: ACCELERATION DIAGRAMS

1

In this programme, we continue with the analysis of mechanisms, begun in Programme 2, extending the graphical technique to include acceleration. To a design engineer, acceleration is more important than velocity, as it is directly related to force. Much modern machinery operates at very high speeds; the ordinary automobile engine is a typical example, and the moving parts undergo accelerations of a very high order. If such machinery is to operate without breaking apart due to internal stresses, the designer must be able to predict the inertial forces accurately, and allow for them.

It must be made clear that in order to draw the vector diagram of acceleration of a mechanism, it is necessary first to draw the velocity diagram. So do not attempt to begin this programme unless you have worked through Programme 2, and can draw a velocity diagram for a simple mechanism.

2

Here is a diagram of a single link, AB, turning about a fixed pivot at A.

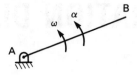

What can you state regarding the acceleration of the point B relative to A? There are four statements you should be able to make. Two refer to acceleration magnitude, and two to direction. Write down as many statements as you can. It might be helpful to look back to Programme 1, Frames 63 and 69.

3

> 1. There is a centripetal acceleration of B relative to A, of magnitude (ω^2AB) where ω is the angular velocity of AB.
> 2. The centripetal acceleration of B relative to A is in the direction B to A.
> 3. If AB has an angular acceleration α, there will be a tangential component of acceleration of B relative to A, of magnitude (αAB).
> 4. The line of action of the tangential acceleration component will be perpendicular to AB.

Thus, in the general case of the acceleration of one point on a single rigid link relative to another point, the acceleration will comprise a **centripetal** component, and a **tangential** component.

4

Work through this simple example yourself.

Example. The link AB (Frame 2) is 0.75 m long. Determine the total acceleration of B relative to A for the following cases.

(a) $\omega = 2$ rad s^{-1}; $\alpha = 4$ rad s^{-2} clockwise.

(b) $\omega = 1$ rad s^{-1}; $\alpha = 2$ rad s^{-2} anti-clockwise.

The answers are: (a) 4.245 m s^{-2} at 45° to AB; (b) 1.677 m s^{-2} at 63.4° to AB. The first is worked out in Frame 5 for you, but do the second yourself.

5

For case (a):

Centripetal acceleration, component $a_c = \omega^2 R = 2^2 \times 0.75 = 3.00$ rad s^{-2}

Tangential acceleration, component $a_t = \alpha R = 4 \times 0.75 = 3.00$ rad s^{-2}

The figure shows the simple vector addition of the components.

The vector sum, ab $= \sqrt{(a_c^2 + a_t^2)} = \sqrt{(3^2 + 3^2)} = \mathbf{4.243\ m\ s^{-2}}$

$$\text{Angle } \theta = \tan^{-1}(3/3) = \mathbf{45°}$$

Since a_c is parallel to AB, the resultant vector makes this angle with AB.

The notation is the same as we used on velocity vector diagrams. a–b, read in that order, is the total acceleration of B relative to A. Similarly b–a, in that order, is the acceleration of A relative to B.

6

If the angular velocity of a link is known, or if the velocity of one point relative to another point on the link is known, the centripetal acceleration of the one point relative to the other can be calculated. This is why the first procedure is to draw the velocity diagram for the mechanism. When this is done, all the relevant centripetal acceleration components can be calculated.

We begin with a four-bar chain. Details are set out in the following frame, and you should go through the procedure yourself. Begin by taking a blank sheet of A4 paper, and construct the configuration and velocity diagrams. This time, dispose the space so that you have enough room to draw an acceleration diagram also; all three diagrams must be on the one sheet. Very roughly, allow about one-third of the sheet for each diagram.

7

Example. Details of a simple four-bar chain are shown in the diagram.

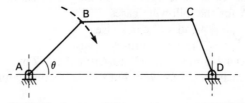

$AB = 1$ m; $BC = 1.5$ m; $CD = 0.8$ m; $AD = 2.5$ m. $\theta = 45°$. Determine the angular accelerations of the links BC and CD when AB is turning clockwise at 5 rad s^{-1} and has an angular acceleration of 10 rad s^{-2} anti-clockwise.

Choose your own scales for the configuration and velocity diagrams, referring if necessary to the remarks in Programme 2, Frame 23, and leaving space to draw an acceleration diagram. As a check on the configuration diagram, link CD should make an angle of 68.5° to AD. The lengths of the velocity vectors bc and dc should be 4.88 m s^{-1} and 3.67 m s^{-1}.

Now calculate all the centripetal acceleration components, and also the tangential component of B relative to A. The calculations appear in Frame 8, but if your own values of velocities vary slightly from the ones given here, use your own values.

8

Centripetal acceleration of B relative to A $= \omega^2 R = 5^2 \times 1 = 25$ m s^{-2}
Tangential acceleration of B relative to A $= \alpha R = 10 \times 1 = 10$ m s^{-2}
Cent. acc. of C rel. to B $= v^2/R = (\text{bc})^2/\text{BC} = 4.88^2/1.5 = 15.88$ m s^{-2}
Cent. acc. of C rel. to D $= v^2/R = (\text{cd})^2/\text{CD} = 3.67^2/0.8 = 16.84$ m s^{-2}

Your configuration and velocity diagrams should look like this.

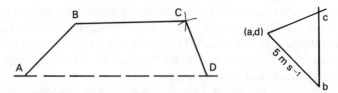

The acceleration diagram is drawn completely in the following frame, with explanatory notes, but of course, it must actually be drawn on the same sheet as the configuration diagram, in order that the vectors may be drawn parallel to, or perpendicular to the links themselves. The configuration diagram is repeated in Frame 9 for this purpose.

Here is a 'repeat' of the configuration diagram, with the acceleration diagram. The vectors are numbered in the order in which they have been drawn.

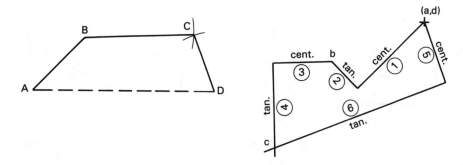

This is the procedure for drawing the acceleration diagram.

1. Draw the centripetal vector from (a,d) in the direction B to A, length 25 m s^{-2}.
2. Draw the tangential vector from the end of this perpendicular to AB, in the 'up-left' direction (corresponding to anti-clockwise angular acceleration), length 10 m s^{-2}. This locates point b.
3. Draw the centripetal vector from b in the direction C to B, length 15.88 m s^{-2}. This is the centripetal acceleration of C relative to B.
4. Draw the tangential acceleration component from the end of this perpendicular to BC, of indefinite length: c must lie on this line.
5. Draw the centripetal vector from (a,d) in the direction C to D of length 16.84 m s^{-2}. This is the centripetal acceleration of C relative to D.
6. Draw the tangential acceleration component from the end of this perpendicular to CD. c must lie on this line, c is located where the line intersects the line drawn under 4 above.

To complete the exercise, measure the two tangential vectors (C rel. to B (4) and C rel. to D (6)). These should scale respectively approximately 23.2 m s^{-2} and 50 m s^{-2}, although small errors of drawing could result in possibly 5% variation on these values. From these values, the angular accelerations of the respective links are calculated:

$$\alpha_{BC} = a_{tan}/R = 23.2/1.5 = \textbf{15.47 rad s}^{-2}$$

$$\alpha_{CD} = a_{tan}/R = 50.0/0.8 = \textbf{62.5 rad s}^{-2}$$

To gain practice in this work, repeat this whole exercise, with the velocity and acceleration of AB the same, but with the angle θ now 30° instead of 45°. Complete details are not given, but small diagrams are shown in Frame 10 with some figures for you to check your own work. The procedure listed above is exactly the same.

10

The three diagrams, (a), (b) and (c) are respectively the configuration, velocity and acceleration diagrams.

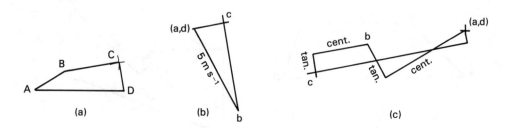

(a) (b) (c)

Here are a few values for you to check your own attempt.

In the configuration diagram, link CD should make an angle of 78.4° with AD.

In the velocity diagram, you should obtain values of 4.75 m s^{-1} and 1.64 m s^{-1} for the vectors bc and dc respectively.

In the acceleration diagram, the tangential component for C relative to D should scale approximately 41.8 m s^{-2}. The tangential component for C relative to B should scale approximately 5.25 m s^{-2}.

You should consider the stated velocity values as accurate, and if you are not close to these values, examine your work carefully and see if you can find any errors. The values for acceleration cannot be considered so accurate, and you can allow an error of 5% either way on the stated values.

To complete the exercise, use your own values of tangential acceleration components to calculate the angular accelerations of the links BC and CD, as was done in the previous frame for the other configuration. For the values given above, you can check that the accelerations will be $\alpha_{BC} = 3.5$ rad s^{-2} and $\alpha_{CD} = 52.19$ rad s^{-2}.

Before we work through the next example, we must establish the concept of the **acceleration image**. If you understood the velocity image in Programme 2, then you will have no difficulty with the acceleration image. The principle can be stated as follows.

When an acceleration vector is defined for any two points on a single link, the vector for any other points on the same link can be determined by extending the vector in geometric ratio of the corresponding points on the link. The resulting extended vector is called the **acceleration image** of the link.

If you refer back to Frame 39 of Programme 2, item (e), you will find that exactly the same wording was used for defining the velocity image. The only additional point which you have to remember is, that before you construct an image, you require the *total* accelerations of points, that is, both centripetal and tangential components. The example in Frame 11 should make this clear.

11

Example. The diagram shows a mechanism of four links. AB is 0.1 m, BC is 0.3 m; BD is 0.2 m; DE is 0.14 m; GC is 0.12 m; EF is 0.3 m. BCDE is a single rigid link with a right-angled branch DE. The slider is horizontal and the line passes through the pivot A. At the instant shown, AB is turning clockwise at 4 rad s^{-1} and also has a clockwise angular acceleration of 12 rad s^{-2}. The angle θ between AB and the horizontal is 20°. For this configuration, determine the sliding acceleration of the slider at F, and the angular accelerations of all the links.

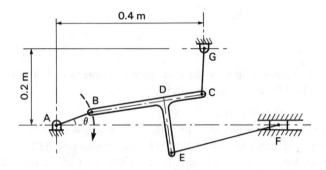

The drawing of the configuration diagram should not present many problems. Remember first that your sheet will have to take all three diagrams, so leave adequate space. A scale of 2 cm $\equiv$ 0.1 m is satisfactory. Do not be misled by the lettering; construct the four-bar chain A–B–C–G first of all, and then D–E–F. You would be unable to construct in the order A–B–C–D–E–F because this part by itself would not constitute a mechanism, whereas A–B–C–G would. Check the angles made to the horizontal by BC and GC; they should be respectively 7.3° and 86°.

A suggested scale for the velocity diagram is 2 cm $\equiv$ 0.1 m s^{-1}. The diagram is reproduced for you in the following frame over the page, with notes, and refer to these if you have difficulty. If you wish to complete your diagram without referring to them, here are some of the values you should obtain.

> Vector bc should scale approximately 0.375 m s^{-1}
> Vector cg should scale approximately 0.085 m s^{-1}
> Vector ef should scale approximately 0.107 m s^{-1}
> Vector af should scale approximately 0.250 m s^{-1}

Remember, you may not arrive at exactly these values, as there must always be some error in a graphical solution, but if your values vary from these by more than about 2%, you should check your work carefully and ensure that you have not made any serious mistake.

12

Here is the configuration diagram and the velocity diagram.

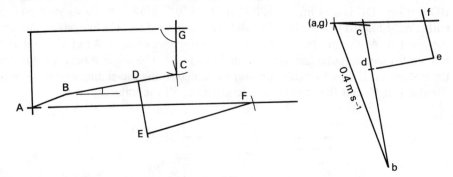

Details of the construction for the configuration diagram should not be necessary. The steps for the velocity diagram follow.

1. Define the 'fixed' points (a,g).
2. Draw vector ab perpendicular to AB, of length $v = \omega R = 4 \times 0.1 = 0.4$ m s^{-1}, 'down-right' (i.e. corresponding to clockwise rotation of AB).
3. Draw vector bc of indefinite length perpendicular to BC; c must lie on this line.
4. Draw vector gc perpendicular to GC, to intersect the above at c.
5. Measure bc and calculate two-thirds of the length (BD is two-thirds of BC). Measure this distance along bc to locate d.
6. Draw line at d perpendicular to bc.
7. Measure de = bc $\times$ DE/BC along this line to locate e. This completes the velocity image of BCDE.
8. Draw vector ef of indefinite length perpendicular to EF.
9. Draw horizontal through (a,g) to intersect above at f. (Velocity of slider at F must be horizontal.)

When drawing the branch de, make sure that your velocity image is a correct one, and not a mirror-image.

Now the various accelerations are calculated. Here, the velocities scaled from the velocity diagram are used. If your values differ, you should of course calculate using your own values, although they should not vary much from the values used here.

Centripetal acceleration of AB $= \omega^2 R = 4^2 \times 0.1 = 1.6$ m s^{-2}

Tangential acceleration of AB $= \alpha R = 12 \times 0.1 = 1.2$ m s^{-2}

Centripetal acceleration of BC $= v^2/R = (\text{bc})^2/\text{BC} = (0.375)^2/0.3 = 0.469$ m s^{-2}

Centripetal acceleration of CG $= v^2/R = (\text{cg})^2/\text{CG} = (0.085)^2/0.12 = 0.0602$ m s^{-2}

Centripetal acceleration of EF $= v^2/R = (\text{ef})^2/\text{EF} = (0.107)^2/0.3 = 0.0382$ m s^{-2}

13

Here follows a step-by-step set of instructions for drawing the acceleration diagram. A scale of 1 cm $\equiv$ 0.2 m s^{-2} will be found to result in a diagram approximately 10 cm by 10 cm.

1. Locate the starting-point (a,g) representing the two fixed points, A and G.
2. Draw the vector from (a,g) for the centripetal acceleration of B relative to A of magnitude 1.6 m s^{-2}, and in the direction B to A.
3. From the end of the above, draw the tangential acceleration vector for B relative to A, of magnitude 1.2 m s^{-2}, and perpendicular to AB in the 'down-right' direction consistent with clockwise angular acceleration of AB. This fixes the point b on the diagram.
4. From point b, draw the centripetal acceleration vector for C relative to B, of magnitude 0.469 m s^{-2} and in the direction C to B.
5. From the end of this, draw the tangential acceleration vector for C relative to B, of indefinite length, perpendicular to BC. The point c must lie on this line.
6. From point (a,g), draw the centripetal acceleration vector for C relative to G, of magnitude 0.0602 m s^{-2} and in the direction G to C.
7. From the end of this, draw the tangential acceleration vector for C relative to G. The length is unknown, but c is found where this vector intersects the one drawn at 5 above.
8. Join the points b and c. Measure bc.
9. Divide bc at d such that bc:cd is the same as BC:CD, i.e. 3:1.
10. Draw a line at d perpendicular to bc to construct the image of DE. Take care that the line is drawn to the correct side of bc, i.e. to the right when looking from b to c.
11. Mark point e on this line such that de:bc is the same as DE:BC, i.e. 0.14:0.3. b–c–d–e is then the acceleration image of B–C–D–E.
12. From point e, draw the centripetal acceleration vector for F relative to E, of magnitude 0.0382 m s^{-2} and in the direction F to E.
13. From the end of this, draw the tangential acceleration vector for F relative to E, of indefinite length, perpendicular to EF. Point f must lie on this line.
14. Draw a vector through point (a,g) parallel to slider at F, i.e. horizontal. Because the acceleration of F relative to A is horizontal, f lies on this line. f is located where the line intersects the vector drawn at 13 above.

The diagram is reproduced in the following frame. You should of course use your own values for the calculated accelerations. You will find that the magnitudes of some of the acceleration components from 12 onwards in the above sequence are extremely small. Note particularly in the construction that the acceleration image is constructed only after the *total* acceleration of B relative to C has been determined.

14

The complete acceleration diagram for the example of Frame 11 is drawn below, along with a 'repeat' of the configuration diagram.

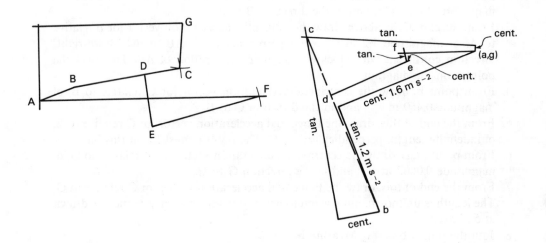

The tangential acceleration components for links BCDE, CG and EF are given below; values from your solution may of course differ slightly from these.

For BCDE: tangential component (b rel. to c) scales 1.96 m s^{-2}

For CG: tangential component (g rel. to c) scales 1.85 m s^{-2}

For EF: tangential component (e rel. to f) scales 0.09 m s^{-2}

The last of these measurements must be considered speculative. The vector is only approximately $4\frac{1}{2}$ mm long, and in such circumstances, very high percentage errors are possible. For example, if your version gave a length of 5 mm, which could be quite probably, as $\frac{1}{2}$ mm is not a large amount to allow for drawing error, the percentage error could be 11%. The angular accelerations are calculated in the next frame. Work them out yourself first.

Angular acceleration of BCDE: $\alpha_{BC} = 1.96/0.3 = $ **6.53 rad s**$^{-2}$
Angular acceleration of CG: $\alpha_{CG} = 1.85/0.12 = $ **15.42 rad s**$^{-2}$
Angular acceleration of EF: $\alpha_{EF} = 0.09/0.3 = $ **0.30 rad s**$^{-2}$
Sliding acceleration of F: af scales **0.776 m s**$^{-2}$

PROBLEMS

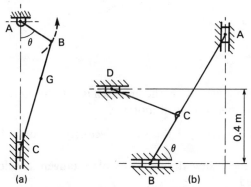
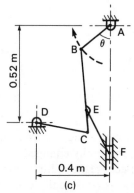

(a)   (b)   (c)

1. Diagram (a) above shows a simple slider–crank mechanism. AB = 0.2 m; BC = 0.6 m. G represents the mass centre of the link BC and BG = 0.2 m. Determine the acceleration of the slider at C and the acceleration of the point G, for values of the angle θ of 0°, 45°, 90° and 180° when the crank AB turns anti-clockwise at a constant rate of 200 rev min^{-1}. [*Ans. 0°: 116.98 m s*$^{-2}$; *97.58 m s*$^{-2}$. *45°: 62.03 m s*$^{-2}$; *74.7 m s*$^{-2}$. *90°: 31.02 m s*$^{-2}$; *59.34 m s*$^{-2}$. *180°: 58.48 m s*$^{-2}$; *77.98 m s*$^{-2}$.]
Hint: diagrams for 0° and 180° need to be sketched only.

2. In the mechanism shown in diagram (b) above, the ends of the link AB move in vertical and horizontal guides. Link CD is pinned to the link AB and D is constrained by a horizontal slideway. AB = 0.8 m; AC = 0.5 m; CD = 0.4 m. Determine the velocities and accelerations of ends B and D when the angle θ is 60° and when A is moving downwards with a constant velocity of 2 m s^{-1}. [*Ans. B: 3.464 m s*$^{-1}$; *40 m s*$^{-2}$. *D: 1.77 m s*$^{-1}$; *27.52 m s*$^{-2}$.]
Hint: the velocity and acceleration of B can be *calculated* from the trigonometry of the velocity and acceleration diagrams which will be right-angled triangles.

3. In the mechanism shown in diagram (c) above, AB = 0.2 m, BC = 0.45 m, CD = 0.28 m, EF = 0.27 m and BE = 0.32 m; BC is a single rigid link to which EF is pinned at E. Determine the acceleration of the slider at F when the angle θ is 50° and AB turns at a constant speed of 36 rev min^{-1} clockwise. [*Ans. 2.32 m s*$^{-2}$.]
Hints: centripetal acceleration of F relative to E is very small, and e and f are practically coincident points on the diagram.

17

So far, we have avoided the problem of a block sliding along a link which is itself turning. This involves a new component of acceleration called the **Coriolis component**. There is no particular mystery attached to the Coriolis component, once you clearly understand that acceleration is a change of velocity, and that velocity, being a vector, changes when its direction changes, as well as its magnitude.

Look carefully at the situation shown in the figure.

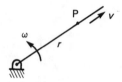

A point P is moving along a line with a velocity v; the line itself is rotating at angular velocity ω. There are two results of this combined motion.

1. Because the line is turning, the *direction* of the sliding velocity vector is being continually changed.
2. Because the radius is continually increasing, the *magnitude* of the tangential velocity, ωr, is continually being increased.

Both of these effects are the result of the *combination* of turning and sliding. If either ω or v were zero, neither would occur.

Before deriving the simple expression for the Coriolis acceleration, we may mention some simple illustrations of its effects. The rotation of the earth means that lines of longitude are rotating, so that a body following a line of longitude suffers a Coriolis acceleration. Thus, an air current which, on a stationary globe, might blow from North to South, cannot do so on the turning earth, as no force can act upon it. The result is that the air currents tend to get 'left behind', so to speak, by the spinning earth, and the prevailing wind directions are normally oblique to the lines of longitude.

Another illustration of the Coriolis acceleration is that of a disc spinning at high speed. If the spinning disc is turned about an axis perpendicular to the spin axis, a simple analysis shows that elements of the disc are subject to a Coriolis acceleration, the result of which is that, in order to turn the disc about the required axis, you have to apply a torque about an axis *perpendicular to this axis*. The required torque is called the **gyroscopic torque**. Thus, if you hold a spinning bicycle wheel in your hands by its axle, so that it spins in a vertical plane, a clockwise twist on the axle, up with the left hand and down with the right, will have the surprising result that the wheel will twist about a *vertical* axis.

The effect was discovered and analysed by the French physicist G. Coriolis as recently as 1835.

18

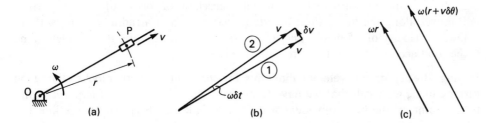

(a)   (b)   (c)

Diagram (a) shows a link pivoted at O, with a sliding block P moving outwards along it at velocity v. We shall consider the two effects mentioned in the previous frame separately.

First, the change of direction of the sliding velocity vector. Diagram (b) shows a vector 1 of length v, and a vector 2, also of length v, after an increment of time δt. In that time, the link will rotate through an angle $(\omega \delta t)$ and this will be the angle between the two vectors. The change of velocity, δv (for a very small angle), will be $(v\omega\delta t)$. The rate of change of velocity, that is, the acceleration, will thus be $(v\omega)$ and in the limit, this is seen to be in the direction perpendicular to the direction of sliding.

Diagram (c) shows a vector representing the tangential velocity at an instant. This will have magnitude (ωr) at an instant. But after a time lapse δt, the radius will increase by an amount $(v\delta t)$ so that the tangential velocity will increase in magnitude by an amount $(\omega v\delta t)$. The resulting acceleration, or rate of change, will be $(v\omega)$, as before, and will also be in the same direction.

Thus, the total acceleration arising out of this condition is $2v\omega$. This is the magnitude of the Coriolis component of acceleration.

19

We may summarise the Coriolis component of acceleration:

When a body moves with a velocity v along a path which is turning with an angular velocity ω, it is subjected to a Coriolis acceleration of magnitude $2v\omega$.

The direction of the Coriolis component is the direction of the sliding velocity, advanced 90° in the direction of the rotation.

You are reminded that this acceleration has been shown to exist on a link turning at a *constant* speed, with a block sliding along it at *constant* speed. If these speeds are not constant, there will be in addition, a tangential acceleration component, and a sliding acceleration component. And, of course, there is also the centripetal acceleration component.

20

Example. A link turns about a fixed pivot with a clockwise angular velocity of 2 rad s^{-1} and an anti-clockwise angular acceleration of 3 rad s^{-2}. A particle P moves along the link and at a certain instant, it is at a radius of 2 m, with an inward velocity of 1.5 m s^{-1} and an outward acceleration of 2 m s^{-2}. Determine the total acceleration of P relative to the pivot.

Having already drawn velocity diagrams for mechanisms with blocks sliding on turning links, we recall that we have to allocate separate letters to the point P and to the point on the link coincident with it. We shall call the point on the link P_L. We begin by calculating the centripetal and tangential acceleration components of acceleration of P_L relative to the plot, which we shall call O.

$$\text{Centripetal acceleration } a_c = \omega^2 r = 2^2 \times 2 = 8 \text{ m s}^{-2}$$

$$\text{Tangential acceleration } a_t = \alpha r = 3 \times 2 = 6 \text{ m s}^{-2}$$

The sliding component of acceleration of the block along the link is given. We calculate the magnitude of the Coriolis component from the formula just derived.

$$\text{Sliding acceleration } a_s = 2 \text{ m s}^{-2} \text{ (given)}$$

$$\text{Coriolis acceleration } a_{cor} = 2v\omega = 2 \times 1.5 \times 2 = 6 \text{ m s}^{-2}$$

The diagram can now be drawn, and is shown here, the vectors drawn in the order calculated. The 'configuration diagram' of the line and point P are also shown.

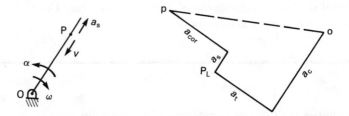

The magnitude of the total acceleration of P relative to O (vector op.) is **13.42 m s^{-2}**.

In this particular example, we could have begun by drawing the tangential component before the centripetal. But when analysing mechanisms, the magnitude of the centripetal component is usually known, and therefore is drawn first.

The direction of the Coriolis component is determined by the rule given. The sliding velocity vector is directed radially inwards; this is 'advanced' 90° in the direction of rotation of OP, which in this case is clockwise.

If you are sure you understand how the diagram has been constructed, make an attempt at drawing the diagram yourself, for the case when all four quantities, v, ω, A_a and α are in the reverse direction to those shown.

21

Here is the diagram for the previous example, with velocities and accelerations all reversed in direction. The magnitudes of all four vectors remain the same.

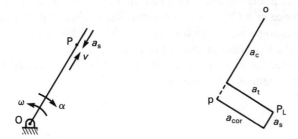

The diagram is seen to be quite different. Of course, the centripetal vector is in the same direction as before: centripetal acceleration is always directed towards the centre of rotation. The direction of the tangential component is in the reverse direction, and so is the sliding acceleration component, a_s. Perhaps surprisingly, the direction of the Coriolis component has not changed. This is because both sliding velocity, and direction of angular velocity have both changed, leaving the Coriolis vector unaltered.

The magnitude of the total acceleration is seen to be **10 m s^{-2}**.

22

PROBLEMS

1. A horizontal pipe of length 8 m is mounted on a central pivot so that it can turn in a horizontal plane at a speed of 30 rev min^{-1}. Water is directed into the pipe at the central pivot and flows radially outwards. The pipe bore is 5 cm diameter and the flow rate is 1.2 m^3 per minute. Calculate the magnitude of the Coriolis acceleration component (a) at the pipe centre, and (b) at the maximum radius of 4 m. [*Ans. 64.00 m s^{-2}.*]
   Hint: answer to both parts is the same; Coriolis acceleration is independent of position.

2. A link turns about a fixed pivot in a vertical plane, with angular velocity ω and angular acceleration of 4 rad s^{-2} clockwise. A point P moves along the link with a sliding velocity of 2 m s^{-1} inwards from the pivot, and a sliding acceleration of 1 m s^{-1} outwards. If, at the instant the link is vertically upwards, P is at a radius of 1.5 m and the total acceleration of P is horizontal, what is the value of ω, and what is the total acceleration of P? [*Ans. $\omega = 0.8165$ rad s^{-1}; a$_{tot} = 2.734$ m s^{-2}.*]
   Hint: sketch the four vectors. It can be seen that for the stated condition, centripetal component = sliding component; hence find ω.

23

We now study an actual mechanism which involves a Coriolis acceleration. Learn to 'spot' the existence of a Coriolis component. Remember that it is found whenever a point is *moving* along a path which is *turning*. When a block moves along a slideway which is fixed, the Coriolis component does not exist.

We shall take for the first example, the simple 'quick-return' mechanism which we looked at in Programme 2, Frame 26.

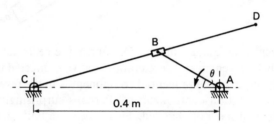

Example. In the mechanism shown, link AB is 0.15 m long and CD is 0.5 m long. At the instant shown, AB is at angle $\theta = 30°$ to AC, and is turning anti-clockwise at a constant rate of 30 rev min^{-1}. Determine the angular acceleration of the link CD, the sliding acceleration of slider B along CD, and the linear acceleration of D.

The first part of the solution should be straightforward by this stage. Draw the configuration diagram and the velocity diagram on a single sheet of A4 paper, leaving plenty of space to include an acceleration diagram. Choose your own scales, recalling the remarks in Frame 23 of Programme 2. When you have completed the velocity diagram, you can then calculate the centripetal acceleration components for both AB and CD. You may need to refresh your memory by referring to Programme 2. Recall particularly that you will need to allocate a letter to the point on CD corresponding to the position of the block; call the point B_L.

As a check on your work you should find that on the configuration diagram, CD makes an angle of 15.5° with CA, and the length of CB_L should be 0.28 m. In the velocity diagram, vectors bb_L and cb_L should scale approximately 0.336 m s^{-1} and 0.330 m s^{-1} respectively.

The two diagrams are reproduced in the next frame, although detailed step-by-step instructions are not included this time, as the sequence will be exactly the same as for the example in Programme 2, detailed in Frame 28, allowing for the different direction of rotation and dimensions.

24

The velocity of B relative to A is first calculated.

$$v = \omega R = (2\pi \times 30/60)(0.15) = 0.471 \text{ m s}^{-1}$$

and the configuration and velocity diagrams should look like these.

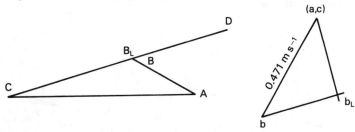

Before beginning the acceleration diagram, we calculate the centripetal acceleration components of both AB and CB_L, and the Coriolis component. Work these out, using your own velocity values, if they are different from the ones shown (although if the difference is considerable, you should check to see where you have made mistakes). The calculations are given in Frame 25.

25

Centripetal acceleration of B rel. to A $= \omega^2 R = (2\pi \times 30/60)^2(0.15) = 1.48 \text{ m s}^{-2}$

Centripetal acceleration of B_L rel. to C $= v^2/R = (cb_L)^2/CB_L = (0.33)^2/0.28$

$$= 0.389 \text{ m s}^{-2}$$

To calculate the Coriolis component, a_{cor}, we use the expression

$$a_{cor} = 2v\omega$$

where v is, in this case, the sliding velocity of the block along CD, bb_L, which is 0.336 m s^{-1}, and ω is the angular velocity of CD.

$$\omega_{CD} = cb_L/CB_L = 0.330/0.28 = 1.179 \text{ rad s}^{-1}$$

$$\therefore \quad a_{cor} = 2 \times 0.336 \times 1.179 = 0.792 \text{ m s}^{-2}$$

If you wish to draw the acceleration diagram, here is the order of procedure.

1. Define 'fixed' point (a,c).
2. Draw centripetal vector ab of length 1.48 m s^{-2} in direction B to A.
3. Draw Coriolis vector of length 0.792 m s^{-2} perpendicular to CD.
4. Draw sliding vector from end of this of unknown length parallel to CD.
5. Draw centripetal vector of length 0.389 m s^{-2} in direction B_L to C.
6. Draw tangential vector from end of this perpendicular to CD. This will intersect the vector drawn under 4 at point b_L.

26

Specific instructions as to the direction of the Coriolis component were omitted from the procedure in the previous frame, to give you the opportunity to work it out for yourself. First, here is the complete solution, with the configuration and velocity diagrams repeated, for clarity.

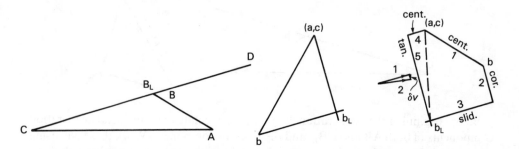

In constructing the acceleration diagram, we identify point b before point b_L. The direction of the Coriolis vector is 90° in advance of the corresponding sliding velocity vector. Now it must be clearly understood that this sliding vector is bb_L on the velocity diagram, not b_Lb because we are drawing the Coriolis and sliding vectors of B_L relative to B, not the other way round.

Now we must determine the direction of rotation of the sliding path. The velocity diagram shows the vector cb_L to be downwards, indicating that B_L is moving downwards relative to C. This clearly indicates a clockwise rotation of CD. Thus, we 'advance' the sliding velocity vector bb_L clockwise by 90°.

If you find this rule difficult to understand or to apply, you may find it simpler to determine the Coriolis direction simply by working out each time which way the sliding velocity vector is being turned. Alongside the velocity diagram, we show a small vector with an arrow, specifically indicating the sliding velocity of B_L relative to B, in positions 1 and 2. The vector cb_L again tells us that link CD is turning clockwise; so in a small increment of time, this sliding vector will be in position 2, that is, advanced clockwise by a small amount. Then the change of velocity, δv, is clearly seen to be in the downward direction.

This determination of the correct direction of the Coriolis vector is the most difficult part of the work, and you will require much practice to be always certain of getting it right. Notice in the discussion above that we have used the velocity diagram to determine the direction of rotation of CD. Although it is obvious from the details of the question that if AB is turning anti-clockwise, CD *must* be turning clockwise, you should never take such obvious facts for granted. Get into the habit of always determining the direction of rotation of a link from the velocity diagram. You will find some examples in which the direction is not obvious.

The calculations for the required values are completed in the next frame.

27

Values scaled from the acceleration diagram are:

Sliding acceleration vector (b_L rel. to b) scales 1.43 m s^{-2}

Tangential acceleration vector (b_L rel. to C) scales 1.83 m s^{-2}

Total acceleration B_L rel. to C (vector cb_L) scales 1.89 m s^{-2}

$$\alpha_{CD} = a_{tan}/r = 1.83/0.28 = \textbf{6.536 rad s}^{-2}$$

Sliding acceleration (as scaled) $= \textbf{1.43 m s}^{-2}$

The linear acceleration of point D can be obtained by constructing the image of link C–B_L–D, but this is not necessary; we may simply calculate the length of the vector by ratio:

$$cd = cb_L \times CD/CB_L = 1.89 \times 0.5/0.28 = \textbf{3.375 m s}^{-2}$$

Repeat this whole exercise, this time taking θ as 45° instead of 30°. The procedure will be exactly the same throughout, of course, and therefore details are not given, but in the following frame there are a few values for you to confirm that your working is correct, as you proceed.

28

For the case when angle $\theta = 45°$:

In the configuration diagram:
CB_L should measure approximately 0.31 m
CD should be at approximately 19.8° to AC

In the velocity diagram:
bb_L should scale approximately 0.43 m s^{-1}
cb_L should scale approximately 0.2 m s^{-1}

In the acceleration diagram:
The sliding component (b_L rel. to b) should scale approximately 0.76 m s^{-2}
The tangential component (b_L rel. to c) should scale approximately 1.88 m s^{-2}
The total acceleration of B_L (cb_L) should scale approximately 1.89 m s^{-2}

These values give the following answers:

$$\text{Angular acceleration of CD} = a_{tan}/r = 1.88/0.31 = \textbf{6.065 rad s}^{-2}$$

$$\text{Sliding acceleration of slider on CD} = \textbf{0.76 m s}^{-2}$$

$$\text{Total acceleration of D} = cb_L \times CD/CB_L = 1.892 \times 0.5/0.31 = \textbf{3.052 m s}^{-2}$$

29

In Frame 30 are two further problems. The first consists of a single link, although a Coriolis acceleration component will be involved. For both problems, the velocity diagram is a right-angled triangle, and the acceleration diagram consists of only four vectors. Accurate drawing is not necessary; once the shape of the diagrams is known, the values of the vectors can be calculated.

We shall see in Programme 4 that we can calculate accelerations mathematically for such simple mechanisms. It is actually simpler to solve graphically, but mathematical analysis offers the advantage that, once an expression for an acceleration has been derived, it can be used for any value of displacement, and therefore, for any configuration of the mechanism. With a graphical method, the diagrams must be drawn for each configuration required.

30

PROBLEMS

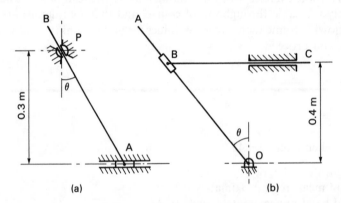

(a)   (b)

1. Diagram (a) above shows a link AB. A is constrained by a horizontal slide and the link passes through a swivel at P which is fixed in position but allows the link to turn, and slide through it. If A moves at constant speed of 2 m s^{-1} to the right, determine the sliding component of acceleration through the swivel, and the angular acceleration of AB when angle θ is 30°. [*Ans. 8.66 m s^{-2}; 28.87 rad s^{-2}.*]
   Hint: (o,p) is a single point on the velocity diagram, and (o,a) a single point on the acceleration diagram.
2. In diagram (b) above, line OA turns about a fixed pivot O. Link BC moves in a horizontal guide and the end B carries a block which slides along OA. Angle θ is 40°.
   (a) If BC moves left with constant velocity 2 m s^{-1}, determine the angular acceleration of OA.
   (b) If OA turns anti-clockwise with constant velocity 2 rad s^{-1}, determine the linear acceleration of BC.
   [*Ans. (a) 14.447 rad s^{-2}; (b) 4.576 m s^{-2}.*]
   Hints: for (a), (o,b) will be one fixed point on the acceleration diagram.

31

We shall go through one further example before the final set of problems, but first, here is a step-by-step set of instructions for drawing acceleration diagrams.

1. Draw a configuration diagram and a velocity diagram, according to the principles set out in Programme 2, Frame 39. Leave sufficient space on the sheet for drawing the acceleration diagram.

2. Calculate all centripetal acceleration components for the mechanism. When the angular velocity of a link is given, the centripetal component can be calculated from the data. For all other links, the component is calculated from values scaled from the velocity diagram. **One** centripetal component should be calculated for each link in the mechanism.

3. Calculate all Coriolis components, using values scaled from the velocity diagram.

4. Make a rough sketch of the acceleration diagram to decide on a scale, and to determine at what point to begin the drawing.

5. Begin by defining a 'fixed point', that is, a point of zero acceleration. Where there is clearly more than one such point in the mechanism, letter the point appropriately.

6. Generally, begin the drawing with the centripetal and tangential vectors for a link whose angular velocity and acceleration are given.

7. Always draw centripetal and Coriolis vectors before tangential and sliding vectors: that is, always draw vectors of known value before those of unknown value.

8. Generally, proceed from one link to an adjacent link in the mechanism.

9. When a link has more than two connections to it in the mechanism, first identify two points on the link on the acceleration diagram, and determine the *total* relative acceleration of the two points. All other points on the link may then be determined by constructing the *acceleration image* of the link.

10. When the diagram is complete, measure all the vector components required for the solution of the problem, using the scale chosen. These will usually be tangential and sliding components.

11. Calculate all angular accelerations required.

It is impossible to set down a complete and absolutely comprehensive guide to the drawing of vector diagrams, and this does not have any pretensions to being one. There will always be some oddity about the occasional problem which requires some extra ingenuity, initiative, or special knowledge of the solver.

The next, and final exercise, is set out generally according to the guide, and we shall make reference to it as we proceed through the solution.

32

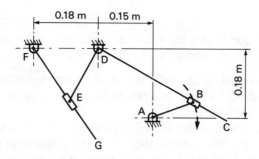

Example. The figure shows part of a mechanism in which CDE is a single rigid link with a right-angled bend, turning about the fixed pivot D. The link AB is connected to the arm CD by a slider at B, so that B slides along CD. Link FG connects to the other arm DE by the slider at E, so that E can slide along FG. At the instant shown, AB is at an angle of 20° to the horizontal and is turning clockwise at the constant rate of 5 rad s^{-1}. AB = 0.12 m; CD = 0.4 m; DE = 0.16 m; FG = 0.3 m. Determine the angular velocities and accelerations of the links CDE and FG.

Begin the solution by studying the data carefully. There are two dimensions given which are not required for the solution. Which are they?

33

> We shall not need the lengths of CD, or FG.

If you do not see why, it will become clear later, but this fact helps in deciding on a scale for the configuration diagram, because we shall not need to include the arm CD beyond the point B. A suitable scale for A4 paper is therefore 4 cm ≡ 0.1 m. Draw your diagram carefully, beginning by locating the 'fixed' points A, D and F, and keeping the diagram well to the top of your A4 sheet. If you locate F almost at the left of the sheet, you will fit B comfortably in, but C will be off the paper. The diagram is reproduced in the following frame, as are the detailed steps in producing it, but if you wish to complete the drawing without referring to the steps, then as a check, you should find that the angle between BD and the horizontal through F and D is 27.9° and that the angle between FG and the same horizontal is 53.4°. Also the length of DB should be 0.297 m, and the length of EF should be 0.176 m. These values have been calculated from the geometry of the diagram; you should accordingly take them as correct, and your values should be close to them.

34

The steps for constructing the configuration diagram are:

1. Locate F at the top-left of the sheet.
2. Draw a horizontal through F.
3. Measure FD = 0.18 m along this line to locate D.
4. Measure 0.15 m along the line to the right of D.
5. Draw a vertical through this last point.
6. Measure 0.18 m below the horizontal, along this vertical, to locate A.
7. Draw horizontal through A.
8. Draw line at 20° to the horizontal through A.
9. Measure AB = 0.12 m along this line to locate B.
10. Join BD. Measure.
11. Draw a line through D perpendicular to BD.
12. Measure DE = 0.16 m along this line to locate E.
13. Join EF. Measure.

And the configuration diagram is reproduced below.

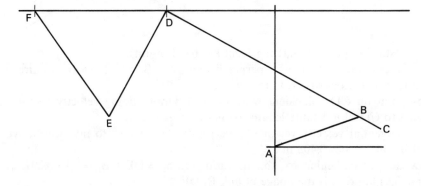

From the diagram, BD scales 0.297 m and EF scales 0.176 m.

The drawing of the velocity diagram comes next. Follow the suggestion made earlier, and make a rough sketch of it, to gain some idea of the shape, and to help in choosing a scale. And of course, calculate the velocity of B relative to A. You should find that a scale of 2 cm ≡ 0.1 m s^{-1} is a suitable scale for a diagram which will then be of reasonable size and yet leave space to draw the acceleration diagram. It need not be considered a disaster, of course, if one diagram runs across another one, but it is clearly better to keep them separate so far as is practical. The diagram is reproduced in Frame 35, with a 'repeat' of the configuration diagram.

35

Velocity of B relative to A is:

$$v = \omega R = 5 \times 0.12 = 0.6 \text{ m s}^{-1}$$

and the pair of diagrams are shown below, with the instructions.

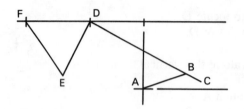
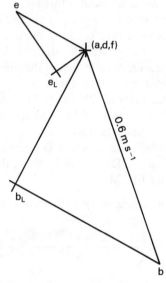

1. Locate 'starting-point' (a,d,f) representing 'fixed' points.
2. Draw vector $ab = 0.6$ m s^{-1} perpendicular to AB, in 'down-right' direction consistent with clockwise rotation of AB.
3. B_L is point on CD coincident with slider B. Draw sliding velocity vector bb_L parallel to CD of indefinite length; b_L lies on this line.
4. Draw tangential velocity vector db_L perpendicular to CD, to intersect above at point b_L. ab_L scales 0.403 m s^{-1}.
5. Draw ae perpendicular to ab_L in ratio $ae:ab_L = DE:DB_L = 0.16:0.297$. (See Frame 33.) b_L–d–e is the image of link $B_L DE$.
6. E_L is point on FG coincident with slider E. Draw sliding velocity vector ee_L of indefinite length parallel to FG: point e_L lies on this line.
7. Draw tangential velocity vector fe_L perpendicular to FG to intersect above at point e_L. This completes the velocity diagram.

$$bb_L \text{ should scale 0.448 m s}^{-1}; \quad db_L \text{ should scale 0.403 m s}^{-1}$$

$$ee_L \text{ should scale 0.196 m s}^{-1}; \quad fe_L \text{ should scale 0.093 m s}^{-1}$$

Once more, the above values have been accurately calculated from the geometry of the diagram, and your scaled values should be close to them.

Calculate the required angular velocities of CDE and FG.

$$\omega_{CDE} = v/R = db_L/DB_L = 0.403/0.297 = \textbf{1.357 rad s}^{-1}$$
$$\omega_{FG} = v/R = fe_L/FE_L = 0.093/0.176 = \textbf{0.528 rad s}^{-1}$$

This completes step 1 of the instruction sheet on Frame 31. Steps 2 and 3 require calculation of all the necessary acceleration components. These consist of a centripetal component for each of the three links of the mechanism, and also two Coriolis components.

$$a_{cen}(\text{B rel. to A}) = \omega^2 R = 5^2 \times 0.12 = 3.0 \text{ m s}^{-2}$$

$$a_{cen}(\text{B}_L \text{ rel. to D}) = v^2/R = db_L^2/DB = (0.403)^2/0.297 = 0.545 \text{ m s}^{-2}$$

$$a_{cen}(\text{E}_L \text{ rel. to F}) = v^2/R = fe_L^2/FE = (0.093)^2/0.176 = 0.049 \text{ m s}^{-2}$$

$$a_{cor}(\text{B}_L \text{ rel. to B}) = 2v\omega = 2(bb_L)\omega_{CDE} = 2 \times 0.448 \times 1.357 = 1.216 \text{ m s}^{-2}$$

$$a_{cor}(\text{E}_L \text{ rel. to E}) = 2v\omega = 2(ee_L)\omega_{FG} = 2 \times 0.196 \times 0.528 = 0.207 \text{ m s}^{-2}$$

The lengths of DB and FE are scaled from the configuration diagram in Frame 34.

We omit step 4, mentioning in passing that you should include it when you are solving a problem unaided, from the beginning. It will suffice to state that sketching the diagram reveals firstly, that a scale of 4 cm $\equiv$ 1 m s^{-2} will result in an acceleration diagram approximately 12 cm wide and 8 cm deep; secondly, that the starting-point (a,d,f) will be at the extreme right of the diagram; and thirdly, that the centripetal vector for B relative to A will be the longest vector in the whole diagram.

The completed diagram is reproduced below, together with the 'repeat' of the configuration diagram. Steps for the drawing follow in the next frame.

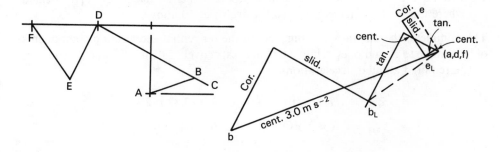

37

These are the stages in drawing the acceleration diagram of the previous frame.

1. Select the 'fixed points' point, (a,d,f) with at least 3 cm space above it, and well to the right of your available space.
2. Draw centripetal vector ab 3.0 m s^{-2} long, in the direction B–A.
3. From b, draw the Coriolis vector of length 1.216 m s^{-2} perpendicular to CD. The sliding velocity vector bb_L points up-left; the tangential velocity vector db_L points down-left indicating clockwise rotation of link CD. Clockwise rotation of sliding vector bb_L informs us that the velocity change must be up-right.
4. From the end of this, draw the sliding acceleration vector of indefinite length, parallel to CD; point b_L lies on this line.
5. From d, draw the centripetal vector for B_L rel. to D, 0.545 m s^{-2} long, in the direction B_L–D.
6. From the end of this, draw the tangential vector perpendicular to CD. b_L is located where this intersects the vector drawn at 4 above.
7. Join points d, b_L. Vector db_L is the *total* acceleration of B_L relative to D. Measure the length. It is not necessary to 'translate' this length into an acceleration. To the scale chosen, the vector should scale approximately 46 mm.
8. Draw vector de perpendicular to $b_L d$ such that $de:b_L d = DE:B_L D$. The configuration diagram gives the length of $B_L D$ as 0.297 m, and DE is 0.16 m. Thus de $= 24.78$ mm. Then b_L–d–e is the acceleration image of $B_L DE$.
9. From e, draw the Coriolis vector perpendicular to link EF. The sliding velocity vector ee_L points down-right; the tangential velocity vector $e_L f$ indicates that link FG is turning clockwise. Clockwise rotation of the sliding velocity vector is consistent with a down-left direction of the Coriolis vector.
10. From the end of this, draw the sliding acceleration vector parallel to FG, of indefinite length; point e_L lies on this line.
11. From f, draw the centripetal vector for E_L relative to F, 0.049 m s^{-2} long, in the direction E_L–F.
12. From end of this, draw the tangential vector perpendicular to EF. e_L is located where this vector intersects the vector drawn at 10 above.

This completes the diagram. Scaling from it, the tangential acceleration components of b_L relative to d, and of e_L relative to f, are respectively 1.01 m s^{-2}, and 0.21 m s^{-2}.
The required angular accelerations are:

$$\alpha_{CDE} = a/R = a/BD = 1.01/0.297 = \textbf{3.37 rad s}^{-2}$$

$$\alpha_{FG} = a/R = a/FG = 0.21/0.176 = \textbf{1.19 rad s}^{-2}$$

38

A few concluding remarks may be helpful.

Even with the completed diagram before you as a guide, it cannot always be easy to follow the instructions, particularly in regard to the acceleration diagram. In an attempt to make the diagram clearer, the acceleration image of the right-angled link CDE has been drawn as a broken line. But you may have found that in following step 11 of the instructions, the direction of the centripetal vector (of length 0.049 m s^{-2}) happens to be almost exactly the same as the direction of vector de, and moreover, is very small, being less than 2 mm long. Thus, even with the scale suggested, it is not easy to see the actual vectors, and it becomes less easy when the diagram is scaled down for the purpose of including it in a printed book.

You will have seen that in an attempt to simplify the instruction, all the points on the acceleration diagram have not been allocated letters. For example, the acceleration of point B_L relative to point B consists of two components: a Coriolis vector and a sliding vector, and there is no need to allocate a letter to the end of the one and the beginning of the other. It has been found that learners are more confused by a comprehensively-lettered diagram than they are by the ones shown.

The question of accuracy also enters into any graphical solution, and it is just not possible to lay down limits to the sort of accuracy you should expect, as this depends on the problem being solved. So, although you should strive to make drawings as accurate as possible, you should not be unnecessarily disturbed if the answers you obtain disagree with the ones in the book.

Finally, it cannot be denied that the complete analysis of a mechanism such as this takes a considerable time. But you should not use this as grounds for not bothering to learn the subject. You may tell yourself that you could not possibly solve such a problem in the limited time allotted to an examination question. This may be true, but you should also remember that examiners, whatever you may think about them, are for the most part, reasonable people, and will set questions which require only so much work as can reasonably be expected from an average student in the allotted time. This may be done in several ways. For example, the examiner may provide you with a completed drawing of the configuration and velocity diagrams and ask you to draw only the acceleration diagram. Or you may be asked only to sketch the diagram or diagrams, instead of drawing them accurately.

The following frame consists of four problems for solution, and this completes the work of this programme.

39

The following set of three problems completes the programme.

PROBLEMS

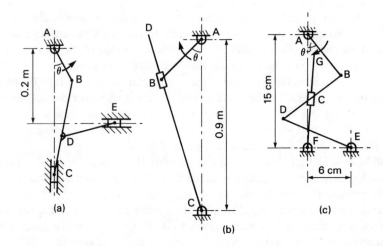

(a) (b) (c)

1. In the mechanism shown in diagram (a), AB is 0.1 m long, BC is 0.25 m long, BD is 0.15 m long, and DE is 0.15 m long. BC is a single link. AB turns anti-clockwise at a constant speed of 15 rev/min. Determine the velocities and accelerations of the two sliders at C and E, and the angular accelerations of the links BC and DE when the angle θ is 30°. [*Ans. $v_C = 0.1063\ m\ s^{-1}$; $v_E = 0.077\ m\ s^{-1}$; $a_C = 0.269\ m\ s^{-2}$; $a_E = 0.054\ m\ s^{-2}$. $\alpha_{BC} = 0.44\ rad\ s^{-2}$; $\alpha_{DE} = 1.587\ rad\ s^{-2}$.*]

2. Diagram (b) shows a quick-return mechanism. AB is 0.3 m long and turns clockwise at 20 rev min^{-1} with angular acceleration 4 rad s^{-2} clockwise. Determine the angular velocity and acceleration of CD and the linear acceleration of the slider at B along the link CD when angle θ is 45°. [*Ans. $\omega_{CD} = 0.408\ rad\ s^{-1}$; $\alpha_{CD} = 1.467\ rad\ s^{-2}$; $1.796\ m\ s^{-2}$.*]

3. In the device shown in diagram (c), AB is 7 cm long, BD is 10 cm, DE is 10 cm long. BD is a single link with a slider attached at the mid-point C, through which link FG passes. FG lies behind links AB, BC, DE. AB turns clockwise at the constant rate of 8 rad s^{-2}. Determine the angular velocity and acceleration of link FG when angle θ is 40°. [*Ans. $\omega_{FG} = 4.4\ rad\ s^{-1}$; $\alpha_{FG} = 64.23\ rad\ s^{-2}$.*]

Programme 4

KINEMATICS OF MECHANISMS: ANALYSIS

1

In Programmes 2 and 3 we dealt with the kinematic analysis of mechanisms by drawing velocity and acceleration diagrams. We found this method time-consuming, and sometimes rather inaccurate.

In this programme, we analyse mechanisms by the use of the calculus instead of by a graphical method. This avoids the disadvantages of the graphical method, but can be used for only very simple mechanisms.

The method consists of writing the displacement of some point, or of some component of a mechanism, as a mathematical function, by analysing the geometry of the mechanism. Calling this displacement x, we then recall:

$$v = \frac{\mathrm{d}x}{\mathrm{d}t}; \qquad a = \frac{\mathrm{d}v}{\mathrm{d}t} = \frac{\mathrm{d}^2 x}{\mathrm{d}t^2}$$

Thus, the velocity of the point, or the component, can be determined simply by differentiating the displacement function. Similarly, the acceleration is found by differentiating the resulting velocity function.

2

Consider the simple case of a point P moving at a constant speed in a circular path about a fixed point. The radius of the path is R. We can look at this in terms of co-ordinate geometry, by including x- and y-axes of reference.

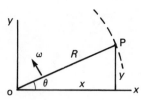

Let us call the angular velocity of the motion ω. If the radius makes an angle θ to the x-axis at some instant, it is easy to see that x and y can be written:

$$x = R \cos \theta; \qquad y = R \sin \theta$$

Thus, we have expressed the displacement components x and y as mathematical functions which we can differentiate. Have a go at this yourself. Think carefully before diving in! Refresh your memory by referring back to Frame 1 for the definition of v.

3

Our displacement functions express displacement components in terms of θ. To determine velocity, we have to differentiate with respect to time, t. Perhaps you forgot this rather important condition.

We use the well-known 'function of a function' technique. If we require dx/dt, and the function is a function of x and θ, we can write:

$$\frac{dx}{dt} = \frac{dx}{d\theta} \times \frac{d\theta}{dt} \quad \text{and similarly} \quad \frac{dy}{dt} = \frac{dy}{d\theta} \times \frac{d\theta}{dt}$$

We shall use the 'dot' notation extensively in this programme:

$$\frac{dx}{dt} = \dot{x}; \qquad \frac{d^2x}{dt^2} = \ddot{x}$$

You should have worked the following out already:

$$\frac{dx}{d\theta} = -R \sin \theta; \qquad \frac{dy}{d\theta} = R \cos \theta$$
$$\therefore \qquad \dot{x} = (-R \sin \theta)\dot{\theta}; \qquad \dot{y} = (R \cos \theta)\dot{\theta}$$

It is not difficult to see at this point that $\dot{\theta} = \omega$, the angular velocity of the radius. Thus:

$$\dot{x} = -\omega R \sin \theta; \qquad \dot{y} = \omega R \cos \theta$$

4

The result obtained in the previous frame is one we might have expected. We know that when a point moves in a circular path, it has a linear velocity of ωR which is tangential to the path. The values of $\dot{x}$ and $\dot{y}$ are the components of this tangential velocity. The figure below illustrates this.

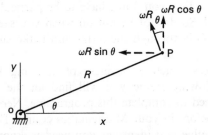

The figure also shows that the x component of the velocity is to the left, and this is consistent with the negative sign for $\dot{x}$ in Frame 3.

Now try and derive the corresponding components of acceleration, by differentiating $\dot{x}$ and $\dot{y}$. Remember again: you need to differentiate with respect to t.

5

$$\ddot{x} = -\omega^2 R \cos \theta; \qquad \ddot{y} = -\omega^2 R \sin \theta$$

and the diagram below shows that these are the components of the centripetal acceleration. In case you had difficulty, here is the working for $\ddot{x}$,

$$\ddot{x} = \frac{d(\dot{x})}{dt} = \frac{d(\dot{x})}{d\theta} \times \frac{d\theta}{dt} = (-\omega R)(\cos \theta)\dot{\theta} = -\omega^2 R \cos \theta$$

recalling again that $\dot{\theta} = \omega$. The derivation of $\ddot{y}$ is similar.

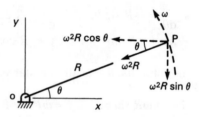

The rest of the programme contains a lot of differentiation, and quite a lot of trigonometry. If you are not the fortunate possessor of a flair for pure mathematics, you might find some of the work a little daunting. Try to avoid this if you can. Although some of the pages appear at first glance to be a dense mass of mathematics, remember that throughout, we are using differentiation only. And although differentiation might be tedious, and may occasionally yield expressions which are too long to fit on to one line, you don't have to be particularly clever to do it; you need only to be careful. So do not be put off when you see the sort of expressions described. Just go carefully through the terms and make sure you follow each step of the working.

Differentiation is very much a business of applying formulae and standard techniques. In the following frame you will find all the formulae and standard differentials you will need to complete this programme. Needless to say, you should have met all of them before in your Mathematics course. Following this is a frame containing all the formulae and identities you need to know from trigonometry to deal with the programme.

Products   When an expression comprises several multiplied terms, e.g. u, v, w:

$$d(u \times v \times w) = (vw)d(u) + (wu)d(v) + (uv)d(w)$$

Example: $y = x^3 \sin x \cos x$

$$\frac{dy}{dx} = (\sin x \cos x)(2x^2) + (x^3 \cos x)(\cos x) + (x^3 \sin x)(-\sin x)$$

Quotient $\dfrac{d(u/v)}{dx} = \dfrac{v\,du/dx - u\,dv/dx}{v^2}$

Example: $y = \dfrac{\sin x}{x^2}$; $\dfrac{dy}{dx} = \dfrac{(x^2)(\cos x) - (\sin x)(2x)}{x^4}$

Function of a function   When y is a function of u which is a function of x, then $dy/dx = dy/du \times du/dx$.
Example: $y = (x^2 + a^2)^{\frac{1}{2}}$; let $(x^2 + a^2)$ be u; then $y = u^{\frac{1}{2}}$

$$\frac{dy}{dx} = \frac{dy}{du} \times \frac{du}{dx} = \tfrac{1}{2}(u)^{-\frac{1}{2}} \times 2x = x(x^2 + a^2)^{-\frac{1}{2}}$$

Implicit differentiation   This is a useful technique when the variables in an expression are not easily separated. To differentiate a 'mixed' function of x and y terms with respect to x, the x terms are treated normally, and the y terms first differentiated with respect to y, and then multiplied by dy/dx.
Example: $y^2 + 2x \sin y = 4$

$$\therefore \quad (2y)\frac{dy}{dx} + (2x)(\cos y)\frac{dy}{dx} + (\sin y)(2) = 0$$

Notice that the second term of the expression is treated as a product.

$$\therefore \quad \frac{dy}{dx}(2y + 2x \cos y) + 2 \sin y = 0$$

giving $\dfrac{dy}{dx} = -\dfrac{2 \sin y}{2y + 2x \cos y} = -\dfrac{\sin y}{y + x \cos y}$

Differentials

Variable	Differential	Variable	Differential
$\sin x$	$\cos x$	$\operatorname{cosec} x$	$\operatorname{cosec} x \cot x$
$\cos x$	$-\sin x$	$\sec x$	$\sec x \tan x$
$\tan x$	$\sec^2 x$	$\cot x$	$-\operatorname{cosec}^2 x$

This frame contains all the trigonometrical formulae and identities you will require for this programme.

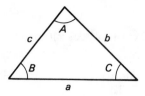

The Sine formula:
$$\frac{a}{\sin A} = \frac{b}{\sin B} = \frac{c}{\sin C}$$

The Cosine formula:
$$a^2 = b^2 + c^2 - 2bc \cos A$$
$$b^2 = c^2 + a^2 - 2ca \cos B$$
$$c^2 = a^2 + b^2 - 2ab \cos C$$

Angle summation:
$$\sin(A + B) = \sin A \cos B + \cos A \sin B$$
$$\sin(A - B) = \sin A \cos B - \cos A \sin B$$
$$\cos(A + B) = \cos A \cos B - \sin A \sin B$$
$$\cos(A - B) = \cos A \cos B + \sin A \sin B$$
$$\tan(A + B) = \frac{\tan A + \tan B}{1 - \tan A \tan B}$$
$$\tan(A - B) = \frac{\tan A - \tan B}{1 + \tan A \tan B}$$

$$\sin^2 \theta + \cos^2 \theta = 1; \qquad \tan^2 \theta + 1 = \sec^2 \theta; \qquad 1 + \cot^2 \theta = \operatorname{cosec}^2 \theta$$

$$\sin \theta = \cos(90° - \theta); \qquad \cos \theta = \sin(90° - \theta); \qquad \tan \theta = \sin \theta / \cos \theta$$

$$\sin \theta = \sin(180° - \theta); \qquad \cos \theta = -\cos(180° - \theta)$$

Particular values:

$$\sin \ \ 0° = 0; \quad \cos \ \ 0° = 1; \quad \tan \ \ 0° = 0$$
$$\sin \ 90° = 1; \quad \cos \ 90° = 0; \quad \tan 90° = \text{infinity}$$
$$\sin 180° = 0; \quad \cos 180° = -1$$

You may recall that many of these formulae appeared in Programme 1, Frames 13 and 14.

8

Now we shall go back to the example of Frame 2 and add a complication. Instead of P moving in a circular path, let it be moving outwards along the radius with a constant speed v, while the radius itself continues to turn at constant speed ω as before.

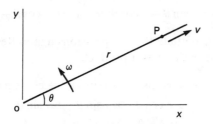

This now means that the radius is a variable, and for this reason, it is denoted by a small r instead of by R as previously. As before, we can state the displacement components of the point P:

$$x = r \cos \theta; \qquad y = r \sin \theta$$

Have a try at determining $\dot{x}$, the differential of x. Remember that now, both terms on the right-hand side of the equation are variables. So use the Product formula.

9

$$\boxed{\dot{x} = r(-\sin \theta)\dot{\theta} + (\cos \theta)\dot{r}}$$

If you failed to derive this, at least make sure you can now see how it is obtained. Treating as a product, we first multiply r by the differential of $\cos \theta$. And as we are differentiating with respect to t, we multiply by $d\theta/dt$. $d(\cos \theta)/d\theta$ is $(-\sin \theta)$ and $d\theta/dt$ is written as $\dot{\theta}$. Then we multiply $\cos \theta$ by the differential of r, which we have written as $\dot{r}$.

Treating the expression for y in exactly the same way, it is left for you to show that the differential of y is given by

$$\dot{y} = r(\cos \theta)\dot{\theta} + (\sin \theta)\dot{r}$$

Now before proceeding, answer this question. What are $\dot{\theta}$ and $\dot{r}$?

10

> $\dot{\theta}$ is ω, the angular velocity of the radius, as before
> $\dot{r}$ is the velocity v at which P moves along the radius

So we can re-write thus:

$$\dot{x} = -\omega r \sin \theta + v \cos \theta; \qquad \dot{y} = \omega r \cos \theta + v \sin \theta$$

The next stage is to differentiate these expressions again. Recalling that both ω and v are constant, we treat $(r \sin \theta)$ as a product.

$$\begin{aligned}\ddot{x} &= -\omega\{r(\cos \theta)\dot{\theta} + (\sin \theta)\dot{r}\} + v(-\sin \theta)\dot{\theta}\\ &= -\omega^2 r \cos \theta - v\omega \sin \theta - v\omega \sin \theta\\ &= -\omega^2 r \cos \theta - 2v\omega \sin \theta\end{aligned}$$

and with this as a guide, it is now your turn to show that the corresponding differentiation of $\dot{y}$ gives:

$$\ddot{y} = -\omega^2 r \sin \theta + 2v\omega \cos \theta$$

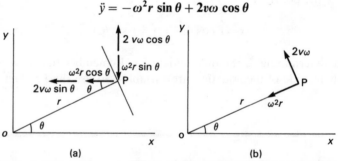

(a)   (b)

The components are shown in diagram (a). Calling the resultant of the four components in the radial direction R_r, and in the tangential direction R_t:

$$\begin{aligned}R_r &= (2v\omega \cos \theta)\sin \theta - (\omega^2 r \sin \theta)\sin \theta - (2v\omega \sin \theta)\cos \theta - (\omega^2 r \cos \theta)\cos \theta\\ &= (-\omega^2 r)(\sin^2 \theta + \cos^2 \theta)\\ &= -\omega^2 r\end{aligned}$$

$$\begin{aligned}R_t &= (2v\omega \cos \theta)\cos \theta - (\omega^2 r \sin \theta)\cos \theta + (2v\omega \sin \theta)\sin \theta + (\omega^2 r \cos \theta)\sin \theta\\ &= (2v\omega)(\cos^2 \theta + \sin^2 \theta)\\ &= 2v\omega\end{aligned}$$

These are respectively the centripetal acceleration, and the Coriolis acceleration. A graphical demonstration of the latter is to be found in Programme 3, Frame 17 *et seq.* The two resultants are shown in diagram (b).

This calculation is one of many which we referred to in Frame 5. There is no inherent difficulty; the working just has to be carried out with care.

11

Now let us examine an actual mechanism. The diagram shows the simple mechanism called the **elliptic trammel**.

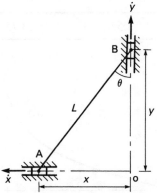

It is so called because as the two ends of the link move along the vertical and horizontal slides, any point on the link traces out the path of an ellipse. The two ends trace straight lines, of course, which is the special case of an ellipse having one axis of zero length. The locus of the centre of the link is a circle, which is another special case of an ellipse, with equal axes.

Example. The length of the link of the elliptic trammel is 1 m. The horizontal slider moves with a constant velocity $\dot{x} = 5$ m s^{-1}. Calculate the velocity of the vertical slider for values of x from 0 to 1 in increments of 0.1 m, and plot a graph of the velocity against x.

We require an expression for y in terms of x. Derive this expression. Call the link length L. The answer is in Frame 12. The configuration of the mechanism is a right-angled triangle.

$$\boxed{y = \sqrt{(L^2 - x^2)}}$$

We differentiate to determine $\dot{y}$, remembering that we require dy/dt, not dy/dx.

$$\dot{y} = \frac{dy}{dt} = \frac{dy}{dx} \times \frac{dx}{dt}$$

$$\therefore \quad \dot{y} = \dot{x}\frac{dy}{dx} = \dot{x}(\tfrac{1}{2}(L^2 - x^2)^{-\frac{1}{2}}(-2x))$$

$$\therefore \quad \dot{y} = \frac{-\dot{x}x}{\sqrt{(L^2 - x^2)}}$$

Values of $\dot{y}$ are calculated in Frame 13, taking $L = 1$ m and $\dot{x} = 5$ m s^{-1}. If you have a programmable calculator, you can draw up the table yourself first, before reading on.

13

x, m	0	0.1	0.2	0.3	0.4	0.5	0.6	0.7	0.8	0.9	1.0
y, m s^{-1}	0	0.502	1.02	1.57	2.18	2.89	3.75	4.90	6.67	10.32	∞

The graph follows.

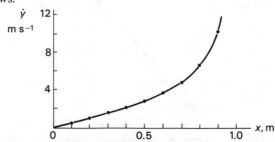

The negative sign is left out of the table, but must be explained. In the diagram in Frame 11, x and y are respectively the distances of the two sliders from O. Implicit in this is that quantities to the left are positive, and quantities upwards are positive. Thus, a negative $\dot{y}$ means that for a velocity $\dot{x}$ to the left, the vertical slider must have a downward velocity. This is clear from the mechanism in this case, but you must always observe a sign convention, so that signs can be correctly interpreted in the derived expressions.

Now, for the same conditions, derive an expression for $\ddot{y}$, the acceleration of the vertical slider. Use the 'quotient' formula when differentiating.

14

$$\ddot{y} = -(\dot{x})^2 \left(\frac{L^2}{(L^2 - x^2)^{3/2}} \right)$$

The calculation follows. Remember that $\dot{x}$ is constant.

$$\dot{y} = \frac{-\dot{x}x}{(L^2 - x^2)^{\frac{1}{2}}}$$

$$\therefore \quad \ddot{y} = \frac{(L^2 - x^2)^{\frac{1}{2}}(-\dot{x}^2) - ((-\dot{x}x)\frac{1}{2}(L^2 - x^2)^{-\frac{1}{2}}(-2x\dot{x}))}{((L^2 - x^2)^{\frac{1}{2}})^2}$$

$$= \frac{(L^2 - x^2)(-\dot{x}^2) - (\dot{x}x)^2}{(L^2 - x^2)^{3/2}} \quad \text{(mult. top and bottom by } (L^2 - x^2)^{\frac{1}{2}})$$

$$= \frac{(\dot{x})^2(-L^2 + x^2 - x^2)}{(L^2 - x^2)^{3/2}}$$

$$\therefore \quad \ddot{y} = -(\dot{x})^2 \left(\frac{L^2}{(L^2 - x^2)^{3/2}} \right)$$

15

Do not be too discouraged if you made any mistakes: if you did, here is a brief 'recap' of the procedure.

We use the Quotient formula: 'u' is $(-\dot{x}x)$ and 'v' is $(L^2 - x^2)^{\frac{1}{2}}$.
du/dt is $(\dot{x})(\dot{x}) = (\dot{x})^2$ (because $\dot{x}$ is constant in this case).
We treat dv/dt as 'function of a function'.
First differentiate the bracket as a whole: $(\frac{1}{2} \times (L^2 - x^2)^{-\frac{1}{2}})$.
Then multiply this by the differential of the contents of the bracket (i.e. $-2 \times x$).
This gives du/dx; we finally multiply by dx/dt, i.e. $\dot{x}$.
The denominator is just 'v'^{2}.
The rest of the calculation is just algebraic simplification.

16

The same method may be used to calculate angular velocity and acceleration. To do this, we require an expression for the angular displacement. On the diagram in Frame 11, the angle θ is shown as the angle the link makes with the vertical. This angle, rather than the angle with the horizontal, is chosen, because it increases with an increase of x.

From the diagram (Frame 11):

$$x = L \sin \theta$$

We could express θ as an inverse sine. But there is no need to do this, if we differentiate implicitly. (See Frame 6.) Thus:

$$\dot{x} = L \cos \theta \, \dot{\theta}$$
$$\therefore \quad \dot{\theta} = (\dot{x}/L) \sec \theta$$

which is the expression we require. The angular acceleration, $\ddot{\theta}$, is determined by a second differentiation.

$$\ddot{\theta} = (\dot{x}/L)(\sec \theta. \tan \theta)\dot{\theta} \text{ (see Frame 6 again)}$$

and substituting for $\dot{\theta}$, this gives:

$$\ddot{\theta} = (\dot{x}/L)(\sec \theta. \tan \theta)(\dot{x}/L)\sec \theta$$
$$\therefore \quad \ddot{\theta} = (\dot{x})^2(1/L^2)\sec^2 \theta. \tan \theta$$

17

PROBLEMS

1. The link of an elliptic trammel has a length L. Assuming the end in the horizontal slide to move with velocity $\dot{x}$ and acceleration $\ddot{x}$, both outwards, show that the acceleration of the end in the vertical slide, $\ddot{y}$, is given by the expression:

$$\ddot{y} = -(\dot{x})^2 \left(\frac{L^2}{(L^2 - x^2)^{3/2}} \right) - (\ddot{x}) \left(\frac{x}{(L^2 - x^2)^{\frac{1}{2}}} \right)$$

2. The horizontal slider A of the elliptic trammel of Frame 11 moves with simple harmonic motion about the point of zero displacement with amplitude 0.5 m and frequency 1 cycle per second. Determine the acceleration of the vertical slider B when the displacement of A is (a) 0; (b) 0.5 m. [*Ans.* (*a*) -9.87 *m* s^{-2}; (*b*) $+11.396$ *m* s^{-2}.]
Hints: determine $\ddot{y}$ as in frame 14, but allowing for $\dot{x}$ being a variable. $x = 0.5 \sin \omega t$; calculate $\dot{x}$ and $\ddot{x}$. $\omega = 2\pi \times$ frequency. Subst. values in $\ddot{y}$.

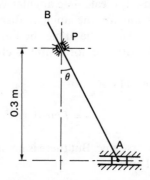

3. In the mechanism shown above, A moves at constant speed of 2 m s^{-1} to the right. Calculate the magnitude of the sliding acceleration of AB through the fixed swivel at P, and also the angular acceleration of AB when angle θ is 30°. [*Ans.* 8.66 *m* *s*$^{-2}$; 28.87 *rad* *s*$^{-2}$.]
Hints: let length of AP be y, displacement of A be x, and vert. height of 0.3 m be h. Prove:

$$\ddot{y} = (\dot{x})^2 \left(\frac{h^2}{(h^2 + x^2)^{3/2}} \right); \qquad \ddot{\theta} = -(\dot{x})^2 \left(\frac{2hx}{(h^2 + x^2)^2} \right)$$

Then substitute the values given. The problem is the same as the one in Programme 3, Frame 30, no. 1.

18

The device called the quick-return mechanism which we analysed graphically in Programme 3, Frame 23 *et seq.* can be analysed mathematically, although the result is somewhat more complex.

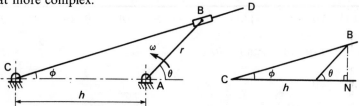

Let the angular velocity of link AB be ω. We shall plot a graph of angular velocity of the link CD against angle θ. If the perpendicular BN is constructed we see from the diagram that:

$$\tan \phi = \frac{BN}{CN} = \frac{BN}{CA + AN} = \frac{r \sin \theta}{h + r \cos \theta}$$

Differentiating implicitly and using the quotient formula (see Frames 6 and 7):

$$(\sec^2 \phi)(\dot{\phi}) = \frac{(\dot{\theta})((h + r \cos \theta)(r \cos \theta) - (r \sin \theta)(-r \sin \theta))}{(h + r \cos \theta)^2}$$

$$= \frac{(\dot{\theta}r)(h \cos \theta + r \cos^2 \theta + r \sin^2 \theta)}{(h + r \cos \theta)^2}$$

$$= (\omega r)\left(\frac{h \cos \theta + r}{(h + r \cos \theta)^2}\right)$$

Recall the trigonometrical identity $\tan^2 \phi + 1 = \sec^2 \phi$ (see Frame 7). We already have the expression for $\tan \phi$ above:

$$\dot{\phi}(\sec^2 \phi) = \dot{\phi}\left(\frac{(r \sin \theta)^2}{(h + r \cos \theta)^2} + 1\right) = \dot{\phi}\left(\frac{r^2 \sin^2 \theta + h^2 + 2hr \cos \theta + r^2 \cos^2 \theta}{(h + r \cos \theta)^2}\right)$$

$$= \dot{\phi}\left(\frac{h^2 + r^2 + 2hr \cos \theta}{(h + r \cos \theta)^2}\right)$$

When substituted in the above, the denominator term $(h + r \cos \theta)^2$ cancels.

$$\therefore \quad \dot{\phi}(h^2 + r^2 + 2hr \cos \theta) = (\omega r)(h \cos \theta + r)$$

$$\therefore \quad \dot{\phi} = (\omega r)\left(\frac{h \cos \theta + r}{h^2 + r^2 + 2hr \cos \theta}\right)$$

19

Taking $h = 0.6$ m, $r = 0.2$ m and $\omega = 8$ rad s^{-1}, draw up the table of values of $\dot{\phi}$ for values of θ from 0° to 180° in increments of 20°.

The table is given in the next frame. Clearly, the use of a programmable calculator or a simple computer program will save time and effort.

20

θ deg.	0	20	40	60	80	100	120	140	160	180
$\dot{\phi}$ rad s^{-1}	2.0	1.95	1.81	1.54	1.10	0.43	-0.57	-1.92	-3.34	-4.0

and this is a graph of $\dot{\phi}$ against θ.

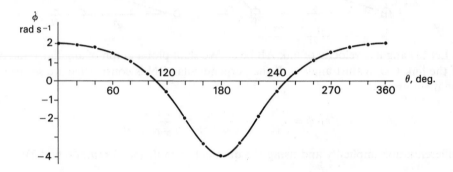

The graph is repeated as a mirror-image for $\theta = 180°$ to $360°$ because it is clear that the motion is symmetrical. The reason for the name 'quick-return mechanism' is now clear. The two points at which $\dot{\phi} = 0$ are the two extreme positions of link CD, when the link stops instantaneously and changes direction. So, from approximately $110°$ to $250°$—a travel of $140°$—it is moving one way. From approximately $250°$ to $110°$—a travel of $220°$—it is moving the other way. The graph and table show that the maximum velocity in the one direction is exactly twice that in the other.

If you refer back to Programme 2, Frames 26 to 31, you will find that this analysis is a mathematical alternative to the graphical exercise in Frame 26. The values of $\dot{\phi}$ called for at $\theta = 60°$, $0°$ and $120°$ in that exercise are found in the above table.

For this same mechanism, we shall develop an expression for the velocity of sliding of the block B on the link CD. See first if you can devise a method for obtaining it. Remember that we must begin with an expression for the appropriate displacement.

21

Look again at the diagram in Frame 18. The required appropriate displacement must be the displacement of the sliding block along CD. Displacement may be measured from any convenient arbitrary datum. So we may define the length CB as the required displacement; the length of CB defines the displacement of the block from the point C at any time. Write down an expression for x, the length of CB. Use the cosine formula.

$$\boxed{x = \sqrt{(h^2 + r^2 + 2hr \cos \theta)}}$$

(From the cosine formula (look back to Frame 7 if you have forgotten):

$$x^2 = h^2 + r^2 - 2hr \cos(180° - \theta)$$

But $\cos(180° - \theta) = -\cos \theta$ (see Frame 7 again) which, on substituting, gives the required expression for x.)

Differentiate this—with respect to t, remember.

$$x = \ldots\ldots\ldots\ldots$$

$$\boxed{\dot{x} = \omega r \left(\frac{-h \sin \theta}{\sqrt{(h^2 + r^2 + 2hr \cos \theta)}} \right)}$$

Here is the working. We use the technique of 'function of a function' (see Frame 6). Call the quantity under the root sign u. Then:

$$x = \sqrt{u} = u^{\frac{1}{2}} \quad \text{(recalling that a square root is raising to power } \tfrac{1}{2})$$

$$\frac{dx}{d\theta} = \frac{dx}{du} \times \frac{du}{d\theta} = (\tfrac{1}{2} u^{-\frac{1}{2}})(2hr)(-\sin \theta)$$

$$\frac{dx}{dt} = \frac{dx}{d\theta} \times \frac{d\theta}{dt} = \frac{dx}{d\theta} \times \dot{\theta} = \omega \times \frac{dx}{d\theta}$$

$$\therefore \quad \dot{x} = \omega \tfrac{1}{2}(u)^{-\frac{1}{2}}(2hr)(-\sin \theta)$$

$$= \omega r \left(\frac{-h \sin \theta}{\sqrt{(h^2 + r^2 + 2hr \cos \theta)}} \right)$$

(recalling also that $u^{-\frac{1}{2}} = 1/u^{\frac{1}{2}}$)

Now use this expression to calculate the values of $\dot{x}$ for values of θ of 60°, 0° and 120°. Take the same values as before for h, r and ω, that is, $h = 0.6$ m, $r = 0.2$ m and $\omega = 8$ rad s^{-1}.

24

$$\boxed{\begin{aligned} &\theta = 60°; &&\dot{x} = -1.153 \text{ m s}^{-1} \\ &\theta = 0°; &&\dot{x} = 0 \\ &\theta = 120°; &&\dot{x} = -1.571 \text{ m s}^{-1} \end{aligned}}$$

Since x is reckoned as the distance from C to the slider B, the negative answer for $\dot{x}$ means that the slider is moving towards C.

In Frame 28 of Programme 2, the graphical solution gave the length of bb_L, the sliding velocity vector, as 1.153 m s^{-1}. The velocity diagram in Frame 29 showed the length bb_L to be zero. The length of bb_L was not actually measured in the diagram of Frame 30 (for $\theta = 120°$)

The expression above, and the expression for angular velocity in Frame 18, may of course be differentiated a second time to determine respectively the sliding acceleration of block on link, and the angular acceleration of the link. The resulting expressions are cumbersome, but the work is not difficult. With a calculator available, there is not much advantage in manipulating the expressions into any particular and economic form. Once an expression has been derived, however cumbersome, values may be substituted, and results obtained. You should remember this when attempting the problems which follow.

25

PROBLEMS

1. In a quick-return mechanism, as shown in the diagram in Frame 18, $r = 0.15$ m, $h = 0.4$ m. Calculate the angular acceleration of the link CD when AB rotates at 30 revolutions per minute anti-clockwise, for values of angle θ of (a) 150°; (b) 135°. [*Ans. (a)* −6.5938 rad s^{-2}; *(b)* −6.0384 rad s^{-2}.]
2. For the same mechanism and data as for problem 1, calculate the magnitude of the sliding acceleration of block A on link CD. [*Ans. (a)* +1.4262 m s^{-2}; *(b)* +0.7578 m s^{-2}.]
   Hints: differentiate the expressions for $\dot{\phi}$ and $\dot{x}$ from Frames 18 and 23. The data are the same as for the example in Frames 23 and 27 of Programme 3. Compare your solution with the graphical one.

The **slider–crank mechanism** is found in many actual devices and machines, and probably most frequently in car engines, as it is the mechanism of the crank, connecting-rod and piston.

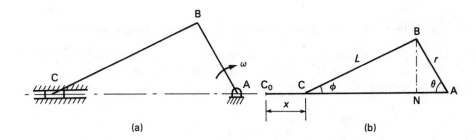

(a)   (b)

Diagram (a) is a representation of the mechanism. The **piston** in the cylinder is represented by the slider at C. AB is the **crank**, which is an integral part of the **crankshaft**. As the crankshaft rotates about the centre A, the other end (the crank-pin end) travels in a circular path. BC is the **connecting-rod**, often abbreviated to 'con-rod', and this connects the sliding piston to the turning crank. The end B of the con-rod, attached to the crankshaft is very much larger than the end secured to the piston, and is, for this reason, called the **big end**. End C is called the **little end**. The purpose of the mechanism, whether used in an engine, or a pump, or in other machines, is to convert rotary motion into reciprocating motion, or vice versa.

Diagram (b) shows the simple geometry of the mechanism. r is the crank radius and L is the length of the connecting-rod. The displacement of the piston may be reckoned from any convenient datum. We have chosen here to reckon it from the point C_0 which is called the position of **inner dead centre**. This is the point at which the crank and connecting-rod are in a straight line, with the crank-pin, B, between the crank centre A and the piston. (When the piston is situated vertically above the crank, as is normal in many car engines, the position is called top dead centre.) The position opposite to this, with crank and connecting-rod in a straight line, this time with the crank-pin B *outside*, angle θ on the diagram being 180°, is called **outer dead centre**.

For the configuration shown, with the crank AB making an angle of θ with AC, the angle between connecting-rod BC and line AC is shown as ϕ. Write down an expression for the displacement x in terms of r, L, θ and ϕ. To start you off, the required displacement is CC_0, which is $AC_0 - AC$ which is $AC_0 - (AN + NC)$.

$$x = r + L - r \cos \theta - L \cos \phi$$

(You can see that the length of AC_0 must be the combined length of $r + L$.)

We cannot differentiate this as it stands, as angle ϕ is a 'dependent variable', that is to say, its value depends on the value of θ. We must express ϕ in terms of θ.

The perpendicular BN is constructed. Then:

$$BN = r \sin \theta = L \sin \phi$$

But $\qquad \sin^2 \phi + \cos^2 \phi = 1$ (see Frame 7)

$$\therefore \qquad \cos \phi = (1 - \sin^2 \phi)^{\frac{1}{2}} = (1 - (r/L)^2 \sin^2 \theta)^{\frac{1}{2}}$$

$$\therefore \qquad x = r + L - r \cos \theta - L(1 - (r/L)^2 \sin^2 \phi)^{\frac{1}{2}}$$

We shall replace the fraction r/L by k. (It must always be a fraction, because the con-rod of an engine must always be much longer than the crank.) Then:

$$x = r + L - r \cos \theta - L(1 - k^2 \sin^2 \theta)^{\frac{1}{2}}$$

We could determine $\dot{x}$ by differentiating at this point, but instead, we shall expand the bracketed terms at the end by using the Binomial Expansion. We shall see that this procedure will result in eliciting more information about the motion of the mechanism than we should gain by straightforward differentiation at this point.

To remind you of the Binomial Expansion:

$$(1 - a)^n = 1 - na + \left(\frac{n(n-1)}{1 \times 2} \right) a^2 - \qquad \text{etc.}$$

You may know that when the term a is small compared with 1, the magnitudes of the terms diminish very rapidly. You can show this for yourself. For the term a substitute $k^2 \sin^2 \theta$. The index n is $\frac{1}{2}$. So work out the first three terms of the expansion yourself, taking a value of k of $\frac{1}{2}$. This is about the largest value k could have; the connecting-rod must be at least twice the length of the crank. So $(1 - a)^n$ becomes $(1 - \frac{1}{4} \sin^2 \theta)^{\frac{1}{2}}$.

$$(1 - \tfrac{1}{4}\sin^2\theta)^{\frac{1}{2}} = 1 - \tfrac{1}{2}(\tfrac{1}{4}\sin^2\theta) + \left(\frac{(\tfrac{1}{2})(-\tfrac{1}{2})}{1 \times 2}\right)(\tfrac{1}{4}\sin^2\theta)^2 - \quad \text{etc.}$$

$$= 1 - \tfrac{1}{8}\sin^2\theta - \tfrac{1}{128}\sin^4\theta - \quad \text{etc.}$$

and when you remember that the maximum value of $\sin\theta$ is 1, it becomes clear that the third term, and all subsequent terms become negligible.

So, taking the first two terms only, we may say:

$$(1 - k^2\sin^2\theta)^{\frac{1}{2}} \simeq 1 - \tfrac{1}{2}k^2\sin^2\theta$$

$$\therefore \quad x = r + L - r\cos\theta - L(1 - \tfrac{1}{2}k^2\sin^2\theta)$$

$$= r - r\cos\theta + \tfrac{1}{2}Lk^2\sin^2\theta$$

Make an attempt to differentiate this. Remember:

Differentiate with respect to t, not θ.
The differential of a constant is 0.
Treat the third term as a 'function of a function' (see Frame 6).

29

Differentiating to obtain the piston velocity $\dot{x}$:

$$\dot{x} = \dot{\theta}(r\sin\theta + \tfrac{1}{2}Lk^2(2\sin\theta\cos\theta))$$

$$= \omega r(\sin\theta + \tfrac{1}{2}k\sin 2\theta) \quad \text{(recalling that } k = r/L)$$

Differentiating a second time to determine the piston acceleration $\ddot{x}$:

$$\ddot{x} = (\dot{\theta})^2 r(\cos\theta + \tfrac{1}{2}k(2\cos 2\theta))$$

$$= \omega^2 r(\cos\theta + k\cos 2\theta)$$

Here are the three expressions: for displacement, velocity and acceleration of the piston.

$$x = r - r \cos \theta + \tfrac{1}{2} L k^2 \sin^2 \theta$$

$$\dot{x} = \omega r (\sin \theta + \tfrac{1}{2} k \sin 2\theta)$$

$$\ddot{x} = \omega^2 r (\cos \theta + k \cos 2\theta)$$

It can be seen that if the last term in each expression were deleted, then displacement would be a simple cosine function, $\dot{x}$ a simple sine function, and $\ddot{x}$ a cosine function again. The motion would indeed be **Simple Harmonic Motion**. You may have forgotten that Simple Harmonic Motion is a reciprocating motion in which the displacement is represented graphically by a pure sine or cosine curve. And because the differential of $\sin \theta$ is $\cos \theta$, and the differential of $\cos \theta$ is $-\sin \theta$, it follows that graphs of velocity and acceleration for Simple Harmonic Motion are also sine or cosine curves. (It also follows that the acceleration is proportional to the displacement, and opposite in sign.)

This would be the case if k were zero, which means that the connecting-rod would be infinitely long. The second terms containing the fraction k are 'harmonics', that is, they are functions of (2θ), and the smaller the value of k, the smaller these terms become. Thus, the longer the connecting-rod of an engine is compared with the crank length, the closer the piston motion becomes to simple harmonic, if the crank turns at constant angular speed. The graphs below are plots of velocity and acceleration for a value of k of 0.4, a crank radius of 0.1 m and a speed of 10 rad s^{-1}, and dotted on the same axes are graphs of the corresponding purely simple harmonic values, to illustrate the effect of the modifying second term.

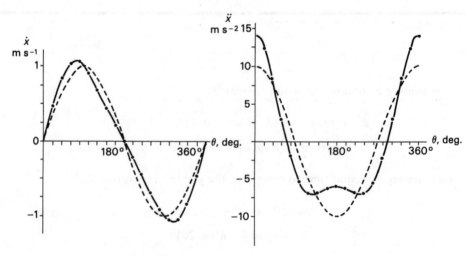

PROBLEMS

1. The crank of a car engine has a length of 64 mm and the connecting-rod length is 153.6 mm. Calculate the maximum piston acceleration when the engine is turning at a speed of 6000 rev. per minute. [*Ans. 35 793.8 m s^{-2}.*]
   Hint: inspection of the expression for acceleration shows that maximum occurs when $\theta = 0°$; differentiating is not necessary.
2. Determine the maximum piston velocity for the engine specified in problem 1. [*Ans. 43.18 m s^{-1} ($\theta = 70.89°$).*]
   Hint: $\dot{v}$ (i.e. acceleration) will be zero. $\therefore$ $\cos \theta + k \cos 2\theta = 0$. $\cos 2\theta = 2 \cos^2 \theta - 1$; substitute and solve the quadratic for θ. Substitute this value in expression for velocity.

32

The answer to the first of the two problems above gives one some idea of the magnitude of the accelerations encountered in high-speed machinery. The acceleration is approximately 3600 times the gravitational acceleration. To express this in practical terms, what it tells us is, that when the piston has moved up to the top of the cylinder, it is being pulled back by the connecting-rod with a force approximately equal to *3600 times its own weight*. This offers some explanation of the reason for manufacturing pistons of light alloy instead of steel.

Determination of the angular velocity and acceleration of the connecting rod requires an expression for the angular displacement. You can use the expression for $\cos \phi$ set down in Frame 27. The differentiation is performed in Frame 33, but you might wish to attempt it yourself first. Use the method of implicit differentiation, that is, do not write the expression as an inverse cosine function.

33

From Frame 27

$$\cos \phi = (1 - k^2 \sin^2 \theta)^{\frac{1}{2}}$$

Differentiating:

$$(-\sin \phi)\dot{\phi} = \tfrac{1}{2}(1 - k^2 \sin^2 \theta)^{-\frac{1}{2}}(-k^2(2 \sin \theta \cos \theta))\dot{\theta}$$

From Frame 27

$$\sin \phi = k \sin \theta$$

Substituting:

$$-\dot{\phi}k \sin \theta = \tfrac{1}{2}(1 - k^2 \sin^2 \theta)^{-\frac{1}{2}}(-k^2(2 \sin \theta \cos \theta))\dot{\theta}$$

$$\therefore \quad \dot{\phi} = \dot{\theta}\left(\frac{k \cos \theta}{(1 - k^2 \sin^2 \theta)^{\frac{1}{2}}}\right)$$

34

Differentiating $\dot{\phi}$ gives the angular acceleration of the connecting-rod. We use the quotient formula again.

$$\ddot{\phi} = (\dot\theta)^2\left(\frac{(1 - k^2 \sin^2 \theta)^{\frac{1}{2}}(-k \sin \theta) - (k \cos \theta)\frac{1}{2}(1 - k^2 \sin^2 \theta)^{-\frac{1}{2}}(-2k^2 \sin \theta \cos \theta)}{((1 - k^2 \sin^2 \theta)^{\frac{1}{2}})^2}\right)$$

We multiply top and bottom lines of the right-hand side by $(1 - k^2 \sin^2 \theta)^{\frac{1}{2}}$:

$$\ddot{\phi} = (\dot\theta)^2\left(\frac{(1 - k^2 \sin^2 \theta)(-k \sin \theta) + (k \cos \theta)\frac{1}{2}(2k^2 \sin \theta \cos \theta)}{(1 - k^2 \sin^2 \theta)^{3/2}}\right)$$

$$\ddot{\phi} = (\dot\theta)^2 k \sin \theta\left(\frac{-1 + k^2 \sin^2 \theta + k^2 \cos^2 \theta}{(1 - k^2 \sin^2 \theta)^{3/2}}\right)$$

$$\ddot{\phi} = (\dot\theta)^2 k \sin \theta\left(\frac{k^2 - 1}{(1 - k^2 \sin^2 \theta)^{3/2}}\right)$$

Remembering that k^2 must always be less than 1, this expression shows that the angular acceleration of the connecting-rod must be negative for all positive values of $\sin \theta$; that is, for $\theta = 0°$ to $180°$. Thus, for the first half-revolution of the crank from the inner dead centre position, the connecting-rod moves outwards, but with a reducing speed, and then returns with an increasing speed. For the second half-revolution, the motion is symmetrical.

Examine the expression and then state (a) what is the condition for maximum acceleration, and (b) what will this maximum acceleration be?

35

For max. $\ddot{\phi}$, $\sin \theta = 1$. $\therefore$ $\theta = \pi/2$ or $3\pi/2$

$$\ddot{\phi}_{\text{max}} = (\dot\theta)^2\left(\frac{-k}{\sqrt{(1 - k^2)}}\right)$$

The expression shows that as $\sin \theta$ increases, the numerator increases, and the denominator decreases; thus, the maximum value must be when $\sin \theta$ has its maximum value of 1. Substituting $\sin \theta = 1$ gives:

$$\ddot{\phi}_{\text{max}} = (\dot\theta)^2 k\left(\frac{k^2 - 1}{(1 - k^2)^{3/2}}\right)$$

$$= -(\dot\theta)^2 k\left(\frac{1 - k^2}{(1 - k^2)^{3/2}}\right)$$

$$\therefore \quad \ddot{\phi}_{\text{max}} = (\dot\theta)^2\left(\frac{-k}{\sqrt{(1 - k^2)}}\right)$$

Answer this question now. For a given value of crank speed, if the length of the connecting-rod were increased, would this result in an increase of the maximum angular acceleration, or a decrease?

36

A decrease

k will be smaller. The numerator will decrease, and the denominator will increase, both resulting in a decrease in $\phi_{\max}$.

A drawing of the mechanism of a trunnion engine is shown.

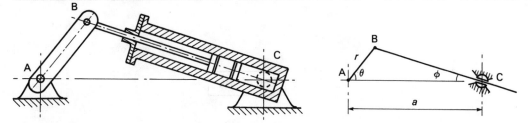

Crank AB rotates at constant speed ω about the fixed pivot A. The piston is integral with the connecting-rod. The cylinder is mounted on a strong transverse axis at C, called a **trunnion**, which allows the cylinder to oscillate up and down as the crank turns. We shall develop expressions for the angular velocity of the cylinder, and the linear velocity of the piston relative to the cylinder.

The equivalent mechanism is shown. Distance a is constant. Begin by obtaining an expression for the angle ϕ. Construct the perpendicular from B to AC.

37

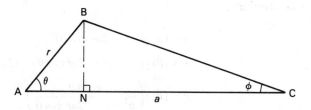

From the diagram, $BN = r \sin \theta - (a - r \cos \theta) \tan \phi$

$$\therefore \quad \tan \phi = \frac{r \sin \theta}{a - r \cos \theta}$$

Angular velocity:

$$\dot{\phi} = (\omega r)\left(\frac{a \cos \theta - r}{a^2 + r^2 - 2ar \cos \theta} \right)$$

It is left for you to derive this expression for $\dot{\phi}$. If you have any difficulty, you will find that the working in Frame 18 is almost identical.

38

To find the linear velocity of the piston, you require an expression for the displacement, x. What dimension on the diagram in Frame 37 can be used to define displacement, x?

39

$$\boxed{\text{Length BC}}$$

The distance of the trunnion centre C from B can be defined as the displacement of the cylinder from a point on the piston rod.

So use the Cosine formula (see Frame 7) to determine x, the length of BC and differentiate.

40

Using the Cosine formula:

$$x = (a^2 + r^2 - 2ar \cos \theta)^{\frac{1}{2}}$$

$$\therefore \quad \dot{x} = (\dot{\theta})\tfrac{1}{2}(a^2 + r^2 - 2ar \cos \theta)^{-\frac{1}{2}}(2ar \sin \theta)$$

$$\therefore \quad \dot{x} = (\dot{\theta}r)\left(\frac{a \sin \theta}{a^2 + r^2 - 2ar \cos \theta}\right)$$

If you need further practice, you can differentiate this again to obtain $\ddot{x}$. The answer is:

$$\ddot{x} = (\dot{\theta}^2)r\left(\frac{ar^2 \cos \theta + a^3 \cos \theta - 2a^2 r}{(a^2 + r^2 - 2ar \cos \theta)^2}\right)$$

The derivation is not included here, but the working is not difficult.

Frame 41 brings this programme to a close with a final set of problems.

PROBLEMS

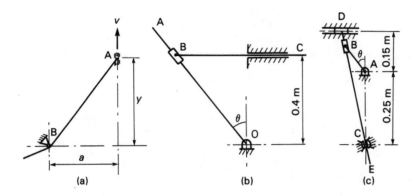

(a)   (b)   (c)

1. A vehicle A moves along a straight track at a constant velocity $v = 25$ m s^{-1}. A rope attached to it passes round a pulley fixed at point B which is at a distance $a = 10$ m from the line of the track. The arrangement is shown at (a) above. Calculate the acceleration of the rope through the pulley when the distance y shown on the diagram is 20 m. [*Ans. 5.59 m s^{-2}.*]

   Hints: let the distance AB be x, and obtain an expression for x in terms of a and y. Differentiate twice, and then substitute the values given. You should find:

$$\ddot{x} = (\dot{y})^2 \left(\frac{a^2}{(y^2 + a^2)^{3/2}} \right)$$

2. In the mechanism shown at (b) above, angle θ is 40°.
   (a) If BC moves left with constant velocity of 2 m s^{-1}, calculate the angular acceleration of link OA.
   (b) If OA turns anti-clockwise with a constant angular velocity of 2 rad s^{-1}, calculate the linear acceleration of BC.
   [*Ans. (a) 14.447 rad s^{-2}; (b) 4.576 m s^{-2}.*]
   Hint: the problem is the same as that in Programme 3, Frame 30, no. 2.

3. The mechanism illustrated at (c) above is a special type of quick-return mechanism. The upper end of link DE is constrained by a horizontal slide, and the link passes through a swivel at C which is fixed in position, but allows the link to slide through it. The link is driven by crank AB of radius 0.125 which is connected by a sliding block at B which slides along DE. Calculate the linear velocity and acceleration of D when AB turns at a constant speed of 2.5 rad s^{-1} in an anti-clockwise direction, when the angle θ is (a) 30°; (b) 0°; (c) 180°. [*Ans. (a) 0.321 m s^{-1}; 0.0142 m s^{-2}. (b) 0.333 m s^{-1}; 0. (c) 1.00 m s^{-1}; 0.*]

Programme 5

NON-LINEAR ACCELERATION

1

In this programme, we shall investigate problems of bodies which move under the direction of a force which is not constant. Also, we shall examine the problem of a body propelled by a constant force, but having a variable mass, such as a rocket. Remember the four equations of linear motion in Programme 1:

$$x = \tfrac{1}{2}(v_0 + v)t \quad (1) \qquad\qquad v = v_0 + at \quad (2)$$
$$x = v_0 t + \tfrac{1}{2}at^2 \quad (3) \qquad\qquad v^2 = v_0^2 + 2ax \quad (4)$$

and four similar and analogous equations for the motion of bodies in pure rotation. You were given a specific warning that they were to be used only when the acceleration of the body was constant. Now force, mass and acceleration are related by the fundamental Equation of Motion which is Newton's Second Law:

$$\Sigma(F) = m \times a$$

so it follows that acceleration will be constant only if the force and the mass remain constant.

2

When acceleration varies, our starting-point for analysis is the basic definition of acceleration in calculus terms, viz.:

$$a = \frac{dv}{dt} = \frac{d^2x}{dt^2}$$

and, if we adopt the convention that small letters are used for variables, and large ones for constants, the equation $\Sigma(F) = ma$ is better written $\Sigma(f) = ma$ where $\Sigma(f)$ now represents the resultant force on a body at any instant. There are two possibilities:

1. $\Sigma(f)$ can be expressed as a *function*, f being a variable with time, velocity or displacement.
2. $\Sigma(f)$ is a variable which cannot be expressed as an algebraic function, but only as a graph of force against some other variable (e.g. time, velocity, displacement).

The first part of this programme, as far as Frame 57, will be devoted to solving problems of force which can be expressed as a function of either time, velocity or displacement.

3

When force can be expressed as a variable of time, velocity or displacement, the Equation of Motion becomes a differential equation, of first or second order. At this point, we need a reminder about the process of integration. The solving of a differential equation is really a process of integration, even though frequently, you do not actually integrate. When integration is performed, you should remember that one must always allow for a *constant of integration*. Why is this necessary?

4

> A constant of integration is required because when differentiating a constant, the result is zero. So, when reversing the process, and integrating, the original function may have had a constant as part of it.

We shall see in this programme that these constants have real meanings in engineering problems. So, if we are solving a first-order equation, we should always remember that a constant of integration must be included, and if we are solving a second-order equation, there must be two constants.

To illustrate the significance of these constants, we shall solve an example of the sort we looked at in Programme 1, but our approach will now be different.

Example. A body is projected vertically upwards with an initial speed of 20 m s^{-1}. How long will it take to reach a height of 15 m? Neglect resistance of the air, and assume $g = 9.81$ m s^{-2}.

Instead of using the equation:

$$x = v_0 t + \tfrac{1}{2} a t^2$$

we shall start with the general Equation of Motion of the body. At any instant, the force acting on the body will be (mg) downwards. So we write the Equation of Motion, $\Sigma(F) = ma$, thus:

$$-(mg) = ma = m\frac{\mathrm{d}^2 x}{\mathrm{d}t^2}$$

$$\therefore \quad \frac{\mathrm{d}^2 x}{\mathrm{d}t^2} = -g = -9.81$$

and here we have a second-order differential equation, which we can solve by integrating twice. You can do this yourself.

5

> Integrating: $\dfrac{dx}{dt} = -9.81t + A$ (1)
>
> Integrating again: $x = -9.81 \times \frac{1}{2}t^2 + At + B$ (2)

We can determine the value of the constant A if we know dx/dt (i.e. the velocity) at some particular value of t. We are told that the initial velocity (i.e. when $t = 0$) is 20 m s^{-1}. So, substituting in equation (1):

$$20 = -9.81 \times 0 + A$$

giving: $\qquad\qquad\qquad\qquad\qquad A = 20$

The constant B can be evaluated if we know the value of displacement x at some particular value of t. The initial displacement (i.e. when $t = 0$) is 0. So, substituting in equation (2):

$$0 = -9.81 \times 0 + A \times 0 + B$$

$$\therefore \qquad B = 0$$

So the complete solution of the equation is:

$$x = -9.81 \times \tfrac{1}{2}t^2 + 20t$$

and this is seen to be the same result as we should have obtained by using the standard equation for constant acceleration in Frame 4. Complete the solution by solving the quadratic equation. The answer is

$$t = 0.991 \text{ s} \qquad \text{or} \qquad 3.087 \text{ s}$$

6

Of course, you would not normally solve this last problem this way. Simple problems, in which the acceleration is constant, should be solved using the four equations developed for the purpose. The aim of Frames 4 and 5 is to introduce you to the more generalised approach needed for problems in which the acceleration is not constant.

The solution here involves solving a **differential equation**, and you will meet differential equations in all the problems and examples in this programme. For the purpose of this text, we may divide differential equations into two classes.

1. Equations in which the variables can be separated easily, so that the equation can be solved by direct integration. (The solution in Frame 5 is an example.)
2. Equations in which the variables cannot be separated.

The second group comprises the much more difficult problems. We shall deal with a few of them later, and shall have some remarks to make about the methods of solving them. But most of the work will consist of equations of the first kind. To help you, you will find in the following frame a list of some standard integrals, many of which will be needed as you work through the text.

7

Useful integrals

$$\int\left(\frac{1}{a+bx}\right)dx = \frac{1}{b}\ln(a+bx); \qquad \int\left(\frac{1}{a-bx}\right)dx = -\frac{1}{b}\ln(a-bx)$$

$$\int\left(\frac{x}{a+bx}\right)dx = \frac{x}{b} - \frac{a}{b^2}\ln(a+bx); \qquad \int\left(\frac{x}{a-bx}\right)dx = -\frac{x}{b} - \frac{a}{b^2}\ln(a-bx)$$

$$\int\left(\frac{1}{a^2+x^2}\right)dx = \frac{1}{a}\tan^{-1}\left(\frac{x}{a}\right); \qquad \int\left(\frac{1}{\sqrt{(a^2-x^2)}}\right)dx = \sin^{-1}\left(\frac{x}{a}\right)$$

$$\int\left(\frac{1}{a^2-x^2}\right)dx = \frac{1}{2a}\ln\left(\frac{a+x}{a-x}\right) = \frac{1}{a}\tanh^{-1}\left(\frac{x}{a}\right)$$

$$\int\left(\frac{1}{\sqrt{(x^2-a^2)}}\right)dx = \ln(x+\sqrt{\{x^2-a^2\}}); \qquad \int\left(\frac{x}{a\pm bx^2}\right)dx = \pm\frac{1}{2b}\ln(a\pm bx^2)$$

$$\int\ln(x)dx = x\ln(x) - x$$

8

The same method of solution is used to solve this next example.

Example. A body having a mass of 25 kg is acted upon by a force f which varies with time according to the expression:

$$f = (10t - 0.4t^3) \text{ newtons}$$

where t is the time elapsed from initiation of the force. Calculate how far the body moves after (a) 4 seconds; (b) 8 seconds, assuming it starts from rest. Determine after what time it will return to its starting-point, and what its velocity will then be.

Begin by setting up the equation of motion, proceeding as in the earlier example. Then integrate to determine dx/dt. Don't forget the constant.

9

> Equation of motion $(\Sigma(f) = ma)$: $10t - 0.4t^3 = 25\dfrac{d^2x}{dt^2}$
>
> Integrating: $25\dfrac{dx}{dt} = 10(\tfrac{1}{4}t^2) - 0.4(\tfrac{1}{4}t^4) + A$ (1)

Constant A can be found straight away, before the second integration, by substituting a known value of velocity at some known value of t. Do this, and thus show that in this case, $A = 0$.

10

The body *starts from rest.* Therefore, when $t = 0$, $v = 0$. Substituting in equation (1) from the previous frame:

$$0 = 5 \times 0 - 0.1 \times 0 + A$$

$$\therefore \quad A = 0$$

So equation (1) now is:

$$25\frac{dx}{dt} = 5t^2 - 0.1t^4 \qquad (2)$$

Now integrate this a second time to determine displacement, x. Again, don't forget the constant, and try to determine the value of it.

11

> Integrating again: $\quad 25x = 5(\frac{1}{3}t^3) - 0.1(\frac{1}{5}t^5) + B \qquad$ (3)

The condition to determine the constant of integration B is clearly, when $t = 0$. $x = 0$ (if we measure displacement from the initial starting-point). Substituting this condition:

$$0 = 5 \times 0 - 0.1 \times 0 + B$$
$$\therefore \qquad B = 0$$

and the circumstance of both constants being proved to be zero in this example should never lead you into *assuming that they will be zero*. You must always determine the values of the constants by substituting known conditions of the motion.

So the final equation may be written:

$$25x = 1\tfrac{2}{3}t^3 - 0.02t^5 \qquad (4)$$

Substitute the two values of t (4 s and 8 s) in this equation; you should obtain answers of **3.4476 m** and **7.9188 m**. To find when the body returns to its starting-point, simply put $x = 0$ in equation (4) and solve for t. You should get $t = $ **9.129 s**. The solution is continued in Frame 12.

12

Substituting the two values of t in equation (4):

$$25x_4 = 1\tfrac{2}{3} \times 4^3 - 0.02 \times 4^5 = 106.667 - 20.48 = 86.19$$
$$\therefore \qquad x_4 = \textbf{3.4476 m}$$
$$25x_8 = 1\tfrac{2}{3} \times 8^3 - 0.02 \times 8^5 = 853.33 - 655.36 = 197.97$$
$$\therefore \qquad x_8 = \textbf{7.9188 m}$$

Substituting $x = 0$:

$$0 = 1\tfrac{2}{3} \times t^3 - 0.02 \times t^5$$
$$\therefore \qquad t^2 = 83.333$$
$$\therefore \qquad t = \textbf{9.129 s}$$

The solution is continued in Frame 13.

13

It may not be immediately obvious from the question that the body does return to its starting-point. But if you examine the expression for the variable force f (Frame 8) you can see that for low values of t (e.g. 1 second) the force will be positive. But as t increases, the negative cubed term increases rapidly, and at some point, the force will be zero, and subsequently will be negative, so that the acceleration of the body will be reversed.

To determine the velocity of the body at the instant it returns to the starting-point, we substitute the value of t for $x = 0$ in the expression for velocity which we obtained in Frame 10 (equation (2)):

$$25v \, (= 25 \mathrm{d}x/\mathrm{d}t) = 5(9.129)^2 - 0.1(9.129)^4 = -277.84$$

$$\therefore \quad v = -\mathbf{11.11} \ \textbf{m s}^{-1}$$

The negative sign clearly indicates that it is now moving in the opposite direction.

See if you can determine how far the body travels before reversing its direction; in other words, calculate its maximum displacement. The answer is, 9.4281 m, but try and find this yourself. The working follows in the next frame.

14

For maximum displacement, $\mathrm{d}x/\mathrm{d}t = 0$. Thus, velocity $= 0$ at maximum displacement.

Substituting in the expression for $\mathrm{d}x/\mathrm{d}t$ (equation (2) in Frame 10):

$$25 \times 0 = 5t^2 - 0.1t^4$$

giving:
$$t^2 = 50$$

$$\therefore \quad t = 7.071 \ \text{s}$$

and substituting this value of t in the expression for x (equation (4) in Frame 11):

$$25x_{\max} = 1\tfrac{2}{3} \times (7.071)^3 - 0.02 \times (7.071)^5 = 235.7$$

$$\therefore \quad x_{\max} = \mathbf{9.4281} \ \textbf{m}$$

The next example is slightly more tricky.

Example. A rocket of mass 700 kg ascends vertically from the earth, propelled by a force of $(4t)$ kN where t is the time, in seconds, measured from the instant the force begins to act. Show that it will take approximately 11.88 s for the rocket to ascend to a vertical height of 1000 m. Neglect resistance of the air, and assume that g is constant at 9.81 m s^{-2}.

It is clear that the force propelling the rocket upwards increases with time from an initial value of zero. But the rocket will not begin to move upwards, that is, lift-off will not take place, until the propulsive force equals the magnitude of the rocket's weight. Before that, the rocket will be resting on the launch pad, and will be subjected to (a) its own weight, (b) the steadily-increasing propulsive force, and (c) an upward reaction force between launch pad and rocket which will decrease as the propulsive force increases, becoming zero at the instant of lift-off. Only then will upward motion begin.

So the first task is to calculate the value of t for which the force just equals the weight. Do this; it is a simple calculation, and you should get an answer of 1.717 s.

$$\begin{array}{l} \text{Propulsive force} = \text{weight} \\ \therefore \quad 4t \times 10^3 = 700 \times 9.81 \\ \therefore \quad t = 1.717 \text{ s} \end{array}$$

Now we write the differential equation of motion for the rocket in flight. Reckoning t from the instant the force begins, and not from the instant of lift-off, for any time t $(t > 1.717$ s) the rocket is subjected to an upward force of $(4t \times 1000)$ N and a downward force of $(700g)$ N. A free-body diagram is not essential for just two forces. Calling upwards positive, the equation is:

$$4000t - 700g = 700a = 700\frac{d^2x}{dt^2}$$

This can be simplified to:

$$\frac{d^2x}{dt^2} = 5.714t - g$$

Now integrate this equation. Don't forget the two constants; call them A and B.

17

$$\frac{dx}{dt} = 2.857\ t^2 - gt + A \qquad (1)$$

$$\text{and} \qquad x = 0.9523t^3 - \tfrac{1}{2}gt^2 + At + B \qquad (2)$$

Read the question and the previous working carefully, and decide how you are to determine A and B.

18

At the instant of lift-off, both velocity and displacement will be 0. But t at this point is 1.717 s, not zero. Substituting in equation (1) of the previous frame:

$$0 = 2.857(1.717)^2 - 9.81 \times 1.717 + A$$

$$\therefore \qquad A = 16.844 - 8.423 = 8.421$$

Substituting $x = 0$ in equation (2) of the previous frame:

$$0 = 0.9523(1.717)^3 - \tfrac{1}{2} \times 9.81(1.717)^2 + 8.421 \times 1.717 + B$$

$$\therefore \qquad B = -4.820 + 14.460 - 14.459 = -4.819$$

So equations (1) and (2) may now be re-written and completed:

$$\frac{dx}{dt} = (2.857t^2 - 9.81t + 8.421)\ \text{m s}^{-1} \qquad (3)$$

$$x = (0.9523t^3 - 4.905t^2 + 8.421t - 4.819)\ \text{m} \qquad (4)$$

and the equations are valid for any value of t greater than 1.717 s.

If you use these equations to determine velocity and displacement for values of t less than 1.717 s, you will obtain what appear to be possible values. But such a procedure is incorrect. We *know* that at $t = 1$ s, the rocket is still on the launching-pad and is acted on by an upward reaction force which was not allowed for when the equations were derived.

If you were to substitute $x = 1000$ m in equation (4), you would be faced with a cubic equation to solve. This is not difficult if you have a programmable calculator, but note the way the question is put. You are not asked to find the value of t, but merely to show that the value given is correct. All that is required, therefore, is to substitute $t = 11.88$ s in the expression for x, and verify that the answer is approximately 1000 m. If you do this, you should find that $x = 999.66$ m, which is close enough for you to assume that the expressions are correct.

Frame 19 comprises a couple of problems for you to try.

19

PROBLEMS

1. A body has a mass of 120 kg. It is travelling with an initial velocity of 100 m s^{-1} when a retarding force of $(0.6t^2)$ newtons begins to act upon it, where t is the time elapsed in seconds from the initiation of the force. Determine the time for the body to come to rest; the time it takes for the body to return to the point at which the force began to act; the maximum distance it travels; the velocity when it returns to the starting-point; and the magnitude of the force at the significant points. [*Ans. 39.15 s; 62.14 s; 2936.3 m; 300 m s^{-1}; 919.6 N; 2316.8 N.*]

2. A body having a mass of 8 kg has an initial speed of 150 m s^{-1} when it is acted upon by a retarding force of (Kt^2) newtons, where K is some constant, and t is the time elapsed from the application of the force. It is observed that the speed is reduced to 100 m s^{-1} after 4 seconds. Calculate the displacement of the mass during this time. Determine also the distance travelled, and the time taken, for the body to come to rest. [*Ans. 550 m; 549 m; 5.769 s.*]

   Hints: solve algebraically, and integrate twice. Expressions for $\dot{x}$ and x will contain three unknowns: A, B and K. $t = 0$, $x = 0$ and $\dot{x} = 150$ m s^{-1}; $t = 4$ s, $\dot{x} = 100$ m s^{-1}. Thus find A, B and K (18.75).

20

Force may also vary with velocity. An example is the resisting force of air, water, or other fluids. A body which moves very slowly through liquid experiences a resistance proportional to the velocity with which it is moving.

Example. A body having a mass of 5 kg and moving with an initial speed of 12 m s^{-1} is subjected to a retarding force of $(0.1v)$ newtons where v is the velocity in m s^{-1}. Determine how long it takes for the speed to fall to (a) 6 m s^{-1}; (b) 3 m s^{-1}; (c) 0.

The equation of motion $(\Sigma(f) = ma)$ is:

$$-0.1v = m\frac{d^2x}{dt^2}$$

We can make this a differential equation in v:

$$-0.1v = m\frac{dv}{dt}$$

So we have a first-order equation in v. The variables can be separated, and the equation integrated. This is done in the following frame.

21

Separating the variables:

$$\int dt = \int \left(\frac{-m\,dv}{0.1v} \right) = \frac{-5}{0.1} \int \frac{dv}{v} = -50 \int \frac{dv}{v}$$

Integrating:

$$t = -50\,\ln(v) + A \qquad \text{(see Frame 7)}$$

The constant A is evaluated by substituting the given condition that when $t = 0$, $v = 12$ m s^{-1}

$$\therefore \quad 0 = -50\,\ln(12) + A$$
$$\therefore \quad A = 50\,\ln(12)$$

So the equation of motion is:

$$t = -50\,\ln(v) + 50\,\ln(12)$$
$$= 50(\ln(12) - \ln(v))$$
$$= 50\,\ln(12/v)$$

Notice that because this was a first-order differential equation, only one constant of integration appears. Completing the solution by substituting values:

Part (a): $t = 50\,\ln(12/6) = 50\,\ln(2) = $ **34.66 s**
Part (b): $t = 50\,\ln(12/3) = 50\,\ln(4) = $ **69.32 s**
Part (c): $t = 50\,\ln(12/0) = 50\,\ln(\infty) = $ **infinite time**

The graph of velocity against time looks like this:

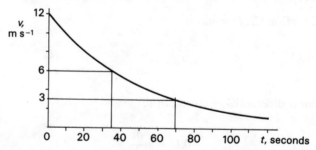

The graph is called an **exponential decay**. One characteristic of such a graph is that for equal increments of time, the dependent variable changes by a *constant fraction*. Thus, after a time interval of 34.66 seconds, the velocity drops to one-half the initial value. What will the velocity be after a total time of 138.64 seconds?

22

$$\boxed{\text{after } 138.64 \text{ seconds, } v = \tfrac{3}{4} \text{ m s}^{-1}}$$

(There are four time-increments of 34.66 s, each diminishing velocity by one-half; thus, the velocities at each interval will be, 12, 6, 3, $1\frac{1}{2}$ and $\frac{3}{4}$ s.)

The diminishing fraction of one-half is quite arbitrary. Calculate the velocities after, say, 10, 20, 30 and 40 seconds. Plot the results in a table.

23

t (seconds)	0	10	20	30	40
v (m s^{-1})	12	9.82	8.04	6.59	5.39

Here is a typical calculation, for $t = 10$ seconds:

$$10 = 50 \ln(12/v)$$
$$\therefore \quad 12/v = e^{0.2}$$
$$\therefore \quad v = 12 \, e^{-0.2} = 9.82 \text{ m s}^{-1}$$

and the remaining calculations are similar. You can verify that for this time-increment of 10 seconds, the reduction ratio—that is, the ratio of any one value of v to the previous value—is 0.8183 for each interval.

For an exponential decay function, the graph of the variable is always asymptotic to the time-axis; in other words, the time for the function to become zero is always infinite. Probably one of the most well-known exponential-decay functions is that of radio-active decay. Because of this feature, some index is needed to describe the rate of change of such a function. One such index is called the **half-life**. This is the time for the function to attain half its initial value. The working in Frame 21 shows that the half-life for this velocity-function is 34.66 seconds.

A second example:

Example. A body of mass 0.5 kg falling vertically from rest is subjected to a resistance of $(0.1v)$ N where v is the velocity at any instant. Sketch a graph of v against t for $t = 0$ to 20 s in increments of 2 s. What is the maximum possible velocity of fall? How long will it be before the velocity is (a) 99%, (b) 99.9% of maximum velocity?

The body moves downwards as a result of its weight and the resisting force acts upwards. So begin by writing the equation of motion. With two forces only, a free-body diagram is not a necessity.

24

> The equation of motion $(\Sigma(f) = ma)$ is:
> $$0.5g - 0.1v = 0.5a = 0.5\frac{dv}{dt}$$

Re-arranging and integrating:

$$\int dt = 0.5 \int \frac{dv}{0.5g - 0.1v}$$

$$\therefore \quad t = 0.5 \ln(0.5g - 0.1v)\left(\frac{1}{-0.1}\right) + A$$

$$= -5 \ln(0.5g - 0.1v) + A \qquad (1)$$

Calculate the value of A by substituting the appropriate condition.

25

> The condition is: when $t = 0$, $v = 0$ (the body starts from rest).
> Substituting in equation (1) of Frame 24:
> $$0 = -5 \ln(0.5g - 0) + A$$
> $$\therefore \quad A = 5 \ln(0.5g)$$

Substituting this value of A in equation (1) (Frame 24):

$$t = -5 \ln(0.5g - 0.1v) + 5 \ln(0.5g)$$

$$= 5 \ln\left(\frac{0.5g}{0.5g - 0.1v}\right)$$

This, though correct, is not in a convenient form to calculate v for given values of t. Recall that if $y = \ln x$, then $x = e^y$. Re-arranging:

$$\frac{0.5g}{0.5g - 0.1v} = e^{t/5} = e^{0.2t}$$

$$\therefore \quad 0.5g - 0.1v = 0.5g\, e^{-0.2t}$$

$$\therefore \quad 0.1v = 0.5g(1 - e^{-0.2t})$$

$$\therefore \quad v = 5g(1 - e^{-0.2t})$$

In this form, we can readily calculate values of v for values of t.

t (s)	0	2	4	6	8	10	12	14	16	18	20
v (m s^{-1})	0	16.2	27.0	34.3	39.1	42.4	44.6	46.1	47.1	47.7	48.2

And here is the graph of velocity against time:

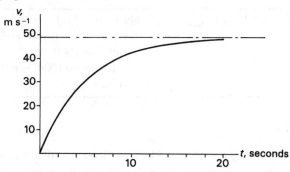

The velocity increases, steeply at first, and then more slowly, as the graph flattens out. The curve is the mirror-image of the curve of exponential decay in Frame 21, and, in fact, is called an **exponential rise**.

Now determine the maximum possible velocity of fall. Look back to the expression for v in Frame 25. Or just re-read the question carefully.

Since $v = 5g(1 - e^{-0.2t})$, it is not difficult to see that for maximum velocity, the e-term must be as small as possible. This condition corresponds with infinite t, when the e-term will be zero.

Going back to the question, if you think of the body falling through the fluid, it will continue to accelerate for as long as the downward weight is greater than the upward resistance. As it goes faster, the resistance increases, the resultant downward force becomes less, and the acceleration gets less. So, when the resistance is equal to the weight, the body will stop accelerating, and will continue at this maximum velocity, which is called the **terminal velocity**. It is a theoretical state insofar as the time to achieve it is infinite, but we calculate the time for the body to attain approximate terminal velocity.

Clearly, when the e-term is zero:

$$v_{max} = 5g = \mathbf{49.05 \ m \ s^{-1}}$$

For 99% of v_{max}:

$$0.99 \times 5g = 5g(1 - e^{-0.2t})$$
$$\therefore \quad e^{-0.2t} = 1 - 0.99 = 0.01$$
$$\therefore \quad e^{0.2t} = 100$$
$$\therefore \quad 0.2t = \ln(100) = 4.605$$
$$\therefore \quad t = \mathbf{23.03 \ s}$$

Using exactly the same reasoning, calculate the time to achieve 99.9% v_{max}.

28

For 99.9% of v_{max}:

$$0.999 \times 5g = 5g(1 - e^{-0.2t})$$
$$\therefore \quad e^{-0.2t} = 1 - 0.999 = 0.001$$
$$\therefore \quad e^{0.2t} = 1000$$
$$\therefore \quad 0.2t = \ln(1000) = 6.908$$
$$\therefore \quad t = \textbf{34.54 s}$$

Another example:

Example. A body having a mass of 4.5 kg is projected vertically upwards with initial velocity of 3.6 m s^{-1}. The resistance due to the air, R, may be assumed to be $R = (0.12v^2)$ newtons where v is the velocity at any instant in m s^{-1}. Calculate (a) the time for the body to reach maximum height; (b) the maximum height reached.

Begin your solution by writing the equation of motion. As in the previous example, there are only two forces. Take care with the signs this time.

29

The equation is: $\quad -4.5g - 0.12v^2 = ma = 4.5\, dv/dt$

We have adopted an 'upwards positive' sign convention. Both the weight and the air resistance will act downwards, as the body is rising, so both forces are negative. Although a free-body diagram is essential for most kinetic problems, when only two forces act on a body, both in the same direction, it can be dispensed with.

Re-arranging the equation in a form suitable for integrating:

$$\int dt = -4.5 \int \frac{dv}{4.5g + 0.12v^2}$$

Calculation is simpler if we divide by the coefficient of v^2:

$$\int dt = -37.5 \int \frac{dv}{367.9 + v^2}$$

The right-hand side is a 'standard' form of integral. Can you recall it? If not, refer to the list of integrals in Frame 7.

You should have found that:

$$\int \frac{dx}{a^2 + x^2} = \frac{1}{a} \tan^{-1}\left(\frac{x}{a}\right)$$

Adapting to this formula, $a = \sqrt{(367.9)} = 19.18$. Now for maximum height, the final velocity must be zero. So, integrating between the two limits, 36 m s^{-1} and 0, remembering to set the *final* value first:

$$\int dt = -\frac{37.5}{19.18}\left[\tan^{-1}\left(\frac{v}{19.18}\right)\right]_{36}^{0}$$

$$\therefore \quad t = -1.955\{\tan^{-1}(0) - \tan^{-1}(36/19.18)\}$$

$$= +1.955\{\tan^{-1}(1.877) - 0\}$$

$$= 1.955 \times 1.083$$

$$= \mathbf{2.114 \ s}$$

You can see that by integrating between limits, we dispense with the need for introducing constants of integration. This is just an alternative way of solving the problem. You can solve it by using constants if you prefer. To determine the distance we modify the original equation of motion. We can express dv/dt as a 'function of a function'. Thus:

$$-4.5g - 0.12v^2 = ma = 4.5\frac{dv}{dt} = 4.5\frac{dv}{dx} \times \frac{dx}{dt} = 4.5v\frac{dv}{dx}$$

and this is arranged with the variables separated:

$$\int dx = -4.5\int \frac{v \ dv}{4.5g + 0.12v^2} \tag{1}$$

This form of integral occurs frequently, wherein the top line can be expressed in terms of the differential of the bottom line. In this example, let the denominator, $4.5g + 0.12v^2$ be u.

$$u = 4.5g + 0.12v^2$$

$$\frac{du}{dv} = 2 \times 0.12v$$

$$\therefore \quad v \ dv = \frac{du}{0.24}$$

Substituting for $v \ dv$ in equation (1) above:

$$\therefore \quad \int dx = -4.5\int \frac{du}{0.24u} = -\frac{4.5}{0.24}\ln(u) = -18.75\ln(4.5g + 0.12v^2)$$

Complete the working yourself. The limits are from initial $v = 36$ m s^{-1} to final $v = 0$. The calculation is completed in Frame 31: the answer is 28.30 m.

31

Completing the integration and putting in the two limit-values:

$$x = -18.75[\ln(4.5g + 0.12v^2)]^0_{36}$$

$$= -18.75(\ln(4.5g + 0) - \ln(4.5g + 0.12(36)^2))$$

$$= +18.75 \ln\left(\frac{4.5g + 0.12(36)^2}{4.5g}\right)$$

$$= 18.75 \ln(199.7/44.15)$$

$$= 18.75 \times 1.5092$$

$$\therefore \quad x_{max} = \mathbf{28.30 \ m}$$

The following frame comprises two problems on acceleration varying with velocity.

32

PROBLEMS

1. A body has a weight of 120 N. Motion through the air is resisted by a force of $(0.01v^2)$ newtons, where v is the velocity of the body in m s^{-1}. If it is projected vertically upwards with an initial velocity of 65 m s^{-1}, calculate the maximum height it reaches, and the time to reach this height. [*Ans. 184.5 m; 5.98 s.*]
   Hints: see Frame 28 *et seq.*
2. A vehicle of mass 1150 kg is subjected to a retarding force R due to air resistance given by:

$$R = (140 + 1.2v^2) \text{ newtons}$$

where v is the velocity in m s^{-1}. Calculate the distance travelled while the speed falls from 15 m s^{-1} to 10 m s^{-1} along a straight level road. Assume that the resistance R is the only force acting on the vehicle. [*Ans. 218.3 m.*]
   Hint:

$$\int\left(\frac{x}{a + bx^2}\right) dx = \frac{1}{2b} \ln(a + bx^2)$$

33

We now consider acceleration varying with displacement. One example is a body acted upon by a spring, or similar elastic member. Another is the motion of a body subject to gravitational force where gravity may not be considered constant, but may vary according to the square of the distance between the bodies. This, of course, is the general case of gravitational attraction. We consider g to be constant only when the distance travelled is small when compared with the size of the earth.

Example. An aircraft has a mass of 18 750 kg. It lands on the deck of a carrier and is brought to rest by an arrester which exerts a retarding force proportional to its extension. The stiffness of the arrester (i.e. the force to extend it by 1 metre) is 75 kN per metre. If the initial speed of the aircraft is 50 m s^{-1}, calculate the time taken to bring it to rest, and the distance travelled.

As always, the first step in the solution is to formulate the equation of motion of the body, writing the acceleration as a differential of velocity or displacement, so that the equation of motion becomes a differential equation. To begin, work in algebra, calling the mass of the aircraft m, and the stiffness of the arrester k. Take care with sign; remember that the arrester exerts a *negative* force.

34

> The required equation of motion ($\Sigma(f) = ma$) is:
>
> $$-kx = m\frac{d^2 x}{dt^2}$$

The arrester force is proportional to its extension, so the tension force when it has stretched a distance x will be (kx). Because it is a retarding force, it is negative. Again, with a single force operating, we do not need a diagram.

To integrate, we use the device we adopted in Frame 30.

$$-(k/m)x = \frac{dv}{dt} = \frac{dv}{dx} \times \frac{dx}{dt} = v\frac{dv}{dx}$$

$$\therefore \quad -(k/m)\int x\,dx = \int v\,dv$$

$$\therefore \quad -(k/m)(\tfrac{1}{2}x^2) = \tfrac{1}{2}v^2 + A \tag{1}$$

We can determine a value for the constant A if we know the velocity when the arrester begins to operate, that is, when $x = 0$. Call this value of velocity v_0, and so work out what is the expression for A. This is done in the next frame.

35

A can be found if we know the velocity when the arrester begins to operate, i.e. when $x = 0$. Retaining algebraic symbols for the time being, and calling this velocity v_0:

$$-(k/m) \times 0 = \tfrac{1}{2}v_0^2 + A$$

$$\therefore \qquad A = -\tfrac{1}{2}v_0^2$$

Substituting this value in equation (1) (Frame 34):

$$-(k/m)(\tfrac{1}{2}x^2) = \tfrac{1}{2}v^2 - \tfrac{1}{2}v_0^2$$

$$\therefore \qquad (k/m)x^2 = v_0^2 - v^2$$

$$\therefore \qquad x^2 = (m/k)(v_0^2 - v^2) \qquad (2)$$

and we may use this to solve the second part of the question first. Substituting the given values, setting final velocity v at 0:

$$x^2 = (18\,750/75\,000)((50)^2 - 0) = 625$$

$$\therefore \qquad x = \mathbf{25\ m}$$

We can re-arrange equation (2) above to express velocity in terms of displacement x:

$$v^2 = v_0^2 - (k/m)x^2$$

$$\therefore \qquad v = \frac{dx}{dt} = \sqrt{(v_0^2 - (k/m)x^2)} = \sqrt{((50)^2 - (75\,000/18\,750)x^2)}$$

$$\therefore \qquad \int dt = \int \frac{dx}{\sqrt{((50)^2 - 4x^2)}} = \frac{1}{2}\int \frac{dx}{\sqrt{((25)^2 - x^2)}}$$

The last integral is a standard 'sine' form (see Frame 7):

$$\int\left(\frac{1}{\sqrt{(a^2 - x^2)}}\right) dx = \sin^{-1}\left(\frac{x}{a}\right)$$

Integrating and substituting values:

$$t = \left[\tfrac{1}{2}\sin^{-1}(x/25)\right]_0^{25}$$

$$= \tfrac{1}{2}\{\sin^{-1}(1) - \sin^{-1}(0)\}$$

$$= \tfrac{1}{2}\left(\frac{\pi}{2} - 0\right)$$

$$\therefore \qquad t = \mathbf{0.7853\ s}$$

This solution is laborious, and demands knowledge of two standard forms of integration. In Frame 36 we shall explore another solution.

36

The problem just completed can be solved another way, by obtaining a direct solution to the differential equation of motion, instead of separating the variables and integration. Before we do this, we shall digress and offer a few remarks concerning differential equations and their solutions.

So far, we have solved the differential equations by 'separating the variables', so that both sides of the equation can be integrated. For example, in Frame 20, the equation of motion was:

$$-0.1v = m\frac{dv}{dt}$$

and this was re-arranged in the form:

$$\int dt = \frac{m}{0.1}\int\frac{dv}{v}$$

the object being to put the differential dt on one side, and the differential dv, together with all terms in v, on the other. With the equation in this form, it is easily integrated. But sometimes, it is just not possible to do this. Take, for instance, the equation:

$$\frac{d^2y}{dx^2} = -Cy$$

As it stands, the variables in this equation cannot be neatly parcelled up to one side or the other. In such a case, you have to solve the equation by finding some function of x which you know will *satisfy the equation*. Now it must be said that this is not easy. If you have a function y of x, it is a fairly simple matter to differentiate it twice and find d^2y/dx^2. But it is very much harder to reverse the process, and deduce what x is from the second differential.

However, there are some aspects of the problem that may make it appear not so formidable as it might at first meeting. Here are three of them.

1. A fairly good knowledge of standard differentials is useful.
2. In Engineering theory, you will not meet very many types of equation.
3. You can memorise some solutions of well-known equations.

We shall discuss these aspects in Frame 37. By way of a lead-in to the discussion, consider this differential equation:

$$\frac{d^2y}{dx^2} = y$$

What you require to solve this equation is some function of x which, if differentiated twice, *remains unaltered*. Can you think of such a function?

37

The answer is: $y = e^x$

If you couldn't think of this yourself, no doubt you now remember that the function e^x has the peculiarity that when differentiated, it does not change.

So a knowledge of some standard differentials is of considerable help in guessing the sort of function that might satisfy an equation.

The second aspect we referred to in the previous frame—the limited number of types of differential equations you are likely to meet—may seem rather like a coward's way out of a problem. But it is a fact that while books on Differential Equations cover a very wide range of types of equation, very few of these are directly applicable to basic engineering theory. To cite an example: in the study of Vibration theory, up to final-year level on an average course, a student will require to solve only three types of equation. (The first of these will be met in Programme 10.)

And finally, remembering standard forms of solution is clearly a help. When you meet an equation that you have solved before, all you need to do is write it down. It is as simple as integrating, when you can remember the standard integrals.

Before returning to solving problems of variable acceleration, there is another very important point to remember when solving differential equations. We shall address this in the following frame.

38

In Frame 4 we stressed that whenever an integration is carried out, one must always include a constant. This is equally true of differential equations. It is often relatively simple to find a *particular* solution to an equation. The solution $y = e^x$ at the head of Frame 37 is an example. It is less simple to obtain the *general* solution to the equation. The general solution is the solution which can satisfy *all possible conditions of the equation*, and it must of necessity include the required constants of integration. When the equation is first-order (i.e. including first differential terms only), a single constant is required. For a second-order equation, including terms of the second differential, then two constants are necessary.

Some of the points just raised will become clearer as we work through the next solution.

Returning to the problem of Frame 33, we have the equation of motion:

$$-kx = m\frac{d^2x}{dt^2}$$

which we can express more simply as:

$$\frac{d^2x}{dt^2} = -Cx \qquad \text{where } C \text{ is a constant, in this case } (k/m)$$

The general solution of the equation is:

$$x = A\,\sin(\sqrt{(C)}t) + B\,\cos(\sqrt{(C)}t) \qquad\qquad (1)$$

Perhaps you know this, although it is unlikely. If you didn't, then you may just accept the solution, but before doing so, differentiate it twice with respect to t, and prove for yourself that it is a valid solution which satisfies the equation of motion. This equation and solution is one of those which you could class as 'standard', and worth remembering, because you will certainly meet it again, in Programme 10, for example. Notice that it includes two constants, A and B.

We find the value of $\sqrt{C}$ by substituting values of k and m:

$$\sqrt{C} = \sqrt{(k/m)} = \sqrt{(75\,000/18\,750)} = \sqrt{4} = 2$$
$$\therefore \qquad x = A\,\sin(2t) + B\,\cos(2t)$$

What are the two conditions we need, to determine A and B?

> The conditions are: 1. When $t = 0$, $x = 0$
> 2. When $t = 0$, velocity $= 50$ m s^{-1}

These conditions for determining the constants are called **initial conditions**. We can substitute the first condition straight away in equation (1) from the previous frame:

$$0 = A\,\sin 0 + B\,\cos 0$$

$$\therefore \quad B = 0 \qquad\qquad \text{(recalling that } \cos 0 = 1)$$

$$\therefore \quad x = A\,\sin(2t)$$

For the second condition, the velocity is required. Differentiate this expression for x to obtain the velocity dx/dt.

41

$$v = dx/dt = 2A \cos(2t)$$

Substituting the second condition, $t = 0$, $v = 50$ m s^{-1}:

$$50 = 2A \cos 0 = 2A$$

$$\therefore \quad A = 25$$

So we now have the final expressions for displacement and velocity:

$$x = 25 \sin(2t) \qquad (2)$$

$$v = 50 \cos(2t) \qquad (3)$$

For the condition of coming to rest, $v = 0$. Substitute in equation (3):

$$\therefore \quad 0 = 50 \cos(2t)$$

$$\therefore \quad 2t = \pi/2 \text{ (the lowest possible value)}$$

$$\therefore \quad t = \textbf{0.7853 s}$$

Then $\qquad x = 25 \sin(\pi/2) = \textbf{25 m}$

For practice, repeat this exercise, taking the aircraft mass at 12 000 kg instead of 18 750 kg, leaving the stiffness, and the initial velocity unchanged. You should find that the distance is 20 m and the time 0.6283 s. The working follows, in condensed form, but avoid referring to it if you can.

42

$$\sqrt{(k/m)} = \sqrt{(75\,000/12\,000)} = \sqrt{(6.25)} = 2.5$$

So the differential equation and corresponding solution are:

$$\frac{d^2 x}{dt^2} = -6.25x; \qquad x = A \sin(2.5t) + B \cos(2.5t)$$

Using the same method as before, you can show that $A = 20$ and $B = 0$.
Then: $\qquad x = 20 \sin(2.5t); \qquad v = 50 \cos(2.5t)$
For $v = 0$: $\qquad 0 = 50 \cos(2.5t)$: $\qquad \therefore \qquad 2.5t = \pi/2$: $\qquad \therefore \qquad t = \textbf{0.6283 s}$
Then: $\qquad x = 20 \sin(\pi/2) = \textbf{20 m}$

The problem of a uniform flexible chain sliding off a smooth table affords an interesting example of acceleration proportional to displacement.

Example. A uniform thin perfectly flexible chain has a total mass m and a length L. It lies partly on a smooth horizontal table, straight, and at right-angles to an edge, with a length x_0 overhanging. It is released from rest and slides off. Derive an expression for the overhang, x, after time t from release, and determine also the velocity of the chain at this point.

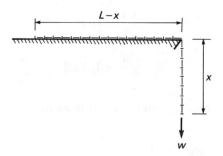

The diagram shows the chain at an instant when the overhang is x. The force causing the chain to accelerate is the weight of the overhang: this is $mg(x/L)$. But the mass accelerated is the total mass of the chain. So the equation of motion is:

$$mg\frac{x}{L} = ma = m\frac{\mathrm{d}^2 x}{\mathrm{d}t^2}$$

$$\therefore \quad \frac{\mathrm{d}^2 x}{\mathrm{d}t^2} = \frac{g}{L}x = Cx \quad \text{(where } C \text{ is } g/L)$$

This differential equation is almost the same as the one in Frame 39, except that the right-hand side is positive instead of negative. Unfortunately, this apparently small difference means that the solution of the equation is completely different from the last one. If you know that the differential of sin is cos, and the differential of cos is −sin, then you are predisposed to look for a solution of the equation of Frame 39 in terms of sin and cos, and indeed, the solution was of this form. But the argument breaks down when the negative sign disappears. We now have to 'guess' some function of x which is unchanged by differentiating twice, except for the emergence of a constant, C.

We shall solve this equation in the following frame, using what may be called a standard method, but you should not be too perturbed if you don't follow all the reasoning. The purpose of this text is to help you to learn to solve engineering problems, not to solve differential equations.

44

To obtain the solution of this type of equation, we assume a solution of the general form:

$$x = Ae^{pt}$$

where p is to be determined by 'trying' the solution, to fit the equation. Thus:

$$\frac{dx}{dt} = Ap\, e^{pt}$$

$$\frac{d^2x}{dt^2} = Ap^2\, e^{pt}$$

We 'try' this in the original equation. This is done in Frame 45.

45

'Trying' this by substituting in the original equation gives:

$$Ap^2\, e^{pt} = C \times Ae^{pt}$$

from which
$$p = \sqrt{C}$$

By 'trying' this solution: $x = Ae^{\sqrt{(C)t}}$ you will find that it satisfies the equation, and thus is a valid solution. But the equation is of second order, and therefore, a complete *general* solution must include two constants of integration. Recall that if $p^2 = C$, then $p = \pm\sqrt{C}$. To ensure we have both our constants in the solution, we must modify it thus:

$$x = Ae^{+\sqrt{(C)t}} + B\, e^{-\sqrt{(C)t}}$$

and you can differentiate this twice and prove that it satisfies the equation.

Now we can turn to the problem of evaluating the constants A and B. What two conditions can we state regarding the motion of the chain?

46

The two conditions are: 1. when $t = 0$, $x = x_0$
                          2. when $t = 0$, $v = 0$

Substituting the first of these conditions, we get:

$$x_0 = A\, e^0 + B\, e^0$$

$$\therefore \quad x_0 = A + B \qquad \text{(recalling that } e^0 = 1)$$

To establish the second condition we require v. Differentiate x:

$$v = dx/dt = A\sqrt{(C)}e^{+\sqrt{(C)}t} - B\sqrt{(C)}e^{-\sqrt{(C)}t}$$

Substituting the second condition gives:

$$0 = A\sqrt{(C)}e^0 - B\sqrt{(C)}e^0$$

$$\therefore \quad 0 = A - B$$

$$\therefore \quad A = B$$

$$\therefore \quad x_0 = 2A$$

$$\therefore \quad A = \tfrac{1}{2}x_0$$

and so the final complete equations become:

$$x = \tfrac{1}{2}x_0\, e^{+\sqrt{(C)}t} + \tfrac{1}{2}x_0 e^{-\sqrt{(C)}t} \qquad \text{where } C = g/L$$

$$v = \tfrac{1}{2}x_0\sqrt{(C)}e^{+\sqrt{(C)}t} - \tfrac{1}{2}x_0\sqrt{(C)}e^{-\sqrt{(C)}t}$$

47

Using the expressions just derived, complete the example following. The answers are given, but the working is not, as all you require to do is to substitute in the two equations.

Example. A flexible chain has a length of 0.9 m and lies partly on a horizontal smooth table with an initial overhang.
(a) If the total time to slide off the table is 1.6 seconds, calculate the initial overhang, and the final velocity.
(b) Given that the initial overhang is 50 mm, verify that the end of the chain will leave the table after 1.085 seconds, and determine the final velocity as the end leaves the table.

The answers are 9.14 mm and 2.97 m s^{-1} for (a). The velocity for (b) is 2.97 m s^{-1}.

48

PROBLEMS

1. A body having a mass of 50 kg is travelling along a straight path at a speed of 4 m s^{-1} when it is acted upon by a retarding force proportional to displacement, which causes the body to be brought to rest in a distance of 5 m. Determine (a) the time to travel 1 m from the point at which the force begins to act; (b) the speed at that point; (c) the time for the body to come to rest. [*Ans. (a) 0.2517 s; (b) 3.919 m s^{-1}; (c) 1.963 s.*]

2. A thin, perfectly flexible uniform chain of total length 1.8 m hangs over a small smooth horizontal peg. It is released from rest when 0.95 m hangs over one side, and 0.85 m hangs over the other. Calculate the time for the chain to slip additionally by 0.5 m, the amount of slip after 0.1 s, and the time for the chain to leave the peg. [*Ans. 1.3229 s; 0.1027 m; 1.5344 s.*]

49

Sometimes, the mass of a body may itself vary.

Example. An experimental rocket is driven along a horizontal frictionless test-track by a constant propulsive force F. It has an initial mass M_0 and discharges fuel at a constant mass-flow rate of k. Obtain an expression for the velocity after time t from starting from rest. Given $M_0 = 40 \text{ kg}$, $F = 200 \text{ N}$ and $k = 2 \text{ kg s}^{-1}$, determine velocity and displacement after 10 s.

We require the general equation of motion after a time t. The mass will then be $(M_0 - kt)$. The equation $(\Sigma(F) = ma)$ will be:

$$F = (M_0 - kt)a = (M_0 - kt)(\mathrm{d}v/\mathrm{d}t)$$

Separating the variables:

$$\mathrm{d}v = F \int \frac{\mathrm{d}t}{M_0 - kt}$$

$$\therefore \quad v = F \ln(M_0 - kt)(-1/k) + A$$

When $t = 0$, $v = 0$

$$\therefore \quad 0 = -(F/k)\ln(M_0) + A; \quad \therefore \quad A = (F/k)\ln(M_0)$$

$$\therefore \quad v = (-F/k)\ln(M_0 - kt) + (F/k)\ln(M_0)$$

$$= \frac{F}{k}\ln\left(\frac{M_0}{M_0 - kt}\right) \tag{1}$$

Substituting the values given:

$$v = \frac{200}{2}\ln\left(\frac{40}{40 - 2 \times 10}\right) = 100 \ln(2) = \textbf{69.3 m s}^{-1}$$

50

Integration will be easier if we write v as two separate log functions. Recalling that $\ln(A/B) = \ln(A) - \ln(B)$, we can expand equation (1) from the previous frame thus:

$$v = \frac{dx}{dt} = \frac{F}{k}\{\ln(M_0) - \ln(M_0 - kt)\}$$

Substituting values, $F = 200$, $M_0 = 40$, $k = 2$ and re-arranging for integration:

$$\int dx = (200/2)\int \ln(40)\,dt - (200/2)\int \ln(40 - 2t)\,dt$$

Frame 7 gives the integral of a log function: $\int \ln(x)\,dx = x\ln(x) - x$

$$\therefore \quad x = 100\ln(40)t - 100(-\tfrac{1}{2})(40 - 2t)\{\ln(40 - 2t) - 1\} + B$$
$$= 100t\ln(40) + 50(40 - 2t)\{\ln(40 - 2t) - 1\} + B$$

When $t = 0$, $x = 0$

$$\therefore \quad 0 = 0 + 50 \times 40[\ln(40) - 1] + B$$
$$= 2000[3.689 - 1] + B$$
$$\therefore \quad B = -5378$$

So the final expression for x is:

$$x = 100t\ln(40) + 50(40 - 2t)\{\ln(40 - 2t) - 1\} - 5378 \qquad (2)$$

Finally substituting $t = 10$ s in equation (2):

$$x = 100 \times 10\ln(40) + 50 \times 20\{\ln(20) - 1\} - 5378$$
$$= 1000 \times 3.689 + 1000[2.996 - 1] - 5378$$
$$= \mathbf{307\ m}$$

51

Example. A test-vehicle has an initial mass $M_0 = 200$ kg. It is propelled along a horizontal frictionless track by a constant force of 50 N. As it moves, it collects water from a channel at a constant rate of 5 kg per second. Its velocity, when it begins to collect, is 2 m s^{-1}. Calculate its velocity after (a) 5 s; (b) 20 s. When will its velocity be 4 m s^{-1}?

This problem is similar to the previous one, except that mass is now being added to the initial mass, instead of being removed. So, write the general equation of motion, after a time t, and integrate, as before.

52

After time t, the mass of the body will be $(M_0 + kt) = (200 + 5t)$ kg.

$$\Sigma(f) = ma: \qquad \therefore \qquad 50 = (200 + 5t)\,dv/dt$$

$$\therefore \qquad \int dv = 50 \int \frac{dt}{200 + 5t}$$

$$\therefore \qquad v = (50/5)\ln(200 + 5t) + A$$

What condition is necessary to evaluate the constant A?

53

The initial velocity (when $t = 0$) is 2 m s^{-1}

$$\therefore \qquad 2 = 10\ln(200 + 0) + A$$

$$\therefore \qquad A = 2 - 10\ln(200)$$

$$\therefore \qquad v = 10\ln(200 + 5t) + 2 - 10\ln(200)$$

$$\therefore \qquad v = 2 + 10\ln\left(\frac{200 + 5t}{200}\right) = 2 + 10\ln(1 + 0.025t)$$

Complete the calculations asked for. You should find that the velocity after 5 seconds is 3.178 m s^{-1}, and after 20 seconds, 6.055 m s^{-1}. The time to reach 4 m s^{-1} is 8.856 s. The exercise is completed in Frame 54.

54

For $t = 5$ s: $\qquad v = 2 + 10\ln(1 + 0.025 \times 5) = \mathbf{3.178}$ s^{-1}
For $t = 20$ s: $\qquad v = 2 + 10\ln(1 + 0.025 \times 20) = \mathbf{6.055}$ s^{-1}

If $v = 4$ m s^{-1}: $\qquad 4 = 2 + 10\ln(1 + 0.025t)$

$$\therefore \qquad \ln(1 + 0.025t) = 0.2$$

$$\therefore \qquad 1 + 0.025t = 1.2214$$

$$\therefore \qquad t = 0.2214/0.025 = \mathbf{8.856}\ \mathbf{s}$$

Now solve the two fairly easy problems in the next frame.

55

PROBLEMS

1. A small projectile of initial mass $M_0 = 40$ kg is subjected to a constant propulsive force $P = 12$ N propelling it along a straight horizontal frictionless track. Its mass is continually being reduced at the rate of $(0.8 \, t^2)$ kg per second, where t is the time elapsed from the beginning of the motion. If it starts from rest, what will be its velocity when the mass is reduced to half its initial value? [*Ans. 1.8697 m s^{-1}.*]

2. A container having an initial mass of 60 kg travels along a straight level track, and is subjected to a retarding force of constant value 20 N. It sheds mass at a rate of 0.4 kg per metre of distance travelled. If it is travelling initially at 4 m s^{-1}, calculate how far it travels before coming to rest. [*Ans. 22.18 m.*]

56

Here is a summary of the methods used.

If force is a function of time t:

$$f(t) = ma = m\frac{d^2 x}{dt^2}$$

Solve the equation by separating variables and integrating twice to determine v and x.
   If force is a function of velocity v:

$$f(v) = ma = m\frac{dv}{dt}$$

Separate the variables and integrate once to determine v as a function of t. Separate the variables again and integrate again to find x.
   If force is a function of displacement x:

$$f(x) = ma = m\frac{dv}{dt} = m\frac{dv}{dx} \times \frac{dx}{dt} = mv\frac{dv}{dx}$$

Separate the variables and integrate once to give v as a function of x. Then write $v = dx/dt$ and integrate again to determine x.
   The remainder of the programme is devoted to problems of accelerating forces which cannot be expressed as mathematical functions, but only in terms of graphs and tables.

57

When the force acting on a body varies in such a manner that we cannot write it as a function of time, velocity or displacement, but can express it only as a graph, we resort to approximate methods of solution of problems.

Example. A body having a mass of 20 kg is acted on by a single force which varies with time according to the graph and the table shown.

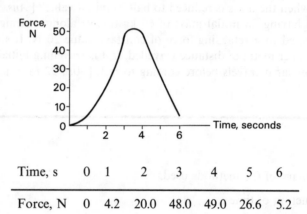

Time, s	0	1	2	3	4	5	6
Force, N	0	4.2	20.0	48.0	49.0	26.6	5.2

Determine the total distance travelled during the 6 seconds the force is acting, and estimate the final velocity. The body starts from rest.

To solve this kind of problem, we break the motion down into convenient 'increments', and calculate the motion over each increment, assuming the force, and therefore the acceleration, to be constant during the increment. Taking six increments, each of 1 second duration, we calculate the force for each increment as being the average of the initial and final value over that period. Thus:

For the first increment: $F_1 = \frac{1}{2}(0 + 4.2) = 2.1$ N
For the second: $F_2 = \frac{1}{2}(4.2 + 20.0) = 12.1$ N

and so on. Because the acceleration is constant, we use the equation $\Sigma(F) = ma$:

For the first increment: $a_1 = F_1/m = 2.1/20 = 0.105$ m s^{-2}
For the second: $a_2 = F_2/m = 12.1/20 = 0.605$ m s^{-2}

and so on. The velocity can be determined using $v = v_0 + at$:

For the first increment: $v_1 = 0 + 0.105 \times 1 = 0.105$ m s^{-1}
For the second: $v_2 = 0.105 + 0.605 \times 1 = 0.71$ m s^{-1}

Displacement may be found from $x = \frac{1}{2}(v_0 + v)t$:

For the first increment: $x_1 = \frac{1}{2}(0 + 0.105) = 0.053$ m
For the second: $x_2 = \frac{1}{2}(0.105 + 0.71) = 0.408$ m

58

The calculations in the previous frame are best presented in the form of a table. Here is the table, completed for the first three increments.

Time, s	0	1	2	3	4	5	6
Force, N	0	4.2	20.0	48.0	49.0	26.6	5.2
Av. force	—	2.1	12.1	34.0			
Acceln, m s^{-2}	0	0.105	0.605	1.70			
Vel., m s^{-1}	0	1.05	0.71	2.41			
Dispt, m	0	0.053	0.408	1.56			

Note that in the third and fourth lines, force and acceleration are assumed to be the values for the increment *immediately before* that point in time, whereas velocity is the velocity *at* that point in time. Displacement is the displacement for *each* increment of time; total displacement will be the sum of all separate displacements. Thus, total displacement after 3 seconds will be 2.021 m.

Make sure you understand the calculations of all the figures, and then complete the table yourself. The completed table appears in the following frame, but refer to it only if necessary. Do not go beyond three decimal places in any calculation. (Notice that displacements for $t = 1$ s and 2 s have been 'rounded off'.) Calculate the final total displacement by adding up the final row.

59

Here is the table complete.

Time, s	0	1	2	3	4	5	6
Force, N	0	4.2	20.0	48.0	49.0	26.6	5.2
Av. force	—	2.1	12.1	34.0	48.5	37.8	15.9
Acceln, m s^{-2}	0	0.105	0.605	1.70	2.425	1.89	0.795
Vel., m s^{-1}	0	0.105	0.71	2.41	4.835	6.725	7.52
Dispt, m	0	0.053	0.408	1.56	3.623	5.78	7.123

The final velocity is seen to be **7.52 m s^{-1}**.
The total displacement is the sum of the final row, which is **18.547 m**.

Do not forget that such methods as this one are at best approximations. Accuracy depends on the size of the increment taken; the more increments, the greater the accuracy, but also, the more work in calculation.

60

We may write:
$$\Sigma(f) = ma = m \, dv/dt$$

$$\therefore \quad \int f \, dt = \int m \, dv = m(\text{velocity change})$$

$$\therefore \quad \text{change of velocity} = (1/m)(\text{area under force–time graph})$$

and if you look back to the fifth line of the table in Frame 59, you will see that the figure of 7.52 is actually the area under the graph divided by 20. The area under each segment will be (average force × time) and as the time-increment is 1 second, average force is numerically equal to area. So total area will be the sum of the terms in line 3, which is 150.4 N s. Dividing this by the mass, 20 kg gives 7.52 m s^{-1}.

61

A similar technique is used when force varies with displacement.

Example. A spring-buffer has a non-linear force–displacement characteristic in compression in accordance with the table.

Compression, mm	0	20	40	60	80	100	120
Force, N		70	82	96	116	144	188	200

A body of mass 4 kg moving with velocity 2.5 m s^{-1} is brought to rest by the buffer. Calculate the approximate time to come to rest, and the compression of the buffer.

In this example, it is convenient to divide the motion into equal increments of displacement, rather than time-increments. We shall take six increments, assuming force to be constant over each one, and equal to the average value. So for the first increment of 20 mm, average force $= \frac{1}{2}(70 + 82) = 76$ N. Then:

$$F = ma: \qquad \therefore \qquad a = 76/4 = 19 \text{ m s}^{-2}$$

The relevant kinematic equation to find velocity change is:

$$v^2 = v_0^2 + 2ax = (2.5)^2 + 2(-19)(20 \times 10^{-3}) = 5.49$$

$$\therefore \quad v = 2.343 \text{ m s}^{-1}$$

Time is calculated from $v = v_0 + at$

$$\therefore \quad t = (2.5 - 2.343)/19 = 0.00826 \text{ s}$$

We begin setting out results in a table in the next frame.

62

Compression, mm	0	20	40	60	80	100	120
Force, N	70	82	96	116	144	188	200
Av. force, N	—	76	89	106			
Acceln, m s^{-2}	—	19	22.25	26.5			
v^2	6.25	5.49	4.60	3.54			
v, m s^{-1}	2.5	2.343	2.145	1.881			
t, s	0	0.00826	0.00890	0.00996			

Make sure you understand all the calculations and then complete the table yourself. The fourth line, v^2, is included because each calculation of velocity requires the square of the previous velocity. The completed table is presented in the next frame.

63

Compression, mm	0	20	40	60	80	100	120
Force, N	70	82	96	116	144	188	200
Av. force, N	—	76	89	106	130	166	194
Acceln, m s^{-2}	—	19	22.25	26.5	32.5	41.5	48.5
v^2	6.25	5.49	4.60	3.54	2.24	0.58	−1.36
v, m s^{-1}	2.50	2.343	2.145	1.881	1.497	0.762	—
t, s	0	0.00826	0.00890	0.00996	0.01182	0.01771	

The table shows that the body comes to rest somewhere between a spring compression of 100 and 120 mm; if a graph of v against compression is plotted, it suggests a value of about 105 mm. The sum of the final row is 0.05665 s. Thus, the time for the body to be brought to rest is slightly above this figure.

An alternative approach is to consider equal increments of time. A reasonable increment in this example would be 0.005 s; this would give about 11 increments. Assuming the spring force for the first increment to be the initial value of 72 N, the acceleration, and thus the velocity change, and displacement, can be worked out. The graph is then used to evaluate the force at the new displacement, and the calculations repeated for the second increment, and so on, until the final velocity becomes zero or negative. This method would not be so accurate, as we should always be measuring the *initial* value of the force for each time-increment, and as the force–compression graph is always rising, every calculation would assume a value of force which was less than the mean value over the increment.

Again, we may make a deduction concerning the area under the curve, which in this case is the work done during compression. A simple square-counting operation on the graph plotted from the table given, up to a compression of 105 mm, gives an area of 12 320 N mm. The initial kinetic energy of the body ($\frac{1}{2}mv^2$) is 12.5 N m; this is a good agreement.

PROBLEMS

1. A body of mass 75 kg moving initially at 12 m s^{-1} is acted upon by a retarding force of $(6t)$ newtons where t is the time in seconds. Calculate how long it takes to come to rest, and how far it travels in that time. [*Ans. 17.32 s; 138.6 m.*]

2. A body of mass 3 kg initially at rest is propelled along a straight path by a single force $f = (5t - kt^3)$ newtons, where t is the time elapsed in seconds, and k is a constant. Given that it returns to its starting-point after 50 seconds, evaluate the constant k, calculate the maximum distance it travels before returning, and calculate its velocity as it passes the starting-point. [*Ans. 1/150; 6455 m; −1388.9 m s^{-1}.*]

3. A body having a mass of 7.5 kg is projected vertically upwards with an initial velocity of 60 m s^{-1}. Resistance to motion due to the air may be assumed to be according to the expression (kv^2) newtons, where v is the velocity at any instant, and k is a constant. It attains a maximum height of 145 m. Write the equation of motion for the body and derive the expression for displacement. Show that the expression is satisfied by a value of $k = 0.0117$. Calculate the time taken to reach maximum height. [*Ans. 5.2359 s.*]

4. A ship of mass 1200 tonnes (1 tonne = 1000 kg) moving through water is resisted by a force of $(240v)$ kN where v is the velocity in m s^{-1}. Its initial speed is 3 m s^{-1}. How far will it move in 20 s, and what will its speed then be? How long will it take before the speed is 0.1 m s^{-1} and how far will it then have gone? [*Ans. 14.725 m; 0.0549 m s^{-1}; 17.00 s; 14.50 m.*]

5. A car has a mass of 950 kg. It may be assumed that the driving force is constant, and that resistance to motion along a straight level track varies as (speed)^2. The maximum speed attainable is 35 m s^{-1} and at this speed, the vehicle is operating at 140 kW. Calculate the time taken for the car to reach a speed of 20 m s^{-1} from rest, and the corresponding distance travelled. [*Ans. 5.400 s; 57.51 m.*]
Hints: at maximum speed, power = tractive force $F \times$ velocity. Hence find F. Also, at maximum speed, $F =$ resistance $= kv^2$. Hence determine k (3.2653).

6. A small truck of mass 50 kg is travelling along a straight level frictionless track at a constant speed of 4 m s^{-1} when it strikes a spring-buffer which has a stiffness of 300 N per metre of compression. Calculate (a) the maximum compression of the buffer; (b) how long the truck is in contact with the buffer before recoiling backwards; (c) the maximum retardation of the truck. [*Ans. (a) 1.633 m; (b) 1.2825 s; (c) 9.798 m s^{-2}.*]

Programme 6

DYNAMICS OF RIGID BODIES

1

We define a **rigid body** as a body which does not change its shape, and which is subjected to a number of forces which do not all pass through a single point. When the forces on a body all pass through a single point, the body is called a **particle**.

For some purposes, a body may be considered to be a particle, while for others, it may be treated as a rigid body. In Programme 1, Frame 95, we made some calculations on a car travelling around a circular track, and in so doing, we drew the free-body diagram as a small rectangle, assuming all three forces to pass through one point. Now it is well-known that if you drive a car around a circular track fast enough, there is a tendency for the inner pair of wheels to lift off the ground, and for the car to turn over. To analyse this effect, we require to know the reaction forces on each pair of wheels, and the position of the mass centre of the car. In such a case, we treat the car as a rigid body.

You will find several examples, later in this programme, of forces acting on cars and other vehicles. We shall also examine the forces on bodies swinging about a fixed pivot, and the motion of discs and wheels on level or inclined tracks. We shall have occasion to examine the *internal* forces and stresses set up when bodies are constrained to move under certain conditions. And finally, we shall talk about d'Alembert's Principle, which offers an alternative method of treatment for the determination of the acceleration of a rigid body.

2

Imagine an abstract rigid body, of indefinite shape, subjected to several forces, which can be reduced to a single resultant force F.

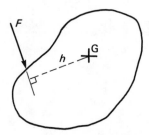

G is the mass centre of the body, and the perpendicular distance from G to the line of action of the resultant force F is h. The force will have two effects.

1. A linear acceleration a of the mass centre G, given by $F = ma$
2. An angular acceleration of the body, α, given by $(Fh) = I_G \alpha$

where m is the mass of the body and I_G its moment of inertia about G. We shall show this in Frame 3.

3

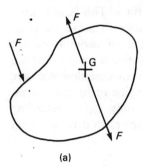
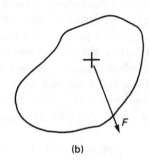
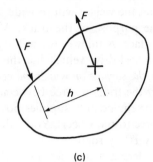

(a)   (b)   (c)

In (a) we have added a pair of equal and opposite forces to the body at G, both parallel to the single force F, and both equal to F. Such an addition cannot alter the motion of the body, as the two forces cancel each other. But we can now treat this system of three forces as a single force F acting at G, as shown in (b), and a couple, of magnitude (Fh) as shown at (c).

The single force F will cause a **linear acceleration** a given by:

$$F = ma$$

and the couple will produce an **angular acceleration** α given by:

$$(Fh) = I_G \alpha$$

4

Frame 3 illustrates the general effect of forces on a rigid body. There are two special cases.

1. The line of action of the resultant force F passes through G. In this case, the body will have no angular acceleration; only a linear acceleration.
2. The body is constrained to rotate about a transverse axis passing through G. Then the body will have no linear acceleration, and the elementary formula $\Sigma(M) = I\alpha$ applies, where $\Sigma(M)$ is the resultant moment of forces acting on the body about G. See Programme 1, Frame 111.

Vehicles travelling on tracks provide an example of the first special case. We shall discuss this in detail in the next frame.

5

When a vehicle travels along a straight or a curved track, it is normally assumed that the weight will provide sufficient force to keep it on the track. This is, of course, the purpose of the track. A road is designed to allow vehicles to move along its surface. A railway is similarly designed to permit the movement of locomotives. But a wheel-drive vehicle has the feature that the driving and retarding forces are applied *at the surface on which the vehicle travels*. A car is pushed forwards, or slowed down, by the friction force between wheels and road, not by the engine or by the brakes. The engine only supplies power to the wheels, and the brakes only apply a retarding force to the wheels. You will know how true this is if you attempt to drive a car on a very icy road.

Here is a sideways look at a car being driven along a level road.

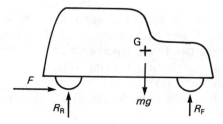

The forward driving force F is called the **tractive force**. If this were the only force acting, it would have the combined effects of both linear and angular acceleration referred to in Frame 2. It can be seen that the force has a moment with respect to an axis through the mass centre G tending to turn the car anti-clockwise. But the weight of the car attempts to pull it downwards. It does not move downwards because the road surface exerts reaction forces at the wheel contact points. But the anti-clockwise moment has the effect of reducing the front-wheel reaction R_F and increasing the rear reaction R_R, to the extent that the resultant moment of all the forces about G is still zero. You may have noticed that when a car pulls away from a standing start, the front of the car tends to rise. When the brakes are applied suddenly, the front drops.

It is theoretically possible, of course, to increase the tractive force until the front reaction force R_F becomes zero. If the tractive force is further increased, the car would actually begin to turn anti-clockwise, because the road cannot exert a negative (i.e. downward) reaction on the car. The condition is hypothetical to the extent that an ordinary car would normally be incapable of providing a tractive force of sufficient magnitude, although when handling the American sporting vehicles called 'hot rods', which consists of very little more than a very powerful engine and four wheels, this condition is quite possible, and part of the skill in driving such vehicles is in learning how to avoid such a catastrophe.

6

Example. A car has a mass of 1150 kg. The distance between front and rear wheels is 2.94 m. The mass centre is 0.42 m above ground level, and is 0.92 m to the rear of the front-wheel centres. Calculate the tractive force, and the magnitudes of the front and rear-wheel reaction forces when the car is driven with a forward acceleration of 1.85 m s^{-2} (a) along a straight level track; (b) up a slope of 8°.

Tractive force was discussed in Programme 1, Frame 45 and also in the previous frame. It is the tangential friction force between the driving wheels and the road. Before drawing a free-body diagram, we review all the forces which most act on the car. These will consist of (a) the weight; (b) the tractive force; (c) the front-wheels reaction force; (d) the rear-wheels reaction force. We shall treat each reaction force as a single force. The diagram follows.

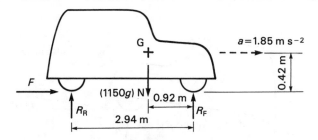

Notice that the question of whether the car is a front- or rear-wheel drive is irrelevant, as the tractive force is in any case tangential to the wheels.

With this type of problem, we always seek three equations:

1. An equation: $\Sigma(F) = ma$ in the direction of the linear acceleration a.
2. An equation: $\Sigma(F) = 0$ in the direction perpendicular to that of the linear acceleration.
3. An equation: $\Sigma(M) = 0$ for moments of all forces about the mass centre.

Write the first two equations before reading on.

7

$$\Sigma(F) = ma: \quad F = 1150 \times 1.85 = \textbf{2127.5 N}$$
$$\Sigma(F) = 0: \quad R_R + R_F = 1150g = 11\,281.5 \text{ N}$$

The first equation gives the value of F. But the two reaction forces cannot be determined from the second. We need the third equation. Write this yourself, adopting a convention anti-clockwise is positive.

8

$$\Sigma(M) = 0 \text{ about } G: \qquad F \times 0.42 + R_F \times 0.92 = R_R \times 2.02$$

Substituting for F and R_R from the first two equations:

$$2127.5 \times 0.42 + R_F \times 0.92 = 2.02(11\,281.5 - R_F)$$

$$\therefore \qquad R_F(0.92 + 2.02) = 2.02 \times 11\,281.5 - 2127.5 \times 0.42 = 21\,895.1$$

$$\therefore \quad R_F = \textbf{7447.3 N} \qquad \therefore \qquad R_R = 11\,281.5 - R_F = \textbf{3834.2 N}$$

For part (b), draw the free-body diagram yourself, before checking in Frame 9.

9

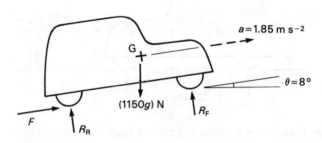

To write the three equations this time, we must resolve the weight force.

$\Sigma(F) = ma$ (in direction of a):

$$F - 1150g \sin 8° = 1150a = 1150 \times 1.85 = 2127.5$$

$$\therefore \qquad F = 2127.5 + 1150 \times 9.81 \times \sin 8° = \textbf{3697.6 N}$$

$\Sigma(F) = 0$ (perpendicular to direction of a):

$$R_R + R_F = 1150g \cos 8° = 11\,171.7 \text{ N}$$

$\Sigma(M) = 0$ (moments about G, anti-clockwise positive):

$$F \times 0.42 + R_F \times 0.92 = R_R \times 2.02$$

The algebra is similar to the first part:

$$3697.6 \times 0.42 + R_F \times 0.92 = 2.02(11\,171.7 - R_F)$$

$$R_F(0.92 + 2.02) = 2.02 \times 11\,171.7 - 3697.6 \times 0.42 = 21\,013.8$$

$$\therefore \qquad R_F = \textbf{7147.6 N}: \qquad R_F = 11\,171.7 - R_F = \textbf{4024.1 N}$$

10

A common mistake is to write a moment equilibrium equation about a point other than the mass centre G—for example, one of the wheel-contact points. This would be correct if the vehicle was in a state of static equilibrium, or if it was travelling at a constant velocity: that is, if there were no resultant force acting on it. But when the vehicle has an acceleration, then you may write a moment equilibrium equation *only about the mass centre*, G. The reason for this is clear if you remember that a vehicle travelling along a track is a special case of rigid-body motion, where the resultant force passes through the mass centre of the body. Now if this is so, it is clear that the resultant force can have no moment about G, but that it does not follow that the moment about any other point will be zero.

Do not forget, also, that a moment equilibrium equation with respect to the mass centre G is a special case of the general equation $(F \times h) = I_G \alpha$ (Frame 3) when the angular acceleration α is known to be zero.

With the second example as a guide, see if you can complete this next example yourself.

Example. The car of the previous example is ascending a slope of 8° at a steady speed of 21 m s^{-1} when it is brought to rest by application of the brakes, in a distance of 35 m. Assuming the retardation is constant, calculate the magnitude of the braking force, and the front and rear-wheel reaction forces. Compare these with the reaction forces when the car is stationary on the slope.

Recall that braking force is exactly like tractive force except that it acts backwards instead of forwards. Call the force B. You will need a simple kinematic equation to calculate the magnitude of the acceleration first.

11

$$v^2 = v_0^2 + 2ax$$

$$\therefore \quad 0 = (21)^2 + 2a \times 35$$

$$\therefore \quad a = -6.3 \text{ m s}^{-2}$$

The complete solution follows, but you should have no trouble.

12

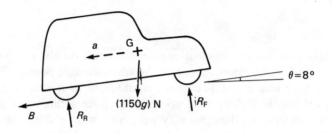

Of course, the direction of the acceleration is down the slope.

The three equations are:

$$\Sigma(F) = ma: \qquad B + 1150g \sin 8° = 1150a = 1150 \times 6.3 = 7245$$

$$\therefore \qquad B = 7245 - 1150 \times 9.81 \sin 8° = \textbf{5674.9 m}$$

$$\Sigma(F) = 0: \qquad R_R + R_F = 1150g \cos 8° = 11\,171.7$$

$$\Sigma(M) = 0: B \times 0.42 + R_R \times 2.02 = R_F \times 0.92$$

and the algebra is similar.

$$5674.9 \times 0.42 + R_R \times 2.02 = 0.92(11\,171.7 - R_R)$$

$$\therefore \qquad R_R(2.02 + 0.92) = 0.92 \times 11\,171.7 - 0.42 \times 5674.9 = 7894.5$$

$$\therefore \qquad R_R = \textbf{2685.2 N}$$

$$\therefore \qquad R_F = 11\,171.7 - R_R = \textbf{8486.5 N}$$

To determine the static wheel reaction forces, which we may call R_{Fs} and R_{Rs}, we write the equations of static equilibrium. Another drawing is not necessary; we may use the free-body diagram above, remembering that force B is removed. Because there is now no acceleration, we may write a moment equilibrium equation about the rear-wheel contact point.

$$R_{Fs} \times 2.94 + 1150g \sin 8° \times 0.42 = 1150g \cos 8° \times 2.02$$

$$\therefore \qquad R_{Fs} = (22\,566.9 - 659.4) \div 2.94 = \textbf{7451.5 N}$$

The equation of equilibrium transverse to the track is the same as before.

$$R_{Rs} + R_{Fs} = 11\,171.7$$

giving $\qquad\qquad\qquad\qquad R_{Rs} = \textbf{3720.2 N}$

If the answers in Frame 9 and these above are compared, it is seen that accelerating up the slope reduces the static front-wheel load by about 300 N, while braking increases it by about 1000 N. The braking retardation is of course much greater than the acceleration.

13

PROBLEMS

1. A car has a mass of 1240 kg. The distance between front- and rear-wheel centres is 3.85 m. The mass centre is 1.26 m to the rear of the front-wheel centre and is 0.69 m above track level. Calculate the tractive or braking force and the magnitudes of front- and rear-wheel reaction forces when the car ascends a slope of 1 in 8 (i.e. $\sin^{-1}\frac{1}{8}$) (a) with a forward acceleration of 1.6 m s^{-2}; (b) with a retardation of 5.8 m s^{-2}. [*Ans. (a)* $R_F = 7491$ N; $R_R = 4578$ N. $F = 3504.6$ N. *(b)* $R_F = 9135.6$ N, $R_R = 2933.4$ N. $B = 5671.5$ N.]

2. A truck has a mass m. The distance between front- and rear-wheel centre is 3.84 m. The mass centre is 2.2 m above ground level and 0.75 m to the rear of the front-wheel centre. The truck is descending a slope of $\sin^{-1}(0.2)$ at a speed of 40 km per hour. Determine the shortest distance in which it can be brought to rest without tipping over the front wheels. Show that for this condition, the coefficient of friction between wheels and road must be at least 0.341. [*Ans. 46.95 m* ($a = 1.3148$ m s^{-2}).]

Hints: $R_R = 0$ for condition stated, $\mu = B/R_F$.

14

Let us examine the situation of a car travelling round a bend.

Example. A car has a mass of 1320 kg. The distance between wheels (the track width) is 2.44 m. The mass centre is centrally between the wheels, and is 0.49 m above ground level. Calculate the magnitudes of total inner and outer wheel reaction forces when the car travels around a flat right-hand bend of mean radius 35 m at (a) 15 m s^{-1}; (b) 25 m s^{-1}.

When drawing the free-body diagram, we must remember that the vehicle will suffer a centripetal acceleration of magnitude v^2/R, directed towards the centre of the bend, i.e. to the right. This acceleration must be provided by a sideways friction force, F. Call the reactions R_i (inner) and R_o (outer).

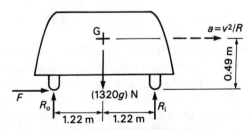

We require the same three equations as before: $\Sigma(F) = ma$ in the direction of the acceleration; $\Sigma(F) = 0$ perpendicular to this; and $\Sigma(M) = 0$ about G.

15

$\Sigma(F) = ma \;(\rightarrow):\qquad F = ma = mv^2/r = 1320(15)^2/35 = 8485.7 \text{ N}$

$\Sigma(F) = 0 \;(\uparrow):\qquad\qquad R_\mathrm{o} + R_\mathrm{i} = 1320g = 12\,949.2$

$\Sigma(M) = 0 \text{ about } G:\quad R_\mathrm{o} \times 1.22 = F \times 0.49 + R_\mathrm{i} \times 1.22$

Substituting for F and R_i in the last equation:

$$1.22R_\mathrm{o} = 8485.7 \times 0.49 + 1.22(12\,949.2 - R_\mathrm{o})$$

$$\therefore\quad R_\mathrm{o}(1.22 + 1.22) = 8485.7 \times 0.49 + 1.22 \times 12\,949.2 = 19\,956.0$$

$$\therefore\quad R_\mathrm{o} = \mathbf{8178.7 \text{ N}}$$

$$\therefore\quad R_\mathrm{i} = \mathbf{4770.5 \text{ N}}$$

As expected, the outer wheel reaction is increased and the inner decreased.

The second part of the exercise is left for you to do yourself, as the calculation follows exactly the same lines. You should obtain values of **11 208.2 N** and **1741 N** for R_o and R_i respectively.

This second result suggests that 25 m s^{-1} is approaching the maximum speed at which the vehicle could negotiate the bend without turning over. We can calculate this limiting speed. Using the same free-body diagram, setting R_i to zero, and calling the acceleration a, the equations now become:

$\Sigma(F) = ma \;(\rightarrow):$

$$F = ma = 1320a$$

$\Sigma(F) = 0 \;(\uparrow):\qquad\qquad R_\mathrm{o} = 12\,949.2$

$\Sigma(M) = 0 \text{ about } G:\quad R_\mathrm{o} \times 1.22 = F \times 0.49$

$$\therefore\qquad 12\,949.2 \times 1.22 = 0.49F$$

$$\therefore\qquad F = 32\,240.9 \text{ N}$$

$$\therefore\qquad a = 24.42 \text{ m s}^{-2} = v^2/R = (v_\mathrm{max})^2/35$$

$$\therefore\qquad v_\mathrm{max} = \sqrt{(24.42 \times 45)} = \mathbf{29.23 \text{ m s}^{-1}}$$

and attempting to drive round this bend in this vehicle at any speed greater than this would result in the vehicle overturning. In this calculation we have made no conditions about friction beyond assuming that a friction force F exists. If the friction coefficient were sufficiently low, then the car could sideslip before it reached the speed for overturning. For the friction force to be capable of resulting in the above limiting acceleration of 24.42 m s^{-2}, the coefficient μ would need to have a minimum value given by $\mu_\mathrm{min} = F/R_\mathrm{o}$ which gives a value of 2.49. This very high figure suggests that in this particular case, sideslip would occur at a lower speed than 29.23 m s^{-1}.

The difficulties of driving cars around bends may be partly overcome by banking the track inwards towards the centre of the curve. This is examined in the next example.

16

Example. A car having the same dimensions as in the example of Frame 14 is driven around a right-hand bend of mean radius 35 m, the track now being banked inwards at an angle of 15°. Calculate the inner and outer wheel reaction forces for the same two speeds of 15 m s^{-1} and 25 m s^{-1}, Calculate the maximum speed at which the car could negotiate the bend without overturning, assuming that it did not slip.

We still have four forces acting: weight, inner and outer reaction, and friction.

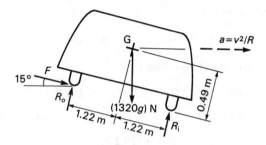

In writing the equations, avoid the temptation to resolve along, and perpendicular to, the track. Always resolve parallel to, and perpendicular to, the acceleration. Attempt the equations yourself before checking in Frame 17.

17

In the direction of acceleration: $\Sigma(F) = ma$:

$$F \cos 15° + (R_o + R_i) \sin 15° = 1320(15)^2/35 = 8485.7 \qquad (1)$$

Perpendicular to the direction of acceleration: $\Sigma(F) = 0$:

$$1320g + F \sin 15° = (R_o + R_i) \cos 15° \qquad (2)$$

Moments about G: $\Sigma(M) = 0$:

$$F \times 0.49 + R_i \times 1.22 = R_o \times 1.22 \qquad (3)$$

The solution is completed by algebraic manipulation. This is done in the next frame.

18

Re-arranging equations (1) and (2) and dividing one by the other:

$$\frac{(R_o + R_i) \sin 15°}{(R_o + R_i) \cos 15°} = \frac{8485.7 - F \cos 15°}{1320g + F \sin 15°}$$

$$\therefore \quad \tan 15°(1320g + F \sin 15°) = 8485.7 - F \cos 15°$$

$$\therefore \quad F(\sin 15° \tan 15° + \cos 15°) = 8485.7 - 1320g \tan 15°$$

$$\therefore \quad F = 4845.0 \text{ N}$$

Substituting in equation (1):

$$(R_o + R_i) = (8485.7 - 4845 \cos 15°) \text{ cosec } 15° = 14\,704.4 \text{ N}$$

Substituting for F and R_o in equation (3):

$$4845 \times 0.49 + R_i \times 1.22 = 1.22(14\,704.4 - R_i)$$

$$\therefore \quad R_i(1.22 + 1.22) = 1.22 \times 14\,704.4 - 4845 \times 0.49 = 15\,565.3$$

$$\therefore \quad R_i = \mathbf{6379.2 \text{ N}}$$

$$\therefore \quad R_o = 14\,704.4 - R_i = \mathbf{8325.2 \text{ N}}$$

19

Again, it is left for you to solve the second part of the example, as the calculations are of exactly the same form. You should obtain a value of **19 416.8 N** for F, and values of **13 203.6 N** and **5405.1 N** for R_o and R_i.

For the final part of the example, when the car is about to tip outwards, the inner wheel reaction force will be zero. We may use the free-body diagram of Frame 16, remembering that $R_i = 0$. The equations now become:

$\Sigma(F) = ma \ (\rightarrow)$: $\qquad F \cos 15° + R_o \sin 15° = mv^2/R$ $\qquad$ (1)

$\Sigma(F) = 0 \ (\uparrow)$: $\qquad mg + F \sin 15° = R_o \cos 15°$ $\qquad$ (2)

$\Sigma(M) = 0$ about G: $\qquad F \times 0.49 = R_o \times 1.22$ $\qquad$ (3)

From equation (3), $F = 2.49 R_o$. Substitute this in equations (1) and (2) and re-arrange thus:

$$\frac{2.49 R_o \cos 15° + R_o \sin 15°}{R_o \cos 15° - 2.49 R_o \sin 15°} = \frac{mv^2}{mgR}$$

Cancelling gives: $\qquad 8.287 = v^2/35g$

$$\therefore \quad v = \sqrt{(2845.3)} = \mathbf{53.34 \text{ m s}^{-1}}$$

The results of the previous example show that the effect of banking is to decrease the sideways friction force F, and to increase *both* wheel-reaction forces. To cause the car to travel around a circular bend, a force must be available to produce the centripetal acceleration. On a flat track, this is a sideways frictional force between wheels and road surface. But if the track is banked inwards, then the normal reaction force between wheels and road will have a horizontal component, which assists in producing the required acceleration. Thus, this force is increased by banking, and the friction force is reduced.

21

PROBLEMS

1. The mass of a car is 1470 kg. The track width is 2.56 m and the mass centre is centrally between the wheels and 0.54 m above ground level.
   (a) Calculate the friction force between wheels and road, and the wheel reaction forces, when the car is travelling at 30 m s^{-1} round a circular track of mean radius 45 m, which is banked at 20°. What is the minimum coefficient of friction necessary for this condition?
   (b) Calculate the required angle of bank of the track in order that the sideways friction force should be zero at the stated speed.
   [*Ans. (a) 22 694.8 N; 7015.0 N, 16 589.4 N, 0.961. (b) 63.87°.*]

2.

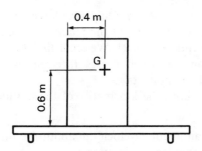

The figure shows the rear view of a crate on the flat floor of a truck. The mass centre G is 0.6 m above the floor and 0.4 m from the left-hand edge.
   (a) Determine the maximum speed at which the truck may travel around a right-hand curve of radius 50 m banked inwards to an angle of 10° without the crate slipping, if the friction coefficient between truck floor and crate is 0.6.
   (b) If the crate is prevented by a stop from slipping, calculate the maximum truck speed such that the crate does not tip outwards, when travelling round the same track.
   [*Ans. (a) 20.64 m s^{-1}. (b) 21.65 m s^{-1}.*]

22

Now let us consider the dynamics of a rigid body turning about a fixed pivot. We shall start with an example of a swinging rod.

Example. A uniform rod of mass m and length L is arranged to swing in a vertical plane about a fixed frictionless pivot at one end. The rod is held initially horizontal, at rest, and is then released, allowing it to swing down. Derive an expression for the angular acceleration of the rod after it has turned through an angle θ from the initial position. Calculate the magnitude of the pivot reaction force when θ is (a) $0°$; (b) $45°$; (c) $90°$.

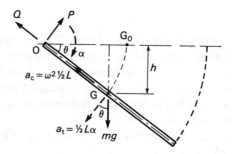

The free-body diagram is shown. Only two forces act on the rod while it is in motion. These are, the weight mg and the reaction force at the pivot. This latter is shown as two components, P and Q. We shall find that it is always preferable to choose components, one of which passes through the mass centre, rather than horizontal and vertical components.

First, be quite clear about the kinematics of the motion. Consider the following points.

1. The road will have an angular velocity ω about the turning point O.
2. It will also have an angular acceleration α.
3. Because of the angular velocity, the mass centre G will have a centripetal acceleration a_c, directed towards the pivot O.
4. Because of the angular acceleration, the mass centre G will have a linear acceleration a_t tangential to its circular path.

Write down expressions for the centripetal acceleration, a_c, and the tangential acceleration, a_t. If you can't see how to do this, refer to Programme 1, Frames 69 and 63.

$$a_c = \tfrac{1}{2}\omega^2 L; \qquad a_t = \tfrac{1}{2}\alpha L$$

The centripetal acceleration is $\omega^2 R$ and the tangential acceleration is αR, where R is the radius of the circular path. Since mass centre G is at the mid-point of the rod, $R = \tfrac{1}{2}L$.

Because there are two accelerations, we shall require two equations of motion of the form $\Sigma(F) = ma$. And a third equation of the form $\Sigma(M) = I\alpha$ is needed in respect of moments of all forces about the mass centre G.

Before we write these equations, notice the necessity for angular and tangential acceleration to be compatible. The angular acceleration α must obviously be clockwise, as shown. Because of this, a_t, the corresponding tangential acceleration of G must be 'down-left' in the direction shown.

Equation $\Sigma(F) = ma$ in direction a_t:

$$mg \cos \theta - P = m \times \tfrac{1}{2}\alpha L \qquad (1)$$

Equation $\Sigma(F) = ma$ in direction a_c:

$$Q - mg \sin \theta = \tfrac{1}{2}m\omega^2 L \qquad (2)$$

Equation $\Sigma(M) = I\alpha$ taking moments clockwise about G:

$$P \times \tfrac{1}{2}L = I_G \alpha \qquad (3)$$

and the advantage of choosing the components P and Q along, and perpendicular to the rod, now becomes clear: equation (1) includes P only and equation (2) includes Q only. The mathematics is thereby made simpler.

The completion of the problem will require a value for I_G, the moment of inertia of the rod about a transverse axis through G. This is given by:

$$I_G = \tfrac{1}{12}mL^2$$

If you didn't know this, then it is one formula that you should remember, as you will certainly require it again. Don't forget that the formula applies only to a *uniform* rod.

Now if you look, you can see that equations (1) and (3) consist of two simultaneous equations in P and α, so you can determine expressions for them. Have a go; the working follows in Frame 24.

24

From equation (1): $\qquad P = mg \cos \theta - \frac{1}{2}mL\alpha$

From equation (3): $\qquad P = (2/L)(\frac{1}{12}mL^2)\alpha$

and equating: $\qquad mg \cos \theta - \frac{1}{2}mL\alpha = \frac{1}{6}mL\alpha$

$$\therefore \qquad mL\alpha(\tfrac{1}{2} + \tfrac{1}{6}) = mg \cos \theta$$

$$\therefore \qquad \tfrac{2}{3}L\alpha = g \cos \theta$$

$$\therefore \qquad \alpha = \frac{3}{2}\frac{g}{L}\cos \theta$$

Substitute this in equation (3):

$$P = \tfrac{1}{6}mL\alpha$$

$$= \tfrac{1}{6}mL\frac{3g}{2L}\cos \theta$$

$$\therefore \qquad \mathbf{P = \tfrac{1}{4}\textit{mg} \cos \theta}$$

In order to find an expression for Q from equation (2) we shall require an expression for ω^2. The easiest way to find this is by using an energy equation. The rod is released from rest in the horizontal position.

$$\text{Loss of potential energy of rod} = \text{gain of kinetic energy}$$

The mass centre G descends a vertical height $h = \frac{1}{2}L \sin \theta$ (see the diagram in Frame 22). The increase of kinetic energy is $\frac{1}{2}I_0\omega^2$. I_0 is the moment of inertia about a transverse axis through the end O now, as this is the pivot about which the rod turns. $I_0 = \frac{1}{3}mL^2$. Again, this is an expression you should try to remember, but you can determine it fairly simply by use of the Parallel Axis theorem. (See Programme 1, Frame 113.)

Substituting in the above energy equation:

$$mgh = \tfrac{1}{2}I_0\omega^2$$

$$\therefore \qquad mg(\tfrac{1}{2}L \sin \theta) = \tfrac{1}{2}(\tfrac{1}{3}mL^2)\omega^2$$

$$\therefore \qquad \omega^2 = 3\frac{g}{L}\sin \theta$$

Substituting in equation (2) of Frame 23 gives:

$$Q - mg \sin \theta = \tfrac{1}{2}mL(3(g/L) \sin \theta) = 1.5 \, mg \sin \theta$$

$$\therefore \qquad Q = mg \sin \theta(1.5 + 1)$$

$$\therefore \qquad \mathbf{Q = 2.5 \, \textit{mg} \sin \theta}$$

25

Summarising the results of the analysis:

$$\alpha = \frac{3}{2}\frac{g}{L} \cos \theta; \qquad P = \tfrac{1}{4}mg \cos \theta; \qquad Q = 2\tfrac{1}{2}mg \sin \theta$$

The total reaction force R at the pivot is given by $R = \sqrt{\{(P^2 + Q^2)\}}$ and substituting the values of θ given yields the following results.

$\theta = 0$: $P = \tfrac{1}{4}mg$; $Q = 0$; $R = \tfrac{1}{4}mg$

$\theta = 45°$ $P = 0.1768\ mg$; $Q = 1.768\ mg$; $R = 1.777\ mg$

$\theta = 90°$: $P = 0$; $Q = 2.5\ mg$; $R = 2.5\ mg$

26

The procedure following will be found applicable to all problems of this type.

1. Draw the free-body diagram:
   (a) If necessary, determine the position of the mass centre, G, and the value of I_G, the moment of inertia with respect to an axis through G perpendicular to the plane of the motion.
   (b) Indicate the angular acceleration, and a compatible linear acceleration of the mass centre G of the body.
   (c) Indicate the reaction force at the pivot in terms of two components, one, P, passing through the mass centre, and the other, Q, perpendicular to this.
2. Calculate the angular velocity ω of the body, using an energy equation.
3. Write the equation of motion $\Sigma(F) = ma$ in the direction of the tangential acceleration of G.
4. Write the equation of motion $\Sigma(M) = I\alpha$ taking moments of forces about the mass centre G.
5. Write the equation of motion $\Sigma(F) = ma$ in the direction of the centripetal acceleration, i.e. G to the pivot O.
6. Manipulate the equations to solve for the unknown terms.

In the next frame, we shall see how this guide applies to another problem.

27

Example. A thin flat uniform metal disc has a diameter of 2 m and a mass of 52 kg. It is mounted on a fixed frictionless pivot at a point on the edge, so that it can swing freely in a vertical plane. It is held initially at rest, with the centre G vertically above the pivot. It is then given a small initial disturbance, causing it to swing downwards. Derive an expression for the angular velocity, and angular acceleration after the disc has swung through an angle θ from rest. Calculate the magnitude of the pivot reaction force when angle θ is 90° and 180°.

The free-body diagram is drawn in Frame 28. The directions of the force components P and Q are not known, and we therefore assume directions.

We shall require the moment of inertia of the disc, both about an axis perpendicular to the plane of the disc through G, and also about a parallel axis through the pivot O. You should remember the expression for the former:

$$I_G = \tfrac{1}{2}mR^2$$

but even if you didn't know this, you can now use it to determine the other value, I_0, using the Parallel axis theorem.

28

$$I_0 = I_G + mh^2 = \tfrac{1}{2}mR^2 + m \times R^2 = 1\tfrac{1}{2}mR^2$$

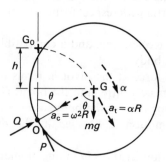

G_0 is the initial position of the mass centre G, and h is the vertical height through which G descends in turning through angle θ.

The tangential acceleration a_t of G is compatible with the angular acceleration, α; its value is αr and its direction is perpendicular to the radius OG.

Taking step 2 of the procedure of Frame 26, write the energy equation and derive an expression for ω^2.

$$\tfrac{1}{2}I_0\omega^2 = mgh = mg(R - R\cos\theta) = mgR(1 - \cos\theta)$$

$$\therefore \quad \tfrac{1}{2}\times 1.5mR^2\omega^2 = mgR(1 - \cos\theta)$$

$$\therefore \quad \omega^2 = \frac{4}{3}\frac{g}{R}(1 - \cos\theta)$$

Steps 3 to 5 of the procedure are the formulations of the three equations of motion. Attempt them first yourself.

$\Sigma(F) = ma$ in direction of tangential acceleration:

$$mg\sin\theta - P = ma_t = m\alpha R \tag{1}$$

$\Sigma(M) = I\alpha$: moments about G:

$$PR = I_G\alpha = \tfrac{1}{2}mR^2\alpha \tag{2}$$

$\Sigma(F) = ma$ in direction of centripetal acceleration:

$$mg\cos\theta - Q = ma_c = m\omega^2 R \tag{3}$$

Step 6: manipulate the equations to find the unknown terms. No doubt you need practice in algebra of this sort, so this is left for you to complete. You can eliminate P from equations (1) and (2) and thus find α. You can then use this to substitute back in either equation (1) or (2) to find P. Finally, the expression for Q can be obtained directly from equation (3) and the expression already derived for ω^2. You should get the following results.

$$\alpha = \frac{2}{3}\frac{g}{R}\sin\theta; \quad P = \tfrac{1}{3}mg\sin\theta; \quad Q = \tfrac{1}{3}mg(7\cos\theta - 4)$$

For $\theta = 90°$ you should get:

$$P = 170\ N; \quad Q = -680\ N; \quad R = 701\ N$$

For $\theta = 180°$ you should get:

$$P = 0; \quad Q = -1870\ N; \quad R = 1870\ N$$

These results are calculated to the nearest whole number.

31

Example. A uniform bar of mass 12 kg and length 1 m rests on a table with its mass centre overhanging the edge by 0.1 m. When released from the horizontal rest position, it is observed that the rod begins to slip on the table edge when it has turned through 10°. Determine the coefficient of friction between rod and table.

Follow the suggested procedure; you are given all the data, and can calculate P and Q. You should find $P = 103.51$ N and $Q = 24.82$ N; $\omega^2 = 3.65$ rad^2 s^{-2} and $\alpha = 10.351$ rad s^{-2}. $\mu = Q/P$ when slip begins. To apply the energy equation, in order to calculate ω, you will require (a) I_G (which is the same as for the example in Frame 22), and (b) the Parallel Axis theorem, in order to determine I_0. You should find the value of I_0 to be 1.12 kg m ^{2}. The solution follows in Frame 32.

32

The free-body diagram is shown here.

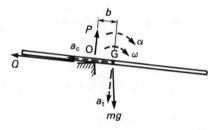

$$I_G = \tfrac{1}{12}mL^2 = 1 \text{ kg m}^2; \qquad I_0 = I_G + mb^2 = 1.0 + 12(0.1)^2 = 1.12 \text{ kg m}^2$$

The energy equation:

$$\tfrac{1}{2}I_0\omega^2 = mg(b \sin \theta)$$

$$\tfrac{1}{2} \times 1.12\omega^2 = 12g(0.1 \sin 10°)$$

$$\therefore \qquad \omega^2 = 3.65 \text{ rad}^2 \text{ s}^{-2}$$

The three equations of motion:

In direction a_t: $\qquad\qquad mg \cos \theta - P = ma_t = m\alpha b$ $\qquad\qquad$ (1)

In direction a_c: $\qquad\qquad Q - mg \sin \theta = ma_c = m\omega^2 b$ $\qquad\qquad$ (2)

$\Sigma(M) = I\alpha$: moments about G: $Pb = I_G\alpha$ $\qquad\qquad$ (3)

The calculations are completed in Frame 33.

33

In this case, working will be simplified by substituting the values given and calculated. The revised equations are then:

Equation (1): $12g \cos 10° - P = 12\alpha \times 0.1$

$\therefore$ $115.9 - P = 1.2\alpha$

Equation (2): $Q - 12g \sin 10° = 12 \times 3.65 \times 0.1 = 4.38$

$\therefore$ $Q = 4.38 + 20.44 = 24.82$ N

Equation (3): $P \times 0.1 = 1 \times \alpha$

Since α is not required, we eliminate α from equations (1) and (3):

$$115.9 - P = 1.2(P \times 0.1)$$
$$\therefore \quad P = 115.9/(1 + 0.12) = 103.5 \text{ N}$$

Since slip is about to occur

$$\mu = Q/P = 24.82/103.5 = \textbf{0.24.}$$

34

Sometimes there may be forces other than weight and pivot force.

Example. A trapdoor is a uniform flat board hinged at one end, 2 m wide and of mass 20 kg. When closed, in the horizontal position, it compresses a spring which exerts an upward force at the free edge of 300 N. When the securing-bolt is released, calculate the instantaneous angular acceleration of the door, and the pivot reaction force.

The problem is straightforward. Draw the free-body diagram, including the upward force of 300 N at the free edge. Because the door is motionless, there is no centripetal acceleration, so only two equations are needed. Begin with a moment equation about the hinge; α can be determined from this. Then write the equation of linear translation to determine the vertical reaction force at the pivot, which we have called P.

It was made very clear in Frame 10 that it is a mistake to write a moment equilibrium equation for a rigid body about any point other than the mass centre. Here, you are being advised to write a moment equation with respect to the hinge. In case this bothers you, understand that this equation is not an equation of *equilibrium*: it is an equation of *motion*, i.e. $\Sigma(M) = I\alpha$. It is permissible to write such an equation with respect to any point on a rigid body.

35

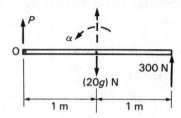

Moments about O $((\Sigma M) = I_0\alpha)$: assume α anti-clockwise:

$$300 \times 2 - 20g \times 1 = I_0\alpha = (\tfrac{1}{3} \times 20 \times 2^2)\alpha \qquad (I_0 = \tfrac{1}{3}mL^2\text{—see Frame 24})$$

$$\therefore \quad \alpha = (600 - 20 \times 9.81) \times 0.0375$$

$$= \mathbf{15.14\ rad\ s^{-2}}$$

Linear translation: $\Sigma(F) = ma$:

$$P + 300 - 20g = 20a = 20(15.14 \times 1) = 302.8$$

$$\therefore \qquad P = 302.8 - 300 + 20g$$

$$= \mathbf{199\ N}$$

36

Example. A uniform thin rod of mass m is held horizontally by two vertical strings attached to the two ends. One of the strings is cut. Show that the tension in the other string immediately after the cut is $\tfrac{1}{4}mg$, and determine the initial angular acceleration of the rod.

This one is left for you to do yourself entirely; the value of the angular acceleration is $1.5(g/L)$. It is actually the same problem as the first part of the example of Frame 22. It is included here, partly to give you practice, but chiefly to emphasise the difference between a static and a dynamic state. Just before the string is cut, the tensions in the two strings must both be $\tfrac{1}{2}mg$. It requires a certain amount of intellectual effort to realise (a) that the tension in the remaining string changes instantaneously, and (b) that it becomes *less* than it was. There is a tendency to think that because it is the only support left, it should be carrying *more* weight.

The same example is developed in the first of the problems that make up Frame 37 which follows.

PROBLEMS

1. A thin uniform rod of length L and mass m is held horizontally suspended by two vertical strings, one attached to the right-hand end and the other a distance a from the left-hand end. The right-hand string is cut. Determine the tension in the left-hand string, as a function of mg the instant after the string is cut, if a is (a) 0; (b) $\frac{1}{4}L$; (c) $\frac{1}{3}L$. Show that the ratio of this tension to the initial static tension is (a) $\frac{1}{2}$; (b) $\frac{6}{7}$; (c) 1. Calculate in each case the angular acceleration of the rod. [*Ans.* $\frac{1}{2}mg$; $\frac{4}{7}mg$; $\frac{3}{4}mg$. $1\frac{1}{2}g/L$; $\frac{12}{7}g/L$; $1\frac{1}{2}g/L$.]

2. A thin uniform rod is 1.2 m long and its mass is 8 kg. It is mounted on a frictionless pivot at the left-hand end, and a weight of mass 1 kg hangs by a light string at a distance b from the pivot. The rod is held horizontally, and then released from rest. Show that if the string supporting the weight is not to go slack, b must be less than 0.8 m. Calculate the initial angular acceleration of the rod. [*Ans.* $\alpha = 1.25g$ rad s^{-2}.]

   Hints: call the string tension T. Write equation of motion also for weight, and eliminate T to determine α. Thus find T; $T = 0$.

3. A thin uniform rod is 1.6 m long with a mass of 12 kg. It stands on a table, vertically on end. It is given a small initial disturbance, causing it to fall. Show that if the lower end begins to slip on the table when the rod has fallen through 19.66°, the coefficient of friction between rod and table must be 0.25.

   Hints: solve in terms of forces P and Q as normally, and then calculate the horizontal and vertical components H and V of the end-force, from P and Q. $\mu = H/V$. Do not try to *prove* that $\theta = 19.66°$ but calculate P and Q for this particular value.

4. A compound pendulum has a mass of 65 kg. It is mounted on a pivot so that it can swing in a vertical plane. It is initially at rest, the mass centre G being 2.2 m below the pivot. The moment of inertia of the pendulum about a transverse axis through the pivot is 420 kg m^2. A torque M of constant magnitude 1500 N m is then applied to the pendulum at the pivot, causing it to be raised.

   (a) Calculate the angular velocity and acceleration of the pendulum when it has turned through 90°, and the components of the pivot reaction force.

   (b) Through what angle must the torque be applied in order that the pendulum turns exactly through 180° before coming to rest?

   [*Ans.* (a) 2.1307 rad s^{-1}, 0.2314 rad s^{-2}, 670.74 N, 649.2 N. (b) 107.17°.]

   Hints: for (b) a simple energy equation: $M\theta = mgh$ where $h = 4.4$ m.

38

When rigid bodies accelerate, they are subjected to internal forces.

Example. A uniform rod has a mass m and length L. It is attached to a pivot at one end so that it can turn in a vertical plane. Show that if it is held horizontally and released from rest, there will be a shearing force and bending moment in the rod. Determine the magnitude of the maximum bending moment, and its location.

Referring to Frames 22 to 24, when the rod is horizontal (i.e. when $\theta = 0$), the angular acceleration is $1\frac{1}{2}(g/L)$, and the pivot force P is $\frac{1}{2}mg$. We shall use these results here.

To determine internal forces, we draw the free-body diagram of a length x only of the rod. The diagram must include the internal forces which are brought to bear on it by the other part of the rod; these consist of a shearing force, F, and a bending moment, M. (In general, there could also be a longitudinal force, due to centripetal acceleration, but in this particular case, with the bar at rest, this will be zero.) Here is the diagram.

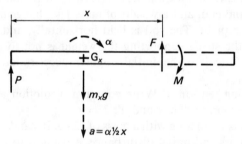

The weight, $m_x g$, and the moment of inertia will be those of the portion of rod, not the complete rod. The directions of F and M are unknown; they have been assumed positive according to a widely-adopted sign convention used in Stress Analysis The tangential acceleration a_t of the mass centre, G_x, will be $\alpha(\frac{1}{2}x)$ since the rod rotates about the fixed pivot at the left-hand end.

The equation of translation of the portion, $\Sigma(F) = ma$, is:

$$m_x g - P - F = m_x a = m_x(\alpha \times \tfrac{1}{2}x) = (m \times x/L)(1\tfrac{1}{2}g/L \times \tfrac{1}{2}x)$$

$$\therefore \quad (m \times x/L)g - \tfrac{1}{4}mg - F = \tfrac{3}{4}mgx^2/L^2$$

$$\therefore \quad F = mgx/L - \tfrac{1}{4}mg - \tfrac{3}{4}mgx^2/L^2$$

Taking a moment equation about G_x: $\Sigma(M) = I\alpha$: assume clockwise $+$ve:

$$M + P \times \tfrac{1}{2}x - F \times \tfrac{1}{2}x = I'\alpha = (\tfrac{1}{12}(mx/L)(x^2))(1\tfrac{1}{2}g/L)$$

$$\therefore \quad M = \tfrac{1}{8}mgx^3/L^2 - \tfrac{1}{4}mg \times \tfrac{1}{2}x + \tfrac{1}{2}x(mgx/L - \tfrac{1}{4}mg - \tfrac{3}{4}mgx^2/L^2)$$

$$= \tfrac{1}{8}mgx^3/L^2 - \tfrac{1}{8}mgx + \tfrac{1}{2}mgx^2/L - \tfrac{1}{8}mgx - \tfrac{3}{8}mgx^3/L^2$$

$$\therefore \quad M = \tfrac{1}{2}mgx^2/L - \tfrac{1}{4}mgx - \tfrac{1}{4}mgx^3/L^2$$

We shall discuss these results in the following frame.

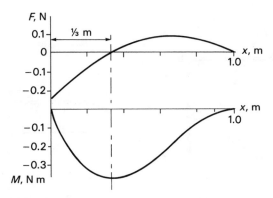

The graphs are drawn for F and M for values of $mg = 1$ N and $L = 1$ m. It is seen from the expressions in Frame 38 that differentiating M results in the expression for F, which is in accordance with Stress Analysis theory. Also, M is seen to be a maximum for zero value of F. You can show for yourself that F will be zero when $x = \frac{1}{3}L$, and this value, substituted into the expression for M results in a value of $M_{max} = -\frac{1}{27}mgL$.

Inertial shearing force and bending moment may appear rather academic, but it is easy to imagine that if you hold a long thin strip of wood in your hands, at the end, it can easily be broken simply by swinging it with a high acceleration. Also, whenever you see pictures of tall industrial chimneys being felled, they are invariably seen to break while falling. Mortared brickwork is not strong enough to resist the bending moment resulting from free fall of the chimney. The fact that the breaking-point is further than one-third the height from the base is accounted for by the chimney not being uniform in section, but tapering.

40

You may have wondered why, having a chosen a 'section', we chose to examine the forces on the part to the left instead of that to the right. There is no special reason, and the same result can be obtained by analysis of the right-hand portion. You should attempt this yourself. To give you some help, here is the complete free-body diagram. You will notice that the directions of F and M are opposite to those of the previous diagram, in accordance with Newton's Third Law of reactions.

41

PROBLEMS

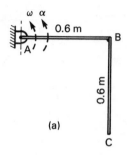

(a)

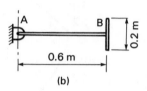

(b)

1. Two uniform rods, AB and BC, each 0.6 m long, and mass 24 kg, are welded together and rotate around a fixed pivot A in a horizontal plane, as shown at (a) above. At a certain instant, the angular velocity ω is 20 rad s^{-1} and the angular acceleration is 48 rad s^{-2}. Calculate the shearing force, tensile force and bending moment at the mid-point of the rod BC at this instant. [*Ans. 2620.8 N; 2505.6 N; 388.8 N m.*]

   Hints: select the portion from mid-point to C. Assume forces P and Q, parallel respectively to tangential and centripetal accelerations, and bending moment M. ($P = 432$ N and $Q = 3600$ N.) Then determine longitudinal and transverse forces T and F from P and Q. Ignore gravity forces.

2. Diagram (b) above shows a thin uniform disc of diameter 0.2 m and mass 15 kg secured to a uniform rod AB of length 0.6 m and mass 6 kg. A is attached to a fixed pivot, permitting the assembly to rotate in a vertical plane. The assembly is held with AB horizontal and released from rest. Calculate the shearing force, bending moment, and tensile force in AB at point B at the instant of release. [*Ans. 7.718 N; 0.644 N m; 0.*]

   Hints: locate G (0.5143 m from A). Calculate I_A (I for disc about diameter is $\frac{1}{4}mR^2$, and use Parallel Axis theorem). Calculate I_G ($I_A = 6.1575$ kg m^2, $I_G = 0.6029$ kg m^2). Determine P and α (20.17 N, 17.21 rad s^{-2}). Then draw AB only, with F and M acting at B. $\Sigma(F) = ma$ yields F; $\Sigma(M) = I\alpha$ yields M.

3. A thin uniform rod of mass m and length L swings in a vertical plane about a fixed pivot at one end. The rod is initially at rest, vertically above the pivot, and is given a small initial displacement so that it swings downwards. Determine the angles through which it must swing in order that (a) the horizontal component of the pivot reaction force is zero; (b) the vertical component of the pivot reaction force is zero. [*Ans. (a) 48.19°. (b) 70.53°.*]

   Hints: assume forces P and Q transverse to, and along the road, and derive expressions ($P = \frac{1}{4}mg \sin\theta$; $Q = mg(2\frac{1}{2}\cos\theta - 1\frac{1}{2})$). Vertical component $= P\sin\theta + Q\cos\theta$; horizontal component $= P\cos\theta - Q\sin\theta$; equate each to zero and solve for $\cos\theta$ ($\cos\theta$ will be respectively, 2/3 and 1/3).

We now look at examples of bodies rolling along surfaces. When a body both rolls and moves laterally, two equations of motion are needed, one for translation, and one for rotation. Also, a compatibility equation is needed.

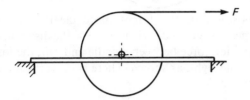

Example. A uniform flat disc of mass 4 kg and diameter 0.15 m is mounted on a central spindle of diameter 6 mm and of negligible mass and inertia. The spindle rests on a pair of horizontal rails, with the disc between, as shown in the diagram above. A light string is attached to the rim of the disc and wrapped round it, and a horizontal force $F = 2$ N applied to the string. Calculate the time for the disc to travel 1 m along the rail, starting from rest, and the final linear and angular velocity. The spindle rolls without slip along the rail.

We begin our solution by writing a kinematic equation relating the linear acceleration of the disc, and its angular acceleration. In the case of a body rolling without slip along a surface, this equation is:

$$a = \alpha R$$

where R is the appropriate rolling radius, in this case, the spindle radius. If this is not immediately obvious, you might find it helpful to think first of the rolling body turning and accelerating about a *fixed* centre. Then the rolling surface would have a peripheral acceleration given by the above equation, and if the disc centre were fixed, and there was no slip, the rail must have a corresponding linear acceleration. But since we know the rail is fixed, then the rolling body must have a corresponding linear acceleration in the opposite direction.

Now the free-body diagram must be drawn, in order to obtain the equations of motion. Attempt the diagram yourself first. You will find it a help to exaggerate the size of the spindle. There are four forces acting on the roller, although only two of these will be found relevant to the solution of the problem. If you have a difficulty finding a fourth force, look at the implications of the phrase: '... rolls without slip ...'.

43

Here is the correct free-body diagram:

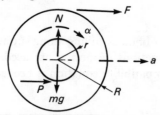

To show the disposition of the forces more clearly, the spindle is drawn disproportionately large, as suggested earlier. Because the disc rolls without slip, there must be a tangential friction force between spindle and rail; the force on the spindle, P, is assumed to act to the right, as shown. There is no vertical acceleration, so that mg is equal to the reaction N.

The translation equation ($\Sigma(F) = ma$) is:

$$P + F = ma = m(\alpha r) \tag{1}$$

The equation of motion for rotation ($\Sigma(M) = I\alpha$) is:

$$FR - Pr = I\alpha = \tfrac{1}{2}mR^2\alpha \qquad (I = \tfrac{1}{2}mR^2 \text{ for uniform disc})$$

Substituting for P:

$$FR - r(m\alpha r - F) = \tfrac{1}{2}mR^2\alpha$$

$$\therefore \qquad FR + Fr = \alpha(\tfrac{1}{2}mR^2 + mr^2) \tag{2}$$

Substituting values in equation (2):

$$2(0.075 + 0.003) = \alpha(\tfrac{1}{2} \times 4(0.075)^2 + 4(0.003)^2)$$
$$\therefore \qquad 0.156 = \alpha \times 0.011\,286$$
$$\therefore \qquad \alpha = 13.822 \text{ rad s}^{-2}$$
$$\therefore \qquad a = \alpha \times 0.003 = 0.0415 \text{ m s}^{-2}$$
$$v^2 = v_0^2 + 2ax = 0 + 2 \times 0.0415 \times 1$$
$$\therefore \qquad v = \mathbf{0.2881 \text{ m s}^{-1}}$$
$$v = \omega r = \omega \times 0.003 \qquad \text{(for no slip of spindle on rail)}$$
$$\therefore \qquad \omega = \mathbf{96.03 \text{ rad s}^{-1}}$$
$$x = v_0 t + \tfrac{1}{2}at^2$$
$$\therefore \qquad 1 = 0 + \tfrac{1}{2} \times 0.0415 t^2$$
$$\therefore \qquad t = \mathbf{6.942 \text{ s}}$$

If the calculated value of α is now substituted into equation (1), you can show for yourself that the value of the force P is 1.834 N, and also, that it acts in the opposite direction to that assumed.

Now see if you can determine how long it would take the disc to roll 1 m down a pair of rails inclined at 5° to the horizontal, without the string attached.

Here is the free-body diagram for the disc rolling down the rail.

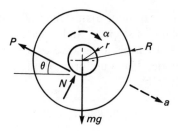

The angle is exaggerated, for clarity. This time, there can be no doubt about the direction of the friction force P. Because the disc is rolling without slip, there must be a force exerting a corresponding torque in the direction of roll. The only force that can do this is P, because the weight acts through the disc centre. So P must exert a clockwise moment about the disc centre, as shown.

Kinematically: $\qquad\qquad a = \alpha r \qquad$ (as before)

Translation: $\qquad mg \sin \theta - P = ma = m\alpha r$

Rotation: $\qquad\qquad Pr = I\alpha$

$\therefore \qquad r(mg \sin \theta - m\alpha r) = I\alpha$

$\therefore \qquad mgr \sin \theta = \alpha(I + mr^2) = \alpha(\tfrac{1}{2}mR^2 + mr^2)$

Substituting values:

$$4g \times 0.003 \sin 5° = \alpha(\tfrac{1}{2} \times 4(0.075)^2 + 4(0.003)^2) = 0.011\,286\alpha$$

$$\therefore \qquad \alpha = 0.909\,09 \text{ rad s}^{-2}$$

$$a = \alpha r = 0.909\,09 \times 0.003 = 0.002\,727 \text{ m s}^{-2}$$

$$x = v_0 t + \tfrac{1}{2}at^2$$

$$\therefore \qquad 1 = 0 + \tfrac{1}{2} \times 0.002\,727t^2$$

$$\therefore \qquad t = 27.08 \text{ s}$$

Imagine now that the disc is in two halves, with the spindle between, and that a string is wrapped round the spindle. The free end of the string is held, and the disc allowed to descend vertically. This is the well-known dynamic toy called the yo-yo. It is also the limiting case of the disc rolling down an inclined rail, the string replacing the rail, and being inclined at 90°. It is left for you to show that it will take **7.995 seconds** for the disc to descend 1 m starting from rest, and that its final linear and angular velocity will be **0.2502 m s^{-1}** and **83.89 rad s^{-1}** respectively. The calculations follow exactly the same lines as those above.

45

PROBLEMS

1. A uniform cylinder having an outer diameter of 30 mm is placed transversely at the top of an inclined plane of slope 5° and released from rest. It rolls down the plane without slipping and travels a distance of 0.5 m in 1.419 s. Determine the inner diameter of the cylinder. For a uniform cylinder, the moment of inertia about its central axis, I_G, is given by:

$$I_G = \tfrac{1}{2}m(R_o^2 + R_1^2)$$

where R_o and R_1 are the outer and inner radii respectively. [*Ans. 20 mm.*]
Hints: calculate the linear acceleration first, and then the angular acceleration. Then treat as the exercise in Frame 44 to find I. Use the given formula to determine R_1. The mass-term will cancel.

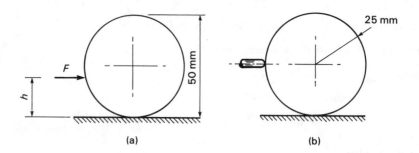

(a)   (b)

2. A uniform solid cylinder of mass 0.6 kg and diameter 50 mm rests on a horizontal surface. The coefficient of friction between cylinder and surface is 0.15. A horizontal force $F = 5$ N acts on the cylinder at a height $h = 20.59$ mm above the surface, as shown in diagram (a) above. Show that the cylinder will have negligible angular motion. Find the linear acceleration. [*Ans. 6.862 m s^{-2}.*]
Hints: friction force acts to left, causing clockwise moment; F acts below centre, causing anti-clockwise moment. Show that the two moments are equal.

3. A uniform solid cylinder of mass 2 kg and radius 25 mm rests on a horizontal surface. A rod moving horizontally moves the cylinder along the surface, the rod centre-line passing through the cylinder centre-line, as shown in diagram (b) above. Determine the angular acceleration of the cylinder, the force F between rod and cylinder, and the force N between cylinder and surface when the rod moves to the right (a) with constant velocity; (b) with acceleration of 1 m s^{-2} to the right. The coefficient of friction between cylinder and surface, and between rod and cylinder, is 0.1. [*Ans. (a) 71.35 rad s^{-2}; 1.9818 N; 19.8182 N. (b) 64.072 rad s^{-2}; 4.002 N; 20.02 N.*]
Hints: surface will exert friction force to left of μN; rod will exert a downward friction force of μR. For case (a), $F - \mu N = 0$. Vertical equilibrium in both cases.

46

For the remainder of the programme, we shall deal with what is known as **d'Alembert's Principle**. And we must begin straight away with a warning:

> **d'Alembert's Principle describes an alternative method of solving dynamics problems. EITHER you use this alternative method, OR you use the methods already described. You MUST NOT use both together.**

Now you may be wondering already why we are bothering with an alternative to something that you by now have become reasonably proficient in. There are two reasons.

The first is, that for certain types of problem, the use of d'Alembert's Principle offers a much simpler solution. This reason is hardly convincing; if you have learned a method of solving a problem, the advantage of learning more theory in order to make a marginal saving of work is dubious.

The second and much more convincing reason is, that it is quite possible that you have already come across this method, but without really being aware of it, with the unhappy result that your thinking in certain areas is muddled and probably incorrect. If this is so, then you need to understand this aspect of Dynamics, if only to enable you to make the decision not to use it again!

The case of a body travelling in a circular path affords a good example to introduce d'Alembert's Principle. We shall shortly select an example from the earlier part of this programme, as an illustration of the application of the method.

When a rigid body is in a state of static equilibrium, we can normally write three equations respecting the forces acting on it. State, if you can remember, what are the three conditions for equilibrium.

47

> Resultant force in any one direction is 0
> Resultant force in direction at right-angles to above is 0
> Resultant moment of all forces about any point is 0

and these conditions enable all the unknown forces to be determined.

When a body has an acceleration, we have to remember that the resultant force ($\Sigma(F)$) in the direction of the acceleration is not zero but is equal to (ma), although $\Sigma(F)$ may still be zero in a direction along which there is no component of acceleration. When a car accelerates along a straight track, the resultant force perpendicular to the track is still zero.

48

d'Alembert's Principle is a device which enables us to treat a dynamics problem as though it was a statics problem. And it achieves this by introducing to the system an extra *and wholly imaginary force* to the free-body diagram.

This is the argument. Suppose a body is known to have an acceleration a in a certain direction. Then we know that the resultant force acting in that direction is (ma). If there is no angular acceleration, we also know that this resultant force must pass through the mass-centre. So, if we add to our free-body diagram, a force of magnitude (ma), at the mass-centre, and acting *in the opposite direction to the acceleration*, then we could use the conditions of static equilibrium, because the resultant would be cancelled by this fictitious force.

An example should make things clear. One follows in Frame 49.

49

Example. A car has a mass of 1320 kg. The distance between wheels (the track width) is 2.44 m. The mass-centre is centrally between the wheels and is 0.49 m above ground level. Calculate the magnitudes of total inner and outer wheel reaction forces when the car travels around a flat right-hand bend of mean radius 35 m at (a) 15 m s^{-1}; (b) 25 m s^{-1}.

This example is copied from Frame 14.

Because the car is travelling at 15 m s^{-1} round a circle, there must be a centripetal acceleration, v^2/R. This is directed towards the centre of the curve. So, we introduce a force of magnitude mv^2/R, acting in the *opposite direction*. Because it is not a real force, we show it by a distinctive arrow. Here is the free-body diagram.

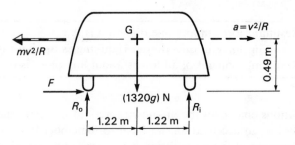

You may recall having done this before in your earlier courses, because many elementary books approach centripetal acceleration in this manner.

In Frame 50, we write the appropriate equations for solving the problem.

50

Because we have included the extra and imaginary force, we may now treat the body as though it were in static equilibrium. The question requires the two reaction forces. To determine R_i, we can write a moment equilibrium equation about the outer-wheel contact-point.

$$R_i \times 2.44 + \text{d'Alembert force} \times 0.49 = 1320g \times 1.22$$

$$R_i \times 2.44 + (1320(15)^2/35) \times 0.49 = 1320g \times 1.22$$

$$\therefore \quad R_i = \textbf{4770.5 N}$$

In Frame 10, you were warned against writing a moment equilibrium equation with respect to any point except the mass-centre. Now, because we have included the extra imaginary force, we may ignore this warning, with the result that we are able to determine the answer more quickly than before, by means of a single equation. The other reaction is found from the vertical-equilibrium equation:

$$R_o = 1320g - R_i = \textbf{8178.7 N}$$

Part (b) of the question is left for you to solve; the working is of course exactly the same.

51

It is clear that this example is solved much more quickly by using this method. Indeed, the only serious criticism one can make in respect of the method is, that it is so frequently used without being properly understood. If you have been taught to solve problems of circular motion this way, and wish to continue doing so, you must realise that this extra force is purely imaginary. Adopt the practice, always, of illustrating this imaginary force in a distinctive manner, as we have done in this example. The force is introduced for the purpose of writing a 'static equilibrium' equation for a body which is not in static equilibrium. There is nothing wrong with this. An accountant will add to the Debit side of a balance-sheet a sum called 'Cash in Hand' simply in order to ensure that both Debit and Credit sides balance, although it is clear that 'Cash in Hand' is not a real Debit at all, but a fictitious one. A force used in this manner is called a **reversed effective force**, because it is opposite in direction (although equal in magnitude) to the true resultant force acting on the body, which is the **effective force**.

When this principle is applied to motion in a circular path, the effective force (i.e. the nett resultant force acting towards the path centre) is called the **centripetal force**, and the reversed effective force (called the d'Alembert force in the example above) is called the **centrifugal force**. (The word 'centrifugal' means 'flying from the centre.'.)

52

The learner is frequently confused about the unreality of centrifugal force. The question is often asked: 'If it is a fictitious force, how can a car be turned over on a bend by a force which does not exist?' The answer is, that it is not the centrifugal force acting outwards at the mass-centre which turns the car over, but the inward-directed friction force between wheels and road, exerted by the road on the wheels. When the line of action of this force is below the mass-centre, it exerts a turning moment on the car, as we have seen in some of the examples (e.g. Frame 14). Moreover, this friction force is not stopping the car from being thrown *outwards*; it is preventing it from travelling *in a straight line*. You may know already (if not, you can easily prove for yourself) that if a weight is whirled round at the end of a string and the string is cut, the weight immediately begins to travel on a straight path tangential to the circular path. It does not move outwards at all.

53

d'Alembert's Principle can also be applied to bodies having angular acceleration. We may summarise.

If a body of mass m is subject to an acceleration a, a reversed effective force of magnitude (ma) may be added to the free-body diagram, at the mass-centre, and in the direction opposite to a.

If a body of moment of inertia I_G with respect to an axis through the mass-centre is subject to an angular acceleration α, a reversed effective moment of magnitude ($I_G \alpha$) may be added to the free-body diagram, in the direction opposite to α.

The body may then be analysed as *though it were in a state of static equilibrium*: thus:

resultant force in any direction $= 0$

resultant moment of all forces about any point $= 0$

The next example shows how we deal with a body having angular acceleration.

Example. A thin uniform rod of mass 32 kg and length 1.2 m turns in a horizontal plane about a pivot at one end. At a certain instant, its angular velocity is 5 rad s^{-1} and its angular acceleration is 10 rad s^{-2}. Determine the shearing force and bending moment at the rod centre. Neglect gravity forces.

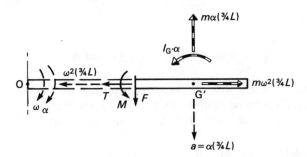

The free-body diagram of the outer half only of the rod is shown. Considering the real forces first, the only forces acting on the outer half are those exerted by the inner half, if we are to neglect gravity forces, as told. These consist of a transverse shearing force, F, a longitudinal tensile force T, and a bending moment, M. The directions of all of these are assumed, those of F and M being positive in accordance with a widely-accepted Stress Analysis sign convention; α and ω are both assumed clockwise.

The 'reversed effective' forces and moments are determined as follows.

1. Angular acceleration α of the rod will cause a linear acceleration a of the centre of mass G' of the half-rod of magnitude $(\alpha r) = (\alpha \times \frac{3}{4}L)$. This will be in a clockwise direction relative to the pivot O; that is, downwards on the diagram. The reversed effective force is therefore $(m\alpha \times \frac{3}{4}L)$ upwards as shown (m is the mass of the half-rod).
2. Angular velocity of the rod will cause a centripetal acceleration of the mass-centre of the half-rod of magnitude $(\omega^2 r) = (\omega^2 \times \frac{3}{4}L)$ radially inwards. The reversed effective force is therefore $(m\omega^2 \times \frac{3}{4}L)$ radially outwards as shown.
3. Angular acceleration α of the rod means also that the half-rod will have the same angular acceleration, clockwise on the diagram. The reversed effective moment is therefore $(I_{G'}\alpha)$ anti-clockwise, as shown. ($I_{G'}$ is the moment of inertia of the half-rod about its own mass-centre).

The appropriate equations are obtained in the following frame.

55

Having introduced the three reversed-effective effects, we may now make use of any conditions of static equilibrium; no equations of motion are necessary—in fact, none are allowed! As with many static problems, work may be saved by choosing an appropriate equation.

A force–equilibrium equation vertically will yield F directly.

$$F - m\alpha \times \tfrac{3}{4}L = 0$$

Substituting values:

$$F = 16 \times 10 \times \tfrac{3}{4} \times 1.2 = \mathbf{144\ N}$$

The positive answer means that the direction is downwards, as assumed.

A moment equilibrium equation, either about G, the whole-rod centre, or about G′, the half-rod centre, will yield M. Taking moments about G:

$$M + I_{G'}\alpha + (m\alpha \times \tfrac{3}{4}L)\tfrac{1}{4}L = 0$$

$$\therefore \quad M = -(\tfrac{1}{12} \times 16 \times 0.6^2 \times 10 + 16 \times 10 \times 0.9 \times 0.3)$$

$$\therefore \quad M = -\mathbf{48.0\ N\ m}$$

the negative sign indicating a clockwise moment.

The question does not require it, but you may show for yourself that the tension force $T = 360$ N. A simple 'left = right' force 'equilibrium' equation is required. T is the centripetal force on the outer half of the rod.

56

A final set of problems follows in Frame 57. But because d'Alembert's Principle is an alternative to writing equations of linear and angular motion, all of the problems so far encountered in this programme can be solved using the method of reversed effective force, or reversed effective moment. So you may gain extra practice and experience by attempting some of the earlier samples using this method.

PROBLEMS

1. The total mass of a motor cyclist and his machine is m, and the height of the mass-centre above the ground is h. Calculate the angle at which the machine must be inclined to the vertical when travelling round a flat circular track of mean radius 20 m at a speed of 15 m s^{-1}. [*Ans. 48.91°.*]
   Hints: include reversed effective force, and then take moments about contact-point of wheel with ground; h and m will be found to cancel.

2. A small cuboidal block of wood, of dimensions a, b and c, is to be used in a car as a brake tester. It is placed on a flat surface in the car, with dimension a parallel to the car's motion, and dimension b vertical. The block is required to tip forward when the car is brought to rest in a distance of 50 m from a speed of 25 m s^{-1} along a straight level track. Calculate the ratio of dimension b to dimension a. If the same block is turned through 90°, so that dimension a is transverse to the car's motion, at what speed would the block tip over sideways if the car were travelling round a circular track of mean radius 25 m (a) if the track were flat; (b) if it were banked at an angle of 15°? Assume that the block never slips on the surface. [*Ans. b/a = 1.5696. (a) 12.5 m s^{-1}; (b) 16.36 m s^{-1}.*]
   Hint: in both cases, take moments about the corner about which the block is about to tip.

3. A small simple pendulum hangs from the roof of a vehicle. It is arranged so that the angle of swing can be read by the string passing over a graduated scale. Calculate the angle indicated when the vehicle accelerates forwards at (a) 2 m s^{-2}; (b) 6 m s^{-2}. Determine also the angle indicated when the vehicle moves with the same accelerations up a slope of sin^{-1} 0.1. [*Ans. (a) 11.52°; (b) 31.45°. (a) 16.979°; (b) 35.57°.*]
   Hints: indicate weight mg and reversed effective force ma on the free-body diagram and take moments about the attachment-point of the string. When the vehicle ascends the slope, first find the *true* angle of the string to the vertical; weight mg acts vertically downward, but reversed effective force will act at angle sin^{-1} 0.1 below the horizontal. Because the scale is attached to the vehicle, the angle of the slope must then be added to these values.

Programme 7

WORK, ENERGY AND POWER

1

The terms Work, Energy and Power should be familiar by now. You have met them in earlier work, and also in Programme 1, as revision. In this programme, following some further revision, we shall apply the principles to solve some more difficult problems. We shall also define **strain energy**, and shall show how this concept can be applied when a load acts suddenly or instantaneously on a member or a structure.

Begin by revising **work** by answering the two questions following.

1. When a force F moves through a distance x, the work done by the force is ...
2. When a moment or torque M turns through an angle θ, the work done by the moment or torque is ...

In each case, state the units of the terms used.

2

> When a force F newtons (N) moves through a distance x metres (m) the work done is:
>
> $$(Fx) \text{ N m, or } \textbf{joules (J)}$$
>
> When a moment or torque M newton metres (N m) turns through an angle θ radians (rad), the work done is:
>
> $$(M\theta) \text{ J}$$

You must also remember that when the force or moment is variable, the work done must be expressed as an integral. Thus, for a variable force f acting through a distance x, the work done, E, is given by:

$$E = \int (f \, \mathrm{d}x)$$

and a similar expression must be used for a variable moment.

Now recall what you know about **energy**. Although energy is manifested in many forms (nuclear; chemical; solar; thermal are just four examples), we shall consider in this programme only those forms of energy relating to Dynamics. First define energy, and then state the three forms of energy relevant to dynamics. By way of a reminder, in Programme 1, examples were given of a hydro-electric power station, a wind-driven generator, and a bow and arrow.

3

Energy is the ability to do work. It is the property possessed by a body or a system when work has been done on it. Because it is interchangeable with work, it is measured in the same unit, i.e. the joule.

In Dynamics, we are concerned with:

(a) **potential** energy (by virtue of position above an arbitrary datum)
(b) **kinetic** energy (by virtue of motion)
(c) **strain** energy (by virtue of deformation of an elastic body)

The energy possessed by a body is determined by a calculation of the work required to be done on it to bring it to its particular state. So write down, if you can, the formulae appropriate to the following.

(a) The potential energy (E_{pot}) of a body of mass m a vertical height h above a datum is ...
(b) The kinetic energy (E_{kin}) of a body of mass m moving with velocity u is ...
(c) The kinetic energy of a body having a moment of inertia I, turning with an angular velocity ω is ...

4

$$E_{pot} = mgh; \qquad E_{kin} = \tfrac{1}{2}mu^2; \qquad E_{kin} = \tfrac{1}{2}I\omega^2$$

You should remember that a body can have both translation and rotational kinetic energy. A body moving with a linear velocity has kinetic energy. Also, a wheel rotating about a fixed axis has kinetic energy, even though it is not moving bodily. A wheel rolling along a track has more kinetic energy than the same wheel turning at the same angular speed about a fixed axis, because it possesses both translational and rotational energy.

An **energy balance equation** is always used as a basis for solving problems using the principle of energy. Thus, for a body, or a system:

Initial energy + energy gained − energy lost = final energy

5

You need to have a clear understanding of translational kinetic energy ($\frac{1}{2}mu^2$) and rotational kinetic energy ($\frac{1}{2}I\omega^2$). As an illustration, consider a vehicle with wheels, which rolls along a straight track.

Let the total mass of the vehicle including wheels be m
Let the total moment of inertia of all wheels be I_ω
Let the wheel rolling radius (i.e. the radius of the rim in contact with the ground) be R
Let the linear velocity of the vehicle be u

Then the wheel angular velocity $\omega = u/R$

Because of the linear velocity u, the vehicle will have kinetic energy E_{kin1} given by:

$$E_{\text{kin1}} = \tfrac{1}{2}mu^2$$

This energy includes that of the wheels, also moving with velocity u, but does not include the additional energy due to rotation of the wheels. Call this E_{kin2}.

$$E_{\text{kin2}} = \tfrac{1}{2}I_\omega\omega^2 = \tfrac{1}{2}I_\omega(u/R)^2$$

$$\therefore \quad \text{total kinetic energy} = \tfrac{1}{2}mu^2 + \tfrac{1}{2}I_\omega(u/R)^2$$

$$= \tfrac{1}{2}u^2(m + I_\omega/R^2)$$

We may call the term $(m + I_\omega/R^2)$ the **effective mass** m_E of the wheeled vehicle. So when calculating the kinetic energy of a vehicle with rotating parts, the effective mass should be used, not the true mass. If there are several wheels of different radii, the effective mass of each should be determined, and the total evaluated. However, in elementary work, for example Programme 6 of this text, this is often neglected, in the interests of simplicity.

If the vehicle ascends or descends a slope, there is a change of potential energy, E_{pot}. Potential energy represents work done against, or by gravity. As such, it is calculated by the product of *weight* and vertical height change, h. Thus:

$$E_{\text{pot}} = (mg)h$$

and here, m is the true mass of the vehicle, not the effective mass. It takes exactly the same amount of work to lift a wheel of weight 400 N a height of 1 metre *whether the wheel is spinning or not*.

Answer this question. Two vehicles start from rest down the same incline, at the same instant. The vehicles have the same total mass, but the total moment of inertia of the wheels of vehicle A is greater than that of vehicle B. Which will reach the foot of the incline first? Neglect any resistance to motion.

6

Vehicle B

Both A and B lose the same potential energy. Therefore both gain the same kinetic energy. Because A has the greater effective mass, it must have a lesser velocity: hence it must travel slower.

An interesting dynamic toy consists of two small cylinders. They are exactly the same weight, and of exactly equal dimensions. One is painted black, and the other white. When placed at the top of an inclined plane and allowed to roll down, it is found that the white one always reaches the foot of the plane before the other. Why is this? A clue to the explanation is the paint.

7

The white one is made of solid steel. The black one is made of brass. Because brass has a greater density than steel, the brass one is bored out in the centre, and the ends plugged, the boring adjusted to make both cylinders the same weight. The paint disguises the fact that the cylinders are of different materials. The brass cylinder has the greater moment of inertia, and hence the greater effective mass when rolling.

Example. A train has a total mass of 300 tonnes, and the effective mass of the rotating parts is 25 tonnes. It is driven by a constant tractive force of 28 kN. Resistance to motion due to air and other sources may be assumed to be a constant force of 4500 N. It begins to ascend a slope of $\sin^{-1} 0.01$ at a speed of 30 m s^{-1}. Calculate the speed after it has travelled 100 m up the incline.

This is revision work, and you ought to be able to solve it without help. The answer is 29.94 m s^{-1}, and the working follows in Frame 8. To start you off, here is the Energy Equation applicable to this problem.

$$\text{Initial energy } (E_{\text{kin}}) + \text{work done by tractive force} - \text{work done to friction}$$

$$= \text{final energy } (E_{\text{kin}} + \text{gain of } E_{\text{pot}})$$

and a reminder that potential energy change is calculated on the *vertical* height change.

8

Initial energy $E_{kin} = \frac{1}{2}m_E u^2$ (m_E is the effective total mass including wheels)

$$= \frac{1}{2} \times 325\,000 \times (30)^2 = 146.25 \text{ MJ}$$

Work by tractive force $= F \times x$

$$= 28\,000 \times 100 = 2.8 \text{ MJ}$$

Work to friction $= F_r \times x$

$$= 4500 \times 100 = 0.45 \text{ MJ}$$

Final potential energy $E_{pot} = mgh$

h is the vertical height. The sine of the slope angle is 0.01.

$$\therefore \qquad h = 100 \times 0.01$$

$$\therefore \qquad E_{pot} = 300\,000 \times 9.81 \times (100 \times 0.01) = 2.943 \text{ MJ}$$

Final kinetic energy $E_{kin} = \frac{1}{2}mv^2$

$$= \frac{1}{2} \times 325\,000 \; v^2 = (0.1625 \; v^2) \text{ MJ}$$

Substituting in the equation (putting all terms in MJ):

$$146.25 + 2.8 - 0.45 = 2.943 + 0.1625 \; v^2$$

$$\therefore \qquad v^2 = 896.34$$

$$\therefore \qquad v = \textbf{29.94 m s}^{-1}$$

If you failed to get the correct answer, you probably made the mistake of confusing actual total mass with effective mass. The effective mass is used in calculating kinetic energy, but the true mass must be used when determining changes of potential energy.

Now write down a definition of power. State the units in which it is measured.

9

> Power is the rate of doing work, or work done per second.
> The unit is the newton metre per second, called the **watt**.

Example. Calculate the power output of (a) a car travelling at 25 m s^{-1}, exerting a constant tractive force of 1100 N; (b) an electric motor delivering a torque of 2.75 N m at a speed of 2950 rev/min.

The answers are: (a) 27.5 kW; (b) 849.5 W. The working follows.

10

(a) Work done per second = force × distance per second

$$= \text{force} \times \text{velocity}$$

$$\therefore \quad W = 1100 \times 25$$

$$= \textbf{27.5 kW}$$

(b) Work done per second = torque × angular displacement per second

$$= \text{torque} \times \text{angular velocity}$$

$$\therefore \quad W = 2.75 \times (2950 \times 2\pi/60)$$

$$= \textbf{849.5 W}$$

Always remember that the use of an energy equation is very often an alternative way of solving a dynamic problem. The example of Frame 7 could have been solved by calculating the acceleration of the train, using an equation of motion, and then applying a kinematic equation.

Some revision problems follow. Frame 11 consists of energy problems and Frame 12 two problems on power.

11

PROBLEMS

1. A body of mass m ascends an inclined plane of slope 15° with initial velocity 12 m s^{-1}. The coefficient of friction between the body and the plane is 0.1. How far up the plane will it travel before coming to rest? How fast will it be moving when it returns to its starting-point? [*Ans. 20.65 m; 8.11 m s^{-1}.*]

2. A truck begins to ascend a slope of 12° with an initial velocity of 5 m s^{-1}. How far up the slope does it travel before the speed is reduced to 1.2 m s^{-1}, assuming that there is a constant resistance to motion of one-fiftieth of the weight of the body? [*Ans. 5.269 m.*]

3. A ballistic pendulum consists of a box filled with sand, suspended by four strings of equal length 2.4 m, attached to four corners of the box. When the box hangs, the four strings are parallel, so that the box can swing sideways without rotating. The total mass of box and sand is 12.5 kg. A bullet of mass 0.08 kg is fired horizontally into the box, and is retained in the sand. The impact causes the box to move sideways and upwards, so that the strings make a maximum angle of 19° to the vertical. Assuming that 99.9% of the initial energy of the bullet is dissipated in the sand at impact, calculate the initial velocity of the bullet. [*Ans. 635.15 m s^{-1}.*)

12

PROBLEMS

1. A car engine is capable of a constant power output of 60 kW. The total mass of the car is 1150 kg. Calculate the steady speed at which it could ascend a slope of 7° against a constant resistance of 375 N, assuming a transmission efficiency of 75%. Neglect the inertia of the wheels. [*Ans. 25.72 m s⁻¹.*]
   Hint: write an energy equation for a period of 1 second.

2. A small generator is driven by a water turbine fed from a tank, the surface level of which is at a constant height of 12 m above the generator. The flow of water is constant at 50 m³ per hour. The generator delivers electricity at a rate of 1 kilowatt. The overall efficiency of turbine and generator combined may be assumed to be 63%. After passing through the generator, the water discharges through an exit pipe at the same level, to waste. Estimate the velocity of the exit flow. [*Ans. 2.62 m s⁻¹.*]
   Hint: write an energy equation in terms of the mass of water flowing per second.

13

Strain energy offers a method of solution of certain problems which would otherwise be very difficult to solve. An example is that of a load which is suddenly applied to a member or a structure. If a crane driver, when lowering a load on to a floor, miscalculates, and allows the load to drop on to the floor for the last few centimetres, instead of lowering it very gently, the load on the floor is much greater than the weight of the load, but there is no simple way of calculating the effect of the load by using Newton's Laws. In some of the examples in this section, we shall find that the magnifying effect of a falling load is often surprisingly and disturbingly high.

Strain energy is also employed by the engineering designer. An example is the tailboard of a truck. The hinges of the tailboard are frequently fitted with springs. This has two advantages. When the board is lowered, it is much easier to control. Instead of dropping heavily, with consequent damage, either to the board itself, or to the operator, it can be lowered slowly with little controlling force. And when being raised again, much less force is needed than would be required if no springs were fitted. The strain energy contained in the springs is re-converted back to potential energy.

Think of a few other examples.

14

> Up-and-over garage doors; vehicle springs; tow-ropes for vehicles and ships; buffers on trucks and locomotives; aircraft arresters on carriers.

All these devices make use of strain energy. The first is similar to the tailboard of the truck. The remaining examples are all devices for absorbing kinetic energy, and are used in conjunction with other components which dissipate the energy absorbed. For example, when a car passes over a stone or a pot-hole, the springs convert the kinetic energy to strain energy. But this alone would result in the car vibrating uncomfortably as the springs gave up the stored energy. Therefore shock absorbers are also included; these have the function of dissipating the energy of the springs, converting it to thermal energy in the fluid of the shock absorber.

All the devices listed employ springs. We shall continue by calculating the work required to extend or compress a spring.

15

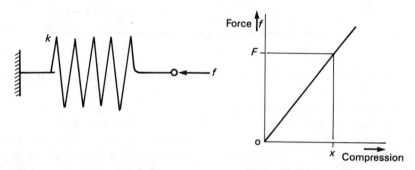

A spring of stiffness k (newtons per metre of compression or extension) is compressed by a steadily-increasing force f. If the compression is within the limit of proportionality, the graph of force against compression will be a straight line, as shown. The work done by a variable force f (see Frame 2) is $\int(f\,dx)$; this is the area under the graph. So the strain energy, E_{str}, will be:

$$E_{\text{str}} = \tfrac{1}{2}Fx$$

where F is the final compressive force, and x the total compression. But $F = kx$.

$$\therefore \quad E_{\text{str}} = \tfrac{1}{2}kx^2$$

The expression in this form allows the energy to be calculated in terms of stiffness and compression.

16

Example. A buffer at the end of a horizontal track consists of two springs, each of stiffness 1600 kN per metre of compression. A truck of mass 4150 kg moving at 1.4 m s^{-1} collides with the buffers. Calculate the resulting maximum compression of the buffers.

You can do this simple example yourself; just equate the kinetic energy of the truck to the strain energy of the buffers. The answer is 50.4 mm.

17

$$\tfrac{1}{2}mu^2 = \tfrac{1}{2}kx^2$$
$$\therefore \quad \tfrac{1}{2} \times 4150 \times (1.4)^2 = \tfrac{1}{2} \times (1600 \times 1000 \times 2)x^2$$
$$\therefore \quad x = \sqrt{\left(\frac{4150 \times (1.4)^2}{1600 \times 2000}\right)} = 0.0504 \text{ m} = \textbf{50.4 mm}$$

You should understand that at the point of maximum compression, the truck will be instantaneously at rest, and therefore the kinetic energy will be zero.

This problem, like many others, can be solved by using the equation of motion, $\Sigma(f) = ma$. Since we are dealing with a variable force, the methods of Programme 5 would need to be employed. Indeed, the example of Frame 33 in that programme is similar to this, and it is interesting to see in that example that the integration required actually results in an energy equation. It is clear that the solution using energy is much simpler. But as we have seen elsewhere, the energy equation would not reveal *how long* it takes for the buffers to compress. For this, we would require the method of Frame 35, Programme 5.

You need to be constantly aware of the assumptions implicit in the methods used. We said in Frame 15 that the spring compression is within the limit of proportionality; that is to say, the graph of force against compression is a straight line. If this were not so, the solution would be more difficult. Suppose for example that the buffer springs could compress a maximum amount of 40 mm. The calculation above would then tell us only that the buffers would compress by this amount, and the remaining kinetic energy would be dissipated elsewhere (possibly by damaging the buffers). You can easily calculate for yourself that for a maximum compression of 40 mm, the maximum truck speed would have to be limited to 1.11 m s^{-1}.

18

When a body falls vertically on to a spring, the problem is a little more difficult, as potential energy also becomes a factor in the equation.

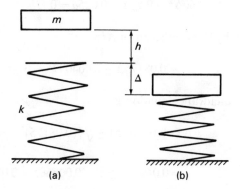

(a)　　　　　(b)

When a weight of mass m falls vertically on to a spring of stiffness k, the spring will compress by a greater amount than if the weight were just lowered on to the spring. Diagram (a) above shows the body, being released from rest at a height h above the top of the spring; (b) shows the spring at the point of maximum compression, which we call Δ.

Write an energy equation, in words, relating the two states. Assume that the system loses no energy.

19

$$\boxed{\text{Loss of potential energy} = \text{gain of strain energy}}$$

although the equation could be expressed in other ways. The important thing to note is, that like the first example, when the spring is at maximum compression, the body will be instantaneously at rest, and therefore, there will be no kinetic energy involved. Substituting the algebraic symbols:

$$mg(h + \Delta) = \tfrac{1}{2}k\Delta^2 \qquad (1)$$

Given the values of m, k and h, Δ can be calculated from this equation. So calculate for yourself the maximum compression when a body of mass 0.5 kg falls from a height of 50 mm on to a spring of stiffness 120 N m^{-1}. The answer is 116.76 mm. Don't be discouraged by the quadratic equation; just use the formula.

20

Substituting the values given:

$$0.5g(0.05 + \Delta) = \tfrac{1}{2} \times 120 \times \Delta^2$$

$$\therefore \quad 60\Delta^2 - 0.5g\Delta - 0.025g = 0$$

Dividing both sides by the coefficient of Δ^2:

$$\Delta^2 - 0.08175\Delta - 0.0040875 = 0$$

The solution to the quadratic equation is:

$$\Delta = \tfrac{1}{2}(0.08175) \pm \sqrt{\{(0.08175)^2 - 4 \times 1 \times (-0.0040875)\}}$$

$$= 0.040875 \pm \tfrac{1}{2}\sqrt{(0.006683 + 0.01635)}$$

$$= 0.040875 \pm 0.07588$$

$$= 0.11676 \text{ m}$$

$$\therefore \quad \Delta = \mathbf{116.76 \ mm}$$

The mere static weight of a mass of 0.5 kg would cause the spring to compress by 40.875 mm. You can see that this figure is the term outside the square root in the solution above. The quantity within the square root is the additional compression of the spring resulting from dropping the weight, as distinct from just lowering it.

The alternative negative solution to the equation was rejected, but it does have a physical significance. If the weight were to fall on to the spring and become attached to it, the spring would expand again after maximum compression, and this negative answer indicates the maximum extension that would result.

21

If you take equation (1) of Frame 17, and solve the quadratic equation in Δ exactly as we have just done in the previous frame, you should have no difficulty in proving that the general expression for Δ is given by:

$$\Delta = \frac{mg}{k} \pm \sqrt{\left\{ \left(\frac{mg}{k} \right)^2 + \frac{2mgh}{k} \right\}}$$

and if you substitute the values given in the example, you will obtain the same result as before.

This general expression for Δ gives an interesting result for a value of $h = 0$. Determine this.

22

$$\boxed{\text{When } h = 0; \quad \Delta = \frac{2mg}{k}}$$

This result may be surprising; one might expect that the result of 'dropping' a weight from zero height is the same as just statically applying the weight. But of course, it is not. If you were to lower a weight on to a spring until it just touches the top, and were then to *suddenly release* it, the spring would compress to twice the amount it would under the static weight only, and the weight would then oscillate up and down about the static compression point.

So far, we have considered maximum spring compression (or extension; exactly the same analysis and result applies to a spring being extended). But now, let us think about the velocity of the falling weight. To determine this, we need a more general energy equation, considering the energy at the initial state (when the weight is a height h above the top of the spring), and also at an instant when the spring has compressed an amount x, where x is less than Δ, the maximum compression. Calling the velocity of the weight v at this instant, try and write down this general equation.

23

$$\boxed{mg(h + x) = \tfrac{1}{2}kx^2 + \tfrac{1}{2}mv^2 \qquad (1)}$$

or, in words:

Loss of potential energy = gain of strain energy + gain of kinetic energy

If values of m, k, h and x are given, the velocity v can be found by using this equation. Use the same data as in Frame 19, and calculate the velocity when x is, say, 100 mm. Your answer should be 0.7369 m s^{-1}.

24

$$0.5g(0.05 + 0.1) = \tfrac{1}{2} \times 120 \times (0.1)^2 + \tfrac{1}{2} \times 0.5\, v^2$$

$$\therefore \quad v = \sqrt{\left(\frac{0.73575 - 0.6}{0.25}\right)} = \sqrt{(0.543)} = \mathbf{0.7369\ m\ s^{-1}}$$

The velocity varies as the weight descends. How do we find the maximum velocity?

25

The energy equation may be re-arranged to make v^2 the 'subject'. We then differentiate v^2 with respect to the variable x. It is not necessary to differentiate v; if v has a maximum value, so must v^2.

You should be able to do this yourself. Take the algebraic equation of Frame 23; don't substitute numbers. When you see the answer, you may also see that there was a simpler way of arriving at it.

26

Re-arranging equation (1), Frame 23:

$$v^2 = 2g(h + x) - (k/m)x^2 \qquad (2)$$

For maximum v^2:
$$\frac{d(v^2)}{dx} = 0$$

$$\therefore \quad 2g - (k/m)2x = 0$$

$$\therefore \quad x = \frac{mg}{k}$$

We could have deduced this result without differentiating. At this value of x, the force in the spring will be $(kx) = mg$, which is the magnitude of the weight. So at this instant, the resultant force acting on the body will be zero; the downward weight is balanced by the upward spring force. No resultant force means no acceleration. And maximum (or minimum) velocity occurs when the acceleration is zero. For all values of x greater than this, the upward spring force will be greater than the body weight, and the weight begins to slow down.

See if you can show that for the data of Frame 19, the maximum velocity will be 1.1756 m s^{-1}. The calculation is given in Frame 27.

27

$$x = mg/k = 0.5g/120 = 0.040875 \text{ m}$$

Substituting in equation (2), Frame 26:

$$v^2 = 2g(0.05 + 0.040875) - (120/0.5)(0.040875)^2$$

$$= 1.78297 - 0.40098$$

$$= 1.38199$$

$$\therefore \quad v_{max} = 1.1756 \text{ m s}^{-1}$$

28

If we apply a force to a spring which already carries a load, the work done by the additional force is still $(\frac{1}{2}Fx)$, where F is the maximum, or final value of the additional force, and x is the additional extension or compression.

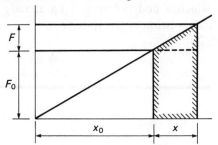

It can be seen that the increase of strain energy—the area shaded under the graph—is now $(\frac{1}{2}Fx + F_0 x)$. How can the same amount of work done produce a greater increase of strain energy? You can probably see how, if you think of a weight of magnitude F_0 hanging from a spring. Here is a clue: E_{pot}.

29

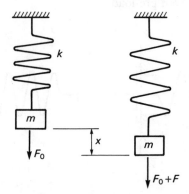

It can now be seen that applying the additional force results in a *loss of potential energy of the hanging weight*. The energy balance equation is:

$$\text{Initial energy } (E_{pot} + E_{str}) + \text{work done} = \text{final energy } (E_{str})$$

$$\therefore \quad \text{work done} = \text{increase of strain energy} - \text{loss of potential energy}$$

$$= \text{shaded area under the graph} - mgx$$

$$= F_0 x + \tfrac{1}{2}Fx^2 - mgx$$

$$= \tfrac{1}{2}Fx^2$$

as it is clear that the initial force F_0 is the weight mg. Therefore:

When a load is applied to a spring, the spring behaves in the same manner, whether it is unloaded, or carries a load.

30

With this last statement in mind, look back to Frame 19, and answer this question.

A weight of mass 0.5 kg falls from a height of 50 mm on to a spring of stiffness 120 N per metre on which a body of mass 1 kg already rests. What will be the additional maximum compression of the spring?

Refer also to Frame 20.

31

116.76 mm

The answer must be the same as the previous answer; the presence of the additional 1 kg weight does not affect the amount of additional deformation.

But the situation is quite different when the spring is pre-tensioned, or pre-compressed, as distinct from pre-loaded.

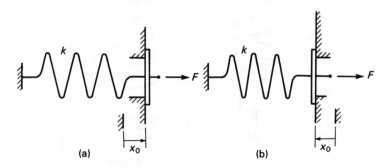

(a)   (b)

The two diagrams show springs which have been strained by an amount x_0 and held in the strained state. In diagram (a) the spring is pre-tensioned, and (b) pre-compressed. This is quite different from a spring carrying an initial load. A force F applied to the free end of the springs will produce no additional strain at all until F reaches the value of the pre-load in the spring.

Assuming a value of k of 400 N m^{-1}, and an initial strain of $x_0 = 0.1$ m, calculate the least value of force F to begin to strain the spring additionally, and calculate what value of F would cause an additional stretch or compression of 0.05 m. Also determine the work done by this extra force.

You should find that F must be at least 40 N, and that the final value must be 60 N. The work done is 2.5 J. The calculation follows.

A pre-strain of 0.1 m means that the initial load is $(kx_0) =$ **40 N**

The final total strain of the spring is $(0.1 + 0.05) = 0.15$ m

Hence the final spring is $(400 \times 0.15) =$ **60 N**

Work done is average force $\times$ extra strain $= (50 \times 0.05) =$ **2.5 J**

When a load is allowed to fall on to a spring which is pre-strained, the resulting additional maximum deflection will be different from what it would be if the spring just carried an initial load.

Example. A spring of stiffness 400 N m^{-1} is pre-compressed by 0.1 m and held between rigid plates, as shown. A body having a mass of 0.4 kg is held a height $h = 0.05$ m above the plate attached to the top of the spring and allowed to fall on to it. Calculate the resulting additional maximum compression, Δ, of the spring, and the corresponding additional load.

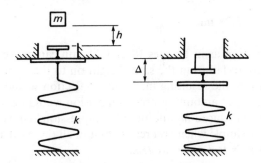

The diagrams show the two states: before the weight falls, and the maximum spring compression, shown as Δ. Write the energy equation applicable to the problem. Work in algebra, calling the mass m, stiffness k, height h, compression Δ. Remember that the spring will have *initial* strain energy. To start you off, here is the equation in words.

Loss of potential energy = increase of strain energy

$$mg(h + \Delta) = \tfrac{1}{2}k(x_0 + \Delta)^2 - \tfrac{1}{2}kx_0^2$$

and the equation is seen to be a quadratic in Δ, which can be solved if all the remaining values are given. So substitute the values and show that Δ is 5.28 mm. As with the example of Frame 20, take the positive solution only of the quadratic.

34

$$mg(h + \Delta) = \tfrac{1}{2}kx_0^2 + \tfrac{1}{2}k \times 2x_0\Delta + \tfrac{1}{2}k\Delta^2 - \tfrac{1}{2}kx_0^2$$

$$= kx_0\Delta + \tfrac{1}{2}k\Delta^2$$

$$\therefore \quad \tfrac{1}{2}k\Delta^2 - \Delta(mg - kx_0) - mgh = 0$$

$$\therefore \quad \Delta^2 - \Delta(2mg/k - 2x_0) - 2mgh/k = 0$$

Substituting values:

$$\Delta^2 - \Delta\left(\frac{0.8g}{400} - 0.2\right) - \frac{2 \times 0.4g \times 0.05}{400} = 0$$

$$\therefore \quad \Delta^2 + 0.18038\,\Delta - 0.000981 = 0$$

$$\therefore \quad \Delta = \tfrac{1}{2}(-0.18038) \pm \tfrac{1}{2}\sqrt{\{(0.18038)^2 + 4 \times 0.000981\}}$$

$$= -0.09019 \pm 0.09547$$

$$= 0.00528 \text{ m}$$

$$\therefore \quad \Delta = \textbf{5.28 mm}$$

Using the same calculation as in Frames 19 and 20, you can prove for yourself that if the same weight were to fall from the same height on to the same spring, this time with no pre-compression, the resulting maximum deflection would be 42.63 mm.

The question arises: what amount of pre-compression would be necessary in order that the falling weight produced *no* additional compression. Think about this for a moment. The answer is simple when you realise that in all these calculations, we have assumed that *no energy is lost to the system.*

35

> There must always be a small additional compression, no matter how small the weight, or the height from which it falls

If we assume no energy is lost, the loss of potential energy of the falling weight must result in an increase of strain energy of the spring, which in turn must mean a further compression.

Of course, in practice, some energy is dissipated, and lost to the system. If a weight is dropped on to a plate, it will inevitably bounce to some extent; this itself means a loss of kinetic energy, with the result that the increase of strain energy of the spring will be less than the calculated amount.

A reminder: remember that in all these calculations we assume that the force–deformation graph for the spring is a straight line.

36

Here is a summary of the work so far on strain energy.

Strain energy E_{str} in a spring of stiffness k ($N\ m^{-1}$) extended or compressed an amount x within the limit of proportionality is given by:

$$E_{str} = \tfrac{1}{2}kx^2$$

When a load falls on to a spring, the loss of potential energy of the weight is assumed to be converted to strain energy and kinetic energy. It is assumed that no energy is lost to the system.

When a load falls on to a spring, the kinetic energy will be zero when the spring suffers maximum deformation: the strain energy is then equal to the loss of potential energy.

When a load falls on to a spring which already carries a load, the *additional* spring deformation can be calculated as if there were no initial load on the spring.

When a load falls on to a spring which is pre-strained, the additional maximum deformation may be calculated by assuming the loss of potential energy to be equal to the increase of strain energy.

37

All the work on springs, beginning at Frame 15, has assumed that the graph of load against deformation (i.e. extension or compression) was a straight line. This was not a mere matter of convenience, to make the work simple. A laboratory test on most springs would show this linear relationship between load and deformation. When a material, or a device exhibits this characteristic, it is said to conform to **Hooke's Law**. You have probably come across Hooke's Law in work on Stress Analysis concerned with the extension of a bar under a tensile load. There are limits to the validity of assuming Hooke's Law. A spring can be loaded so much that all the coils are pressed together, and the law then ceases to be valid. Also, when subjected to a tensile load, the coils could be stretched so much that a graph of load against extension would begin to depart from the straight line. The load at which this begins to occur is called the Limit of Proportionality, and again the law would not apply. But in all the work in this programme, it is to be assumed that the loads applied are within the limit of proportionality.

38

1. A spring of stiffness 1200 N m^{-1} rests on a rigid surface with its axis vertical. A body having a mass of 0.9 kg falls on to the top of the spring from rest from a height h.
   (a) Calculate the maximum instantaneous compression of the spring if $h = 15$ mm.
   (b) Calculate what value of h would result in a maximum compression of the spring of 40 mm.
   In each case calculate the value of the Equivalent Static Load, i.e. the force which would cause the same value of maximum compression. [*Ans. (a) 23.94 mm; 28.73 N. (b) 68 mm; 48 N.*]

2. A spring of stiffness 850 N m^{-1} hangs vertically with a load of 12 kg hanging from the lower end. A weight of 0.5 kg is held above the 12 kg load and dropped on to it from a height of 50 mm. Assuming no loss of energy on impact, calculate the resulting maximum force in the spring. [*Ans. 143.63 N.*]
   Hint: solve as problem 1, and then add the weight of the 12 kg load (see Frame 29).

3. A load of 6 kg hangs vertically from the lower end of a spring of stiffness 1100 N m^{-1}. The upper end of the spring is moving downwards at a steady speed of 1.5 m s^{-1} when it is suddenly brought to rest. Determine the resulting maximum load in the spring. [*Ans. 189.4 N.*]
   Hint: equate the kinetic energy to increase of strain energy − loss of potential energy.

4. A spring of stiffness 1300 N m^{-1} is pre-compressed by 15 mm and held between rigid plates. A weight of 1 kg is held a height h above a plate connected to the top of the spring, and released from rest.
   (a) If $h = 50$ mm, calculate the resulting instantaneous maximum force in the spring.
   (b) What value of h would result in an instantaneous maximum force in the spring of 100 N?
   [*Ans. (a) 46.81 N. (b) 315.25 mm.*]
   Hint: see Frames 32 to 34.

In all the examples and problems so far on strain energy, we have dealt with springs. But in this context, a spring is merely a component which conforms to Hooke's Law, that is, it has a straight-line graph of force against deformation. So provided this condition applies, we may use the same methods of calculation for any member or structure which conforms to Hooke's Law. A steel bar under a tensile load; a beam subject to a transverse load; a bridge; a building; provided that the limit of proportionality is not exceeded, we may adopt the same methods of calculation to determine the effects of suddenly applied loads. Of course, care is required in determining stiffness. For example, the stiffness of a beam subject to a transverse load is not a constant quantity: it depends on where the load is applied. In calculating the stiffnesses of bars in tension and torsion, we shall have to trespass into Stress Analysis theory. An example follows in Frame 40.

Example. A uniform steel bar has a length of 1.5 m and is 12.5 mm diameter. It is mounted vertically with its upper end attached to a rigid mounting, and a light plate attached to the lower end allows a weight to drop suddenly on to the bar. A weight of 20 N is held 15 mm above the plate and released from rest. Calculate the resulting maximum stress in the bar, and the value of the corresponding static load (the Equivalent Static Load) which would produce the same value of stress. It may be assumed that the limit of proportionality is not exceeded. Assume a value of E of 200 GN m^{-2} for the bar material.

We are not given the stiffness of the bar, but can calculate it from simple Stress Analysis theory. A load F on a bar produces an extension x given by:

$$x = \frac{FL}{aE}$$

where L and a are the length and cross-sectional area of the bar, and E is Young's Modulus. Re-arranging:

$$\frac{F}{x} = \frac{aE}{L}$$

But F/x is of course the slope of the load–deformation graph, i.e. the stiffness, k. So, begin your solution by calculating k. Watch your units; particularly the multiples of 10.

41

$$k = \frac{aE}{L} = \frac{(\pi/4 \times (12.5)^2 \times 10^{-6}) \times (200 \times 10^9)}{1.5} = 16.362 \times 10^6 \text{ N m}^{-1}$$

Perhaps you arrived at this figure and thought it must be wrong, being so large. But of course, a steel bar will have a much greater stiffness than a spring, and the figure is not unreasonable.

Now you have a value for k, you can use the same energy equation we used in Frame 19. This was:

$$mg(h + \Delta) = \tfrac{1}{2}k\Delta^2$$

Do this; substitute values and determine Δ. The value you should get is 0.1927 mm.

42

Working is easier if we re-arrange the quadratic in Δ with the coefficient of Δ^2 equal to 1:

$$\Delta^2 - \Delta\left(\frac{2mg}{k}\right) - \frac{2mgh}{k} = 0$$

We can write the solution of the quadratic algebraically:

$$\Delta = \frac{1}{2}\left(\frac{2mg}{k} \pm \sqrt{\left\{\left(\frac{2mg}{k}\right)^2 + 4 \times \frac{2mgh}{k}\right\}}\right)$$

$$= \frac{mg}{k} \pm \sqrt{\left\{\left(\frac{mg}{k}\right)^2 + \frac{2mgh}{k}\right\}}$$

$$= \frac{20}{16.362 \times 10^6} + \sqrt{\left\{\left(\frac{20}{16.362 \times 10^6}\right)^2 + \frac{2 \times 20 \times 15 \times 10^{-3}}{16.362 \times 10^6}\right\}}$$

$$= 10^{-6}(1.2223 + \sqrt{\{1.4942 + 36\,670\}})$$

$$= 10^{-6}(1.2223 + 191.5)$$

$$= 0.1927 \times 10^{-3} \text{ m}$$

$$\therefore \qquad \Delta = 0.1927 \text{ mm}$$

As with earlier examples, we reject the alternative negative root. The resulting stress σ is simply determined:

$$\sigma = \frac{\Delta E}{L} = \frac{(0.1927 \times 10^{-3}) \times 200 \times 10^9}{1.5} = 25.69 \times 10^6 \text{ N m}^{-2} = \textbf{25.69 MN m}^{-2}$$

To complete, calculate the static force F_{eq} required to produce this stress.

43

$$F_{eq} = \sigma a = (25.69 \times 10^6)(\pi/4 \times (12.5)^2 \times 10^{-6}) = \mathbf{3152.6 \ N}$$

where σ = stress and a = area of cross-section.

This is the Equivalent Static Load that we have referred to earlier. When you recall that the magnitude of the falling weight is 20 N, it is seen that the effect of dropping this weight on to the bar from a height of a mere 15 mm has the effect of magnifying the weight by a factor of about 158 times. It should come as no surprise that engineering designers faced with the possibility of sudden loads, or shock-loads, allow very generous safety-factors in their calculations.

44

A close look at the calculations in Frame 42 reveals the reason for such a high value of stress, and also of equivalent static load. In Frame 19, we calculated the effect of a weight of 0.5 kg falling on to a spring of stiffness 120 N m^{-1} from a height of 50 mm. You can easily show that the resulting spring deformation of 116.76 mm corresponds to an equivalent static load of 14.01 N. Since the weight of a mass of 0.5 kg is 4.905 N, the magnifying effect of dropping this load is about 2.5. The reason for the much higher equivalent load in this case is seen to lie in the value of stiffness, k. It is clear that the stiffer the spring, or bar, the greater is the stress, and the greater the equivalent static load. A steel bar is obviously very much stiffer than a spring, and for this reason, the damaging effect of a sudden load acting on it is likely to be very much greater than a sudden load on a spring. This is, of course, the reason for the inclusion of springs into places where shock-loads are to be expected: railway buffers, for example.

45

The previous problem was solved by calculating deflection Δ by solving the quadratic, and from this, the stress was calculated. We could derive a formula which enables us to calculate stress directly. Given that $\Delta = \sigma L / E$, and that stiffness k of a bar is aE/L, you can prove for yourself that the stress, σ, can be determined directly from the formula:

$$\sigma = \frac{mg}{a} \pm \sqrt{\left\{ \left(\frac{mg}{a} \right)^2 + \frac{2mghE}{aL} \right\}}$$

and this formula also shows clearly that the very high value of E is responsible for the high stress arising in this particular case. Stiffness, k, is of course directly proportional to E. This expression shows clearly that the term outside the root is the stress resulting from the static weight of the falling body. In the example in Frame 42, this component is almost negligible in comparison with the effect of the falling load.

The expression above also reveals the result of 'dropping' the weight from a height of zero, namely a stress exactly double the stress due to the static weight. We looked at this effect on a spring in Frame 22.

Expressions such as the one above for stress offer a useful exercise in dimensions. Show that all terms have dimensions of $ML^{-1}T^{-2}$.

46

$$\sigma = \frac{\text{force}}{\text{area}} \equiv \frac{\text{mass} \times \text{acceleration}}{L^2} \equiv \frac{M \times L/T^2}{L^2} \equiv ML^{-1}T^{-2}$$

mg/a has the same units: a weight, or force divided by area. Similarly, $\sqrt{\{(mg/a)^2\}}$ is dimensionally the same as mg/a.

Dimensions of $\sqrt{\left(\dfrac{2mghE}{aL} \right)}$ are:

$$\sqrt{\left(\frac{(M)(L/T^2)(L)(M/LT^2)}{(L^2)(L)} \right)} \equiv \sqrt{\left(\frac{M^2 L}{T^4 L^3} \right)} = ML^{-1}T^{-2}$$

(Dimensions of E are those of stress, derived in the first line.)

Another and slightly less obvious aspect of the expression for stress in Frame 45 is that the length, L, is on the bottom line. So that, a larger value of L will reduce the stress due to a sudden or shock load. If you think about it, this is right; a long bar stretches more for the same load than does a short one. We make this the subject of the next example.

Example. A tow-rope used for towing vessels can withstand a maximum safe load of 75 kN. When a length of 1 metre of the rope is tested in a machine, it is seen that a load of 1 kN causes an extension of 0.62 mm. In use, the rope connects a tug to a stationary vessel. The tug has a mass of 45 tonnes, and the rope tightens suddenly, while the tug is moving away at 2.5 m s^{-1}. Assuming all the kinetic energy of the tug to be converted to strain energy in the tow-rope, calculate the minimum length of the rope, if the maximum safe load is not to be exceeded.

Begin by calculating the kinetic energy of the tug. In this example, we shall not need to determine the stiffness of the rope. We know that the maximum force in the rope will be the maximum safe load. So we can use the expression for work done by a force F extending an elastic rope by a distance x. Look back to Frame 15 if you can't remember this. Then, equating work done to kinetic energy, you can calculate x. This value of x is the stretch for the maximum allowable load of 75 kN. So from it, calculate the extension for a load of 1 kN. And from this last figure, you should easily be able to calculate the length of rope. The final answer should be 80.65 m. See if you can get this answer without referring to the solution following.

48

$$E_{kin} = \tfrac{1}{2}mu^2 = E_{str} = \tfrac{1}{2}F_{max}x$$

$$\therefore \quad \tfrac{1}{2} \times 45\,000 \times (2.5)^2 = \tfrac{1}{2} \times 75\,000 \times x$$

$$\therefore \quad x = 6.25 \times 45/75 = 3.75 \text{ m}$$

Extension per kN of load $= 3.75/75 = 0.05$ m $= 50$ mm

Given that 1 m of rope extends 0.62 mm per kN:

$$\text{required length} = 50/0.62 = \textbf{80.65 m}$$

and if the rope were shorter than this, the kinetic energy of the tug would cause the safe load to be exceeded. This is perhaps a pessimistic conclusion. What would probably happen is, that as the rope tightens, the towed vessel would begin to move also, so that when the rope is at maximum stretch, *both* vessels are moving. The problem is actually one of momentum, and we shall undertake a more accurate analysis in Programme 8. But it is worth remembering that in energy calculations of this kind, it is not a bad procedure to assume no energy loss or dissipation, because then, your solution is assuming the *worst possible circumstances*, which is always sound practice in engineering design.

49

Example. A load of 1 tonne is placed at a point on a horizontal steel beam and it is observed that the resulting deflection due to this load is 3.65 mm. If the load is then removed, and a load of 10 kg is dropped on to the beam at the same point from a height of 10 mm above the beam, what will be the resulting maximum deflection?

Apart from the circumstance that we are now considering a beam instead of a vertical steel bar, the problem is essentially similar to the one set out in Frame 40. It is actually simpler, as in this case, we do not have to use Stress Analysis theory to find the stiffness; this can be very simply determined from the data in the first part of the question.

So see if you can work through the complete problem yourself, first calculating the stiffness, and then using the general expression for deflection Δ which we set out in Frame 21. The answer should be 0.8916 mm. The solution follows in Frame 50, but obviously, it is much better for you to obtain the answer yourself, rather than merely follow someone else's solution.

50

$$\text{stiffness } k = \frac{\text{load}}{\text{deformation}} = \frac{(1000g)}{3.65 \times 10^{-3}} = 2.688 \times 10^6 \text{ N m}^{-1}$$

$$\Delta = \frac{mg}{k} \pm \sqrt{\left\{ \left(\frac{mg}{k}\right)^2 + \frac{2mgh}{k} \right\}} \qquad \text{(refer to Frame 21)}$$

$$= \frac{10g}{2.688 \times 10^6} \pm \sqrt{\left\{ \left(\frac{10g}{2.688 \times 10^6}\right)^2 + \frac{2 \times 10g \times 10 \times 10^{-3}}{2.688 \times 10^6} \right\}}$$

$$= 10^{-6}(36.50 + \sqrt{\{1332 + 729\,911\}})$$

$$= 891.6 \times 10^{-6} \text{ m}$$

$$\therefore \qquad \Delta = \mathbf{0.8916 \text{ mm}}$$

The answer informs us that dropping a 10 kg load from a height of only 100 on to the beam produces a deflection (and therefore a corresponding stress in the beam) which is roughly one-quarter of the deflection produced by a static, or 'dead' load of 1000 kg. This is another illustration of the tremendous capacity for damage of falling, or suddenly-applied loads. In this case, the effect of dropping 10 mm has a magnifying effect of approximately 25 times the weight of the load itself. If you have ever watched a crane operator at work, you will have observed the great care with which loads are very gently lowered on to the floor of a building. And of course, the problem is reversed when a load is raised. Then, the sudden load acts on the crane itself, and carelessness could result in the crane being pulled from its mounting.

51

It has been seen in all the examples how stiffness of a member is directly related to the effects of sudden loads, or falling loads. The greater the stiffness, the worse the effect of the load. When the effect of a sudden load is to be kept as small as possible, then the stiffness must be kept low. In Frame 47, we find that the stiffness of a tow-rope can be kept down by making the rope longer. It must be understood that this does not increase the static strength of the rope, which remains the same; it merely makes it more suitable to accept sudden loads. If you were to examine a tow-rope, or the cable of a crane, you would see that it is made of a number of strands of wire, which are wound spirally, around a core of hemp, or rope. This is not merely to make the cable flexible, but to make it less stiff; winding on a spiral makes it more like a spring. Sometimes, a prudent car driver towing a vehicle will insert a spring in the rope itself, to minimise the chance of the rope breaking, or a bumper being torn off, due to a sudden start. If you take a piece of fairly thin string, and wrap it around both hands, you could break it by pulling your two hands smartly apart. But if you were to insert a spring in the string, you would find it quite impossible to break the string this way.

52

PROBLEMS

1. A truck having a mass of 22 tonnes runs on a rail, and is brought to rest from a speed of 1.8 m s^{-1} by spring buffers which have a total stiffness of 300 kN per metre. Calculate the value of the equivalent static load (the force which would cause the same maximum compression of the buffers (a) if the rail is horizontal; (b) if the rail slopes down at an angle of 2° to the buffers. [*Ans. (a) 146.23 kN; (b) 153.96 kN.*]
   Hint: for (b) there is also a loss of potential energy.

2. The cable of a crane has a stiffness per metre length of 2 MN per metre. It is lowering a load of 4500 N at constant velocity of 2 m s^{-1} when the rope is suddenly stopped. The length of cable extended at this instant is 6 metres. Calculate the value of the equivalent static load which would produce the same maximum extension of the cable. [*Ans. 29.23 kN.*]

3. A horizontal steel cantilever supports a load at its free end of 1.5 kN. The load causes a static deflection at this point of 4.22 mm. If the maximum safe load at this point is 5 kN, calculate from what height above the cantilever a weight of 20 N may be allowed to fall on to the cantilever at the same point, (a) with the 1.5 kN load removed; (b) with the 1.5 kN load still in place. [*Ans. (a) 1.7443 m; (b) 0.8517 m.*]
   Hints: see Frame 28 *et seq.* Calculate the maximum allowable deflection (i.e. for a load of 5 kN); this is then Δ. For (b) reduce this by the 4.22 mm initial deflection.

4. Show that when a uniform bar is subjected to a tensile stress σ which is within the Limit of Proportionality, the strain energy in the bar, E_{str}, is given by:

$$E_{str} = \frac{\sigma^2}{2E} \times \text{volume of bar}$$

Two steel bars are each 1 m long. Bar A is 10 mm diameter for the whole of its length. Bar B is 10 mm diameter for half its length and 20 mm diameter for the remaining half. The maximum permissible stress in the material is 30 MN m^{-2}. Show that when the bars are subjected to the maximum permissible tensile load, the work done on bar A is 1.6 times that done on bar B. If a load W is allowed to fall from a height of 20 mm, show that if the maximum stress is not to be exceeded, the value of W for A will be 8.77 N, and for B, 5.50 N. Take a value of 200×10^9 N m^{-2} for E.
   Hints: the first part of the problem may be solved algebraically, calling the area of bar A a, and calculating the area and corresponding stress in the larger half of the bar B.

53

In the final part of this programme, we shall look at some situations in which the energy equation is not so simple to derive, or so easy to solve. Look at this, for a start.

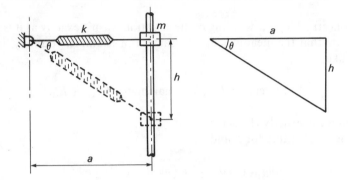

A body is constrained to slide along a frictionless vertical rod, and a spring, anchored at one end, is attached to the body. We shall assume that initially, the spring is horizontal, and just unstrained. Clearly, when the body is released, the spring will be stretched, and eventually, the body will be brought to rest. We shall determine how far the body falls, and also the maximum speed of its fall.

Imagine the body to fall a distance h, as shown, causing the spring to stretch by an amount x. Begin by deriving expressions for h and x in terms of the angle θ and the distance a. The first is simple; the second, not quite so simple. The triangle drawn by the diagram will help.

54

It is clear that $h = a \tan \theta$

The length of the hypotenuse is $(a + x)$

$$\therefore \quad x = a \sec \theta - a$$
$$= a(\sec \theta - 1)$$

Potential energy can be expressed in terms of h, and strain energy can be expressed in terms of x. If we call the velocity at this point v, we can write the energy equation. Try to do this yourself before turning to Frame 55. Begin (as you ought to begin every energy equation) by writing it in words first.

55

> Loss of potential energy = gain of strain energy + gain of kinetic energy
>
> $$\therefore \quad mgh = \tfrac{1}{2}kx^2 + \tfrac{1}{2}mv^2$$

Don't be concerned if your wording of the equation wasn't exactly as it is given here; just make sure that the meanings are the same. For example, you may have written something like:

$$\text{Initial energy } (E_{\text{pot}}) = \text{final energy } (E_{\text{kin}} + E_{\text{str}})$$

which of course is exactly the same.
We can now substitute for h and x:

$$mg\, a \tan \theta = \tfrac{1}{2}ka^2(\sec \theta - 1)^2 + \tfrac{1}{2}mv^2 \qquad (1)$$

If we begin by determining how far the body will fall, what is the first thing to do with this equation?

56

> We must write, velocity $v = 0$

At this point, let's put in some actual values. Take values of $m = 4.2$ kg, $k = 400$ N m^{-1}, and $a = 0.75$ m. Of course, $v = 0$.

$$4.2g(0.75 \tan \theta) = \tfrac{1}{2} \times 400 \times (0.75)^2 (\sec \theta - 1)^2$$

The equation will be slightly easier to handle if we put all the numerical terms to one side, and the 'trig' terms to the other:

$$\frac{\tan \theta}{(\sec \theta - 1)^2} = \frac{\tfrac{1}{2} \times 400 \times (0.75)^2}{4.2 \times 9.81 \times 0.75} = 3.6406$$

There is no simple mathematical solution to this equation; we resort either to plotting or to a process of trial and error. With a programmable calculator, this latter process is not difficult. But to save you trouble at this stage, verify for yourself that a value of $\theta = 50.72°$ will satisfy the equation. It is also left to you to show that this corresponds to a value of $h = 0.917$ m.

57

Suppose we now wish to determine the maximum speed at which the body falls. Then, we can go back to equation (1), Frame 55 and re-arrange it to make v the 'subject'. We can then differentiate v with respect to θ, which is the condition for maximum or minimum. Actually, we do not need to go quite so far as this; we can leave the 'subject' as v^2. If v has a maximum value, then so must v^2, and we can therefore differentiate v^2 with respect to θ.

See if you can show that the general equation can be written:

$$v^2 = 14.715 \tan \theta - 53.57 (\sec \theta - 1)^2$$

and if you can, continue by differentiating this, to find the condition for maximum v^2. You ought to be able to prove that:

$$\tan \theta - \sin \theta = 0.1373$$

58

Here is the working.
From equation (1) of Frame 55, re-arranging and substituting the given values:

$$\tfrac{1}{2} \times 4.2v^2 = 4.2g \times 0.75 \tan \theta - \tfrac{1}{2} \times 400 \times (0.75)^2(\sec \theta - 1)^2$$

Dividing all terms by the coefficient of v^2 reduces the equation to:

$$v^2 = 14.715 \tan \theta - 53.57 (\sec \theta - 1)^2$$

Differentiating:

$$\frac{d(v^2)}{d\theta} = 14.715 \sec^2 \theta - 53.57 \times 2(\sec \theta - 1)(\sec \theta \tan \theta)$$

Equating to zero (for maximum v^2), re-arranging and cancelling $\sec \theta$ gives:

$$14.715 \sec \theta = 107.14(\sec \theta - 1) \tan \theta$$

and bringing the arithmetical terms to one side and the trig. terms to the other:

$$0.1373 = \tan \theta - \tan \theta \cos \theta$$
$$= \tan \theta - \sin \theta$$

59

Although the final equation of Frame 58 could be reduced to a quadratic in $\sin \theta$, it is simpler to solve by trial and error, and you can do this, or just check for yourself that a value of $\theta = \mathbf{35.89°}$ is a satisfactory solution to the equation. You can complete the solution by substituting this value of θ in the expression for v^2 in the previous frame, and thus showing that the maximum velocity $v_{\max}$ is $\mathbf{2.776\ m\ s^{-1}}$.

Now complete the work on this example, firstly, by taking $\theta = 50.72°$ and showing that the energy equation balances, assuming kinetic energy to be zero; and secondly, by taking $\theta = 35.89°$ and checking again that the energy equation balances. If your equations don't balance, check against the work in Frame 60.

60

Taking $\theta = 50.72°$ (the condition for maximum displacement):

$$h = 0.75 \tan 50.72° = 0.917\ m$$

$$x = 0.75(\sec 50.72° - 1) = 0.4346\ m$$

$$E_{pot} = mgh = 4.2 \times 9.81 \times 0.917 = \mathbf{37.78\ J}$$

$$E_{str} = \tfrac{1}{2}kx^2 = \tfrac{1}{2} \times 400 \times (0.4346)^2 = \mathbf{37.38\ J}$$

$$\therefore \quad \text{loss of } E_{pot} = \text{gain of } E_{str}$$

Taking $\theta = 35.89°$ (the condition for maximum velocity):

$$v_{\max}^2 = 14.715 \tan 35.89° - 53.57(\sec 35.89° - 1)^2 = 7.7056$$

$$\therefore \quad v_{\max} = 2.776\ m\ s^{-1}$$

$$h = 0.75 \tan 35.89° = 0.5427\ m$$

$$x = 0.75(\sec 35.89° - 1) = 0.1758\ m$$

$$E_{pot} = mgh = 4.2 \times 9.81 \times 0.5427 = 22.36\ J$$

$$E_{str} = \tfrac{1}{2}kx^2 = \tfrac{1}{2} \times 400 \times (0.1758)^2 = 6.18\ J$$

$$E_{kin} = \tfrac{1}{2}mv^2 = \tfrac{1}{2} \times 4.2 \times 7.7056 = 16.18\ J$$

$$E_{pot} = \mathbf{22.36\ J}$$

$$E_{str} + E_{kin} = 6.18 + 16.18 = \mathbf{22.36\ J}$$

$$\therefore \quad \text{loss of } E_{pot} = \text{gain of } E_{str} + \text{gain of } E_{kin}$$

The second calculation is based on a potential datum which is 0.3743 m higher than the first. Relative to the first datum, the additional potential energy is $(4.2 \times 9.81 \times 0.3743) = 15.42\ J$. This accounts for the difference of the two totals.

With the previous example as a guide, you ought to be able to complete this next one without help. Follow the same procedure, and particularly note that you are not required to *determine* the significant values of the angle θ, but merely to *verify* that the values stated satisfy the appropriate equation. A brief solution of the problem follows in Frame 62.

Example.

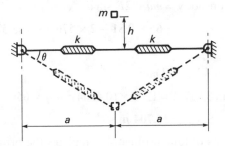

Two springs, each of stiffness $k = 1200$ N m^{-1} are joined, and the outer ends attached to two fixed mountings so that initially, they are horizontal and unstrained, the initial length of each spring being $a = 2.4$ m. A weight of mass $m = 65$ kg is held vertically above the centre-point a vertical height $h = 0.5$ m and is released from rest. When it strikes the springs, it remains attached and does not rebound. The lines of the springs deflect an angle θ from the horizontal, as shown in the diagram. Using an energy equation, show that when $\theta = 50.04°$, the weight will have a maximum displacement of 2.864 m. Also show, by calculating the forces acting on the weight, that a value of $\theta = 33.57°$ corresponds to a maximum velocity of the falling weight of magnitude 5.704 m s^{-1}. Assume that the springs are not extended beyond the limit of proportionality.

The reference to calculating forces should remind you of Frame 26. At maximum velocity, the acceleration (which of course is dv/dt) must be zero, which means that the resultant force on the body at this instant must also be zero.

62

For $\theta = 50.04°$:

Distance weight falls $= h + a \tan \theta = 0.5 + 2.4 \tan 50.04° = 3.364$ m

$$E_{pot} = mgh = 65 \times 9.81 \times 3.364 = 2145 \text{ J}$$

Spring extension $x = 2.4(\sec 50.04° - 1) = 1.337$ m

$$\therefore \qquad E_{str} = 2 \times \tfrac{1}{2}kx^2 = 1200 \times (1.337)^2 = 2145 \text{ J}$$

$$E_{pot} = E_{str} \qquad \therefore \qquad \text{no } E_{kin}, \text{ i.e. } \textbf{maximum displacement}$$

For $\theta = 33.57°$:

$$x = 2.4(\sec 33.57° - 1) = 0.4804 \text{ m}$$

$$\therefore \qquad \text{spring force } F = kx = 1200 \times 0.4804 = 576.5 \text{ N}$$

$$\therefore \qquad \text{nett force on body} = mg - 2F \sin \theta$$

$$= 65 \times 9.81 - 2 \times 576.5 \sin 33.57° = 0.09 \text{ N} \simeq 0$$

Energy equation:

$$mgh = 2 \times \tfrac{1}{2}kx^2 + \tfrac{1}{2}mv^2$$

$$\therefore \qquad 65g(0.5 + 2.4 \tan 33.57°) = 1200 \times (0.4804)^2 + \tfrac{1}{2} \times 65v^2$$

$$\therefore \qquad v_{max} = \textbf{5.704 m s}^{-1}$$

Frame 63, which consists of four problems, completes the programme.

63

PROBLEMS

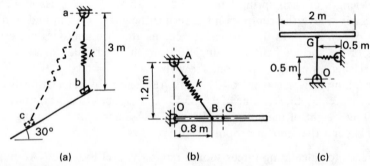

(a) (b) (c)

1. Figure (a) above illustrates a truck of mass 900 kg which rests on a frictionless inclined plane of slope 30°. It is connected to an elastic spring of stiffness $k = 4 \text{ kN m}^{-1}$ which is anchored at its upper end and is initially vertical, unstrained, and 3 m in length, when the truck is at rest at the top of the incline. Show that if the truck is released from this position, it will descend a maximum distance of 3.787 m down the slope before coming to rest.

Hint: use the Cosine formula to solve the triangle abc; hence determine the spring extension and show that $E_{pot} + E_{str}$.

2. In problem 1, show that when the truck has descended a distance of 2.0175 m down the slope, its velocity will be at maximum value, and calculate this value. [*Ans. 3.378 m s^{-1}.*]

   Hints: solve the triangle as for problem 1; calculate the corresponding spring force, and show that there is no resultant force acting on the truck. Then $E_{pot} = E_{str} + E_{kin}$.

3. In figure (b) opposite, a swing door hinged at one side is shown. The mass of the door is 350 kg, it is 2.2 m long, and may be considered as a uniform bar rotating about one end. When horizontal, the door is partially restrained by a spring of stiffness k which is attached to the door at a point 0.8 m from the hinge, and to a fixed anchorage 1.2 m vertically above the hinge. In the position shown, the spring is unstrained. The door is released from rest in the horizontal position. Calculate the required value of k in order that the door will just reach the vertical position as it comes to rest. For this spring stiffness, show that the maximum angular velocity of the door will occur when it has descended through an angle of 27.35° from the horizontal, and calculate this velocity. [*Ans. 24 279 N m^{-1}; 1.674 rad s^{-1}.*]

   Hints: fully-stretched spring is clearly 2 m long; unstretched length is simply calculated, as the hypotenuse of a right-angled triangle. For second part, use Sine formula to solve triangle.

4. In figure (c) opposite, a simple 'up-and-over' door is shown, which may be considered as a uniform bar of length 2 m and mass 160 kg. It is attached to the hinge at O by a light rigid rod 1 m long. A spring of stiffness 4 kN m^{-1} is attached to the mid-point of this rod and to a fixed anchorage as shown. The door is pulled down manually, anti-clockwise, through 90° and locked in the vertical position. Calculate the required pre-load in the spring in order that, when released from the closed position, the door reaches the horizontal open position with an angular velocity of 1 rad s^{-1}. [*Ans. 1477 N.*]

   Hints: calculate the increase of spring stretch from geometry of figure (0.618 m). Initial $E_{str} =$ gain of $E_{pot} +$ gain of E_{kin}. Calculate I with respect to axis through O using the Parallel Axis theorem. For a spring with a pre-load, refer to Frame 31.

Programme 8

MOMENTUM

1

This programme begins with a summary of what has already been covered in Programme 1 on Momentum and we shall examine some problems which need a little more ingenuity to solve. We shall introduce and define the Coefficient of Restitution. Then Angular Momentum will be defined and discussed, and the results of 'collision' of two rotating systems, or one rotating and one translating system. This will require a close investigation into the principle of Conservation of Angular Momentum, and an explanation will be required for this principle apparently failing to apply to certain situations. We shall look at some examples which emphasise the vector aspect of momentum, and finally, we shall examine the effect of an impulsive blow on a single body which rotates, or which simultaneously rotates and translates.

Without looking back, answer these three simple questions.

1. A body of mass m having a velocity u has momentum of magnitude ...
2. A body of mass m, having initial velocity u and final velocity v suffers a change of momentum of ...
3. Change of momentum in unit time (i.e. rate of change of momentum) is ...

2

| 1. mu; | 2. $mv - mu = m(v - u)$; | 3. force |

and if by chance, your answer to 2. was $mu - mv$, then this is wrong. The change is always the *final* value minus the *initial* value.

We showed in Programme 1 that force = rate of change of momentum. This may be written as follows:

$$f = \int \frac{\mathrm{d}(mu)}{\mathrm{d}t}$$

which may be written:

$$\int (f \, \mathrm{d}t) = mv - mu$$

and the quantity $\int(f \, \mathrm{d}t)$, the time-integral of force, is called the **impulse**. This term is useful in cases of sudden blows, such as hammer-blows, or forces experienced when bodies collide.

3

The Conservation of Momentum is a principle which follows from the definition of momentum. If force = rate of change of momentum, then if no force acts on a body, it cannot experience a change of momentum. A more familiar way to express this is, that change of momentum must be the result of the action of an *external* force. This is Newton's Second Law stated another way. The word 'external' becomes important when we begin to consider systems instead of a single body.

Consider a 'system' of two bodies. If they collide, the force between them due to the collision is an *internal* force, and thus cannot affect the *total* momentum of the two bodies, although the momentum of each single body may change.

Consider an explosive shell moving at high speed. When it explodes, it is an internal force which blows the shell into many fragments which all move off at different speeds in various directions. But this principle tells us that the total momentum remains unaltered; thus, the centre of mass of the various fragments continues along the same path, at the same speed, as the whole shell did before the explosion.

4

The principle of Conservation of Momentum makes no pronouncement about energy, and must not be confused with the principle of Conservation of Energy. When two bodies collide, the Conservation of Energy applies, as always. But frequently, we cannot make use of this, because we may be unable to calculate some of the energy involved. If a bullet is shot into a sandbag, although we know that a great deal of the initial kinetic energy is converted to heat in the sand, we have no direct way of calculating this; all we can be certain of is, that the final *kinetic* energy of the system (bullet and sandbag) is much less than the initial. An energy balance equation cannot be used. Similarly, it is highly probably that the total *kinetic* energy of the fragments of an exploding shell will be much greater than the initial energy of the whole shell. But we don't know by how much. Again, an energy balance equation cannot be used.

You should not forget that momentum, because it is a function of velocity, is a **vector**, whereas energy is not. Two bodies of equal mass, moving in opposite directions at the same speed, and colliding, have a total momentum of zero, both before and after collision. This is true whether they remain together, and bring each other to a stop, or whether they rebound with the same velocity. The kinetic energy lost will be total in the first case, and zero in the second.

5

Here is a revision example which you ought to be able to solve.

Example. A body of mass 20 kg moving at 4 m s^{-1} along a straight track collides with a body of mass 30 kg moving at 2 m s^{-1} in the opposite direction. Calculate the final velocities of the two bodies, (a) assuming that they remain together after collision; (b) assuming that no kinetic energy is lost to the system on collision.

In solving part (a) you ought to be able to show for yourself that the two bodies move together at 0.4 m s^{-1} in the direction of the first body. For part (b), you will be able to produce two equations: call the two unknown velocities v_1 and v_2. The first equation is obtained from the Conservation of Momentum, and the second from the Conservation of Energy. The solution of the pair of simultaneous equations should give you the results that v_1 is -3.2 m s^{-1} and v_2 is $+2.8$ m s^{-1}. An abbreviated solution follows in Frame 6.

6

Part (a) Calling the common final velocity v, the momentum equation is:

$$20 \times 4 + 30 \times (-2) = (20 + 30) \times v$$

which can be simplified to:

$$80 - 60 = 50v$$

$$\therefore \qquad v = +\mathbf{0.4 \ m \ s^{-1}}$$

Part (b)

Momentum:

$$20 \times 4 \times 30 \times (-2) = 20v_1 + 30v_2$$

which can be simplified to:

$$2v_1 + 3v_2 = 2 \qquad\qquad (1)$$

Energy:

$$\tfrac{1}{2} \times 20 \times (4)^2 + \tfrac{1}{2} \times 30 \times (2)^2 = \tfrac{1}{2} 20v_1^2 + \tfrac{1}{2} \times 30v_2^2$$

which can be simplified to:

$$2v_1^2 + 3v_2^2 = 44 \qquad\qquad (2)$$

We can re-arrange equation (1) to give:

$$v_2 = \tfrac{1}{3}(2 - 2v_1)$$

and we substitute this into equation (2):

$$2v_1^2 + 3(\tfrac{1}{3}(2 - 2v_1))^2 = 44$$

This can be simplified to the quadratic:

$$v_1^2 - 0.8v_1 - 12.8 = 0$$

which gives the two solutions:

$$v_1 = +4.0 \text{ or } -3.2$$

The first solution is the original velocity, so we adopt the second. Substituting $v_1 = -3.2$ into equation (1) gives a value of $v_2 = +2.8$

$$\therefore \quad v_1 = \textbf{3.2 m s}^{-1} \textbf{ in reverse direction}: \quad v_2 = \textbf{2.8 m s}^{-1} \textbf{ also reversed}$$

We shall find later that there is a simpler method for solving this second part.

7

We used the term 'impulse' in Frame 2. The equation of Conservation of Momentum is obtained by eliminating the impulse when two bodies collide, but it can be interesting to make an approximate calculation of the order of force in a typical impulsive blow. For an example, let us consider striking a golf ball with a club. A golf ball has a mass of approximately 0.045 kg. When driven off from a tee, we may assume that it attains a velocity of approximately 60 m s^{-1}. The length of time that the ball is in contact with the club is speculative. Modern instrumentation, or high-speed photography could determine this reasonably accurately, but for this example, let us assume that the contact-time is one-thousandth of a second. Since impulse = change of momentum:

$$\text{impulse} = m(v - u) = 0.045(60 - 0) = 2.7 \text{ kg m s}^{-1}$$

Although this change of momentum seems a very modest figure, if we recall that it takes place in 0.001 seconds, the *average* force F_{av} is given by:

$$\text{Impulse} = F_{av} \times \text{time} = F_{av} \times 0.001 = 2.7$$

$$\therefore \quad F_{av} = 2700 \text{ N}$$

A reasonable assumption would be, that the maximum value of the force would be approximately twice this figure, i.e. 5400 N. Reverting to old-style Imperial units for a moment, the ball is subjected to a force of about half a ton!

8

When two bodies collide, we can determine something about the nature of the collision by finding the **Coefficient of Restitution**. During collision, bodies deform to some extent, and this coefficient is an index of the degree to which they recover from this deformation. ('Restitution' means recovery.) If for example, two billiard-balls collide, we expect that the recovery of any deformation is very high; if you examine a billiard-ball, you would have difficulty in finding obvious signs of distortion. This suggests a high value of Coefficient of Restitution. On the other hand, the impact of a billiard-ball on a wooden surface would involve quite a high degree of deformation; one should not make a regular habit of dropping billiard-balls on to polished-table tops. In such a case, a low value of Coefficient of Restitution would be expected. Quantitatively, the Coefficient of Restitution (denoted by e) is defined as the ratio of the relative velocity of separation to the relative velocity of approach:

$$-e = \frac{\text{relative velocity of separation}}{\text{relative velocity of approach}} = \frac{v_2 - v_1}{u_2 - u_1}$$

and you should particularly note the negative sign before e. When bodies collide and rebound, the relative separation and approach velocities must clearly be in opposite directions, and this is recognised by including the negative sign.

9

The Coefficient of Restitution, e, can be determined only by experiment, and various values can be found in data-tables and books. When $e = 1$, there is no deformation which is not fully recovered, and hence no kinetic energy loss to the system when bodies collide. Such a collision is called a **perfectly elastic** collision. When e has the lowest possible value of 0, colliding bodies remain in contact after collision, and the collision is said to be **perfectly plastic**. This does not mean that all the kinetic energy is necessarily lost to the system, as some examples will show later.

Example. Two steel balls, each having a mass of 0.4 kg, collide on a straight frictionless track. Ball A has an initial velocity of 1.5 m s^{-1}, and ball B is initially stationary. Calculate the velocities of both balls after collision (a) if $e = 1$; (b) if $e = 0.9$. Calculate the loss of kinetic energy to the system in both cases.

The solution of this example follows in the next frame.

For two bodies of masses m_1, m_2 in collision, Conservation of Momentum gives:

$$m_1 u_1 + m_2 u_2 = m_1 v_1 + m_2 v_2$$

Substituting values: $0.4 \times 1.5 + 0 = 0.4v_1 + 0.4v_2$

$$\therefore \quad v_1 + v_2 = 1.5 \tag{1}$$

Substituting values given in the Restitution equation of Frame 8:

$$-1 = \frac{v_2 - v_1}{u_2 - u_1} = \frac{v_2 - v_1}{0 - 1.5}$$

$$\therefore \quad v_2 - v_1 = 1.5 \tag{2}$$

Adding the equations: $2v_2 = 3$

$$\therefore \quad v_2 = \textbf{1.5 m s}^{-1}$$

Substituting in equation (1): $v_1 = \textbf{0}$

A calculation of energy is unnecessary. It is clear that all the kinetic energy is transferred from A to B.

Part (b) Momentum: substituting terms results in the same equation (1) as before.

Restitution:

$$-0.9 = \frac{v_2 - v_1}{0 - 1.5}$$

$$\therefore \quad v_2 - v_1 = 1.35 \tag{1}$$

Adding the equations: $2v_2 = 2.85$

$$\therefore \quad v_2 = \textbf{1.425 m s}^{-1}$$

Substituting in equation (1) gives: $v_1 = \textbf{0.075 m s}^{-1}$

$$\text{Initial } E_{\text{kin}} = \tfrac{1}{2} \times 0.4(1.5)^2 = 0.45 \text{ J}$$

$$\text{Final } E_{\text{kin}} = \tfrac{1}{2} \times 0.4(1.425)^2 + \tfrac{1}{2} \times 0.4(0.075)^2$$

$$= 0.40725 \text{ J}$$

$$\text{loss of } E_{\text{kin}} = \textbf{0.04275 J}$$

Now, with the above calculations as a guide, solve the example again, this time taking the mass of A as 0.4 kg (as previously) but mass B as 0.8 kg. Answers: (a) $v_1 = \textbf{-0.5 m s}^{-1}$, $v_2 = \textbf{+1.0 m s}^{-1}$; (b) $v_1 = \textbf{-0.4 m s}^{-1}$, $v_2 = \textbf{+0.95 m s}^{-1}$. For (a) and (b), equation (1) is $v_1 + 2v_2 = 1.5$, and equation (2) is (a): $v_2 - v_1 = 1.5$; (b) $v_2 - v_1 = 1.35$. Energy loss for (b) is **0.075 J**. The solution is not given.

11

PROBLEMS

1. Two bodies, A and B, located on a straight frictionless track, collide. Initially, B is stationary and A moves towards B with velocity u. The coefficient of restitution for the collision is 1. Show that (a) if the masses are equal, the final velocity of B is u, while A is brought to rest; (b) if the mass of B is three times that of A, both bodies recoil with velocity $\frac{1}{2}u$.

2. Bodies A and B, respectively of mass 6 kg and 9 kg, collide on a straight level track. Initially, A moves towards B at 2 m s^{-1} and B moves towards A at 1 m s^{-1}. After collision, A recoils with a velocity of 1.24 m s^{-1}. Determine the coefficient of restitution and calculate the kinetic energy lost at the collision. [*Ans. e = 0.8 5.832 J.*]

12

The Coefficient of Restitution is really a constant for a particular material, or a particular combination of two materials. Thus, it is correct to state a value of e for, say, steel on steel, or steel on glass, but it is not strictly correct to refer to the coefficient of restitution when two trucks on a rail collide. But if two such trucks collide with a perfectly elastic impact, it is convenient to assume that the relative velocity of separation of the collision is the same as the relative velocity of approach. Here is a simple proof that this is so, which does not assume a value for e.

Considering two bodies, of masses m_A, m_B, with initial and final velocities u_A, u_B, v_A and v_B, the equation of conservation of momentum is:

$$m_A u_A + m_B u_B = m_A v_A + m_B v_B \tag{1}$$

For a perfectly elastic collision, there is no loss of kinetic energy.

$$\therefore \quad \tfrac{1}{2}m_A u_A^2 + \tfrac{1}{2}m_B u_B^2 = \tfrac{1}{2}m_A v_A^2 + \tfrac{1}{2}m_B v_B^2 \tag{2}$$

Equation (1) can be written:

$$m_A(u_A - v_A) = m_B(v_B - u_B)$$

Equation (2) can be re-arranged and simplified:

$$m_A(u_A^2 - v_A^2) = m_B(v_B^2 - u_B^2)$$

$$\therefore \quad m_A(u_A - v_A)(u_A + v_A) = m_B(v_B - u_B)(v_B + u_B)$$

and the crossed-out terms are seen to cancel, which gives:

$$u_A + v_A = u_B + v_B$$

$$\therefore \qquad u_A - u_B = -(v_A - v_B)$$

which is the result we would obtain if we assumed a value of $e = 1$. The use of this equation makes a simpler solution to problems of perfectly elastic collision when it is incorrect to assume a value for e. The problem solved in Frame 6 is solved much more easily using this method, and you should satisfy yourself that you can solve it this way.

13

Now we shall look at some problems which require some extra thinking.

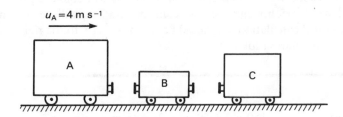

Example. Three trucks, A, B and C, are located on a straight level frictionless track in that order. The masses are A, 150 kg, B, 50 kg, and C, 100 kg. Initially, B and C are stationary, and A moves towards B at 4 m s^{-1}. Assuming all collisions to be perfectly elastic, determine the final speeds of the trucks after all collisions have ceased.

It is immediately clear that A collides with B, so you can begin the solution by determining the final velocities of A and B after this first collision. Since collision is perfectly elastic, you can use the equation at the end of the previous frame, together with a simple momentum conservation equation. You should obtain values of $v_A = 2$ m s^{-1} and $v_B = 6$ m s^{-1}, both to the right. This part of the solution follows, for you to check on.

14

Momentum:
$$m_A u_A + m_B u_B = m_A v_A + m_B v_B$$
$$150 \times 4 + 50 \times 0 = 150 v_A + 50 v_B$$

Simplifying:
$$3v_A + v_B = 12 \tag{1}$$

For perfectly elastic collision:

$$\frac{v_B - v_A}{u_B - u_A} = -1$$

$$\therefore \quad v_B - v_A = -1(u_B - u_A) = u_A - u_B = 4 \tag{2}$$

Use equation (2) to substitute for v_B in equation (1):

$$12 = 3v_A + (4 + v_A) = 4v_A + 4$$

$$\therefore \quad v_A = \tfrac{1}{4}(12 - 4) = +2 \text{ m s}^{-1} \text{ (i.e. to right)}$$

Substituting in equation (2): $v_B = 4 + v_A = +6 \text{ m s}^{-1}$ (i.e. to right)

From this result, it now becomes clear that B must collide with C. So continue by calculating the result of this second collision. u_B will now be $+6 \text{ m s}^{-1}$, and u_c is **0**. The calculation follows exactly the same lines as the first one so it is not given this time, but the answers are: $v_B = -2 \text{ m s}^{-1}$ and v_c is $+4 \text{ m s}^{-1}$.

From this second result, it emerges that A and B will collide again. This time, u_A will be $+2 \text{ m s}^{-1}$ (following the first collision) and u_B will be -2 m s^{-1}. So go through this third calculation: v_B should be $+4 \text{ m s}^{-1}$ (i.e. to the right) and v_A should be **zero**. This calculation follows.

15

Momentum:
$$150 \times 2 + 50 \times (-2) = 150 v_A + 50 v_B$$

Simplifying:
$$3v_A + v_B = 4 \tag{1}$$

Elastic impact:
$$v_B - v_A = -1(u_B - u_A) = -1(-2 - 2) = 4 \tag{2}$$

Using equation (2) to substitute for v_B in equation (1):

$$3v_A + (4 + v_A) = 4$$

$$\therefore \quad v_A = 0$$

Substituting in equation (2):

$$v_B = 4 + v_A = 4 \text{ m s}^{-1}$$

Thus, the final situation is, that A is stationary, while B and C both move to the right at 4 m s^{-1}. So B will not catch up with C and there will be no more collisions.

Finally, you should check for yourself that the final kinetic energy (of B and C) is equal to the initial kinetic energy (of A).

16

Here is another problem, rather different from the previous one.

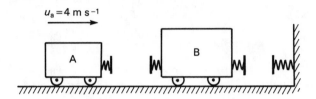

$u_a = 4$ m s^{-1}

A   B

Example. Two trucks, A and B, are on a straight frictionless horizontal track. The masses are, A, 100 kg, B, 200 kg. Initially, B is stationary and A is moving towards B at 4 m s^{-1}. To the right of B is a perfectly elastic buffer. Determine the final speeds of both trucks, after all collisions have ceased.

Again, it is clear that the first collision must be between A and B, and it is left for you to show that the speeds after this first collision will be $1\frac{1}{3}$ m s^{-1} to the left for A, and $2\frac{2}{3}$ m s^{-1} to the right for B. The calculation follows exactly the same lines as for the previous example.

After the first collision, B strikes the buffer, and because this is perfectly elastic, no energy is lost, and B recoils at the same speed. Because this is greater than the speed of A, it must catch A up, and a second collision will take place. For this, $u_A = -1\frac{1}{3}$ m s^{-1} (following the first collision) and $u_B = -2\frac{2}{3}$ m s^{-1}. So analyse this second collision. You should obtain values of $v_A = -3\frac{1}{9}$ m s^{-1}, and $v_B = -1\frac{7}{9}$ m s^{-1}. As previously, the calculations are quite straightforward, and so the solution is not given. Since both trucks are now moving to the left, and A is faster than B, this second collision must be the last one. It is also left for you to check that the final kinetic energy of the two trucks is the same as the initial kinetic energy of A before the first collision.

17

Calculations of collisions are always simpler when there is no energy loss. As a small exercise involving energy loss, take the first part of the previous example—A moving at 4 m s^{-1} towards B which is stationary—and calculate the velocities after collision if 20% of the initial kinetic energy is lost to the system on collision. The answers are: $v_A = \mathbf{0.8977}$ **m s^{-1}** in the reverse direction, and $v_B = \mathbf{2.449}$ **m s^{-1}**. You will have to revert to the method we used in the solution in Frame 6. The working follows in Frame 18.

18

Here is the working for the example of Frame 17.

Momentum:
$$100 \times 4 + 200 \times 0 = 100v_A + 200v_B$$

Simplifying:
$$v_A + 2v_B = 4 \tag{1}$$

$$\text{Initial } E_{kin} = \tfrac{1}{2} \times 100(4)^2 = 800 \text{ J}$$

With 20% loss:
$$\text{residual } E_{kin} = 800 \times 0.8 = 640 \text{ J}$$

Energy:
$$\tfrac{1}{2} \times 100v_A^2 + \tfrac{1}{2} \times 200v_B^2 = 640$$

Simplifying:
$$v_A^2 + 2v_B^2 = 12.8 \tag{2}$$

From equation (1):
$$v_B = 2 - \tfrac{1}{2}v_A$$

Substituting in equation (2):
$$v_A^2 + 2(2 - \tfrac{1}{2}v_A)^2 = 640$$

Expanding:
$$v_A^2 + 8 + \tfrac{1}{2}v_A^2 - 4v_A = 640$$

$$\therefore \quad 1\tfrac{1}{2}v_A^2 - 4v_A - 4.8 = 0$$

$$\therefore \quad v_A = \frac{-(-4) \pm \sqrt{\{(4)^2 - 4 \times 1\tfrac{1}{2}(-4.8)\}}}{2 \times 1\tfrac{1}{2}} = \frac{4 \pm 6.693}{3}$$

$$\therefore \quad v_A = +3.564 \text{ or } -0.898$$

$$v_B = 2 - \tfrac{1}{2}v_A = +0.218 \text{ or } +2.449$$

The first pair of solutions is impossible; A cannot move to the right faster than B. Thus:

$$v_A = -\textbf{0.898 m s}^{-1} \text{ (i.e. to left)}; \qquad v_B = +\textbf{2.449 m s}^{-1} \text{ (i.e. to right)}$$

Check final energy:

$$E_{kin} = 1 \times 100(0.898)^2 + \tfrac{1}{2} \times 200(2.449)^2 = 640.08 \text{ J}$$

19

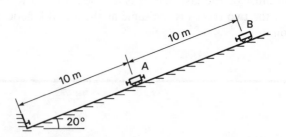

Example. Two trucks, A and B, run on a smooth rail inclined at 20°. The masses are, A, 150 kg, and B, 100 kg. They are initially 10 m and 20 m from the bottom of the slope, where there is a perfectly elastic buffer. Collision between the trucks is also perfectly elastic. The trucks are released from rest at the positions shown. Calculate how far up the track B will come to rest after colliding with A.

This example requires some revision. You will need an energy equation, and also some kinematic equations. The first part of the motion is clear. Both trucks must move with the same acceleration and speed until A reaches the bottom of the slope, when it must rebound with the same speed it strikes the buffer. And B must have this same speed, because it has descended the same slope for the same time. So begin by determining this velocity.

20

$$\text{Gain of } E_{\text{kin}} = \text{loss of } E_{\text{pot}}$$
$$\therefore \quad \tfrac{1}{2}mv^2 = mgh = mg \times 10 \sin 20°$$
$$\therefore \quad v = \sqrt{(2g \times 10 \sin 20°)}$$
$$= 8.192 \text{ m s}^{-1}$$

A diagram helps at this stage.

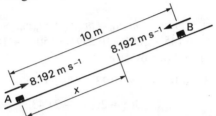

We assume the trucks meet at a point distance x from the bottom of the slope. We shall need the value of x, and also the two velocities at the instant before collision, which we may call u_A, u_B.

Use the kinematic equation $x = v_0 t + \tfrac{1}{2}at^2$ for both trucks. The component of weight down a slope of θ on a mass m is $mg \sin \theta$. So the acceleration for both bodies will be $(g \sin 20°)$ down the slope. And, of course, the time t must be the same for both trucks. This time will be 0.61 s and x is 4.373 m. See if you can do the calculations yourself, before checking.

21

For A: $$x = v_0 t + \tfrac{1}{2}at^2 = 8.192t + \tfrac{1}{2}(-g \sin 20°)t^2$$
For B: $$10 - x = v_0 t + \tfrac{1}{2}at^2 = 8.192t + \tfrac{1}{2}(g \sin 20°)t^2$$
Adding the equations: $$10 = 2 \times 8.192t$$
$$\therefore \quad t = 0.61 \text{ s}$$

Substitute in 1st equation:

$$x = 8.192 \times 0.61 - \tfrac{1}{2}g \sin 20°(0.61)^2 = 4.373 \text{ m}$$

Notice that velocity up the slope is treated as positive in the first equation, and velocity down the slope positive in the second. It would be unnecessarily tedious to adopt a rigorously correct sign convention for both equations.

Now calculate the two velocities, using the equation $v = v_0 + at$. These should work out at 6.145 m s^{-1} for A and 10.239 m s^{-1} for B.

22

$$v = v_0 + at$$

For A: $\qquad u_A = 8.192 + (-g \sin 20°)(0.61) = 6.145 \text{ m s}^{-1}$
For B: $\qquad u_B = 8.192 + (g \sin 20°)(0.61) = 10.239 \text{ m s}^{-1}$

Again, we have taken the initial direction in each case as positive. Thus, A is moving up, and B is moving down the slope when they collide. But now, when we write the momentum conservation equation, we must take care to use a correct sign convention. Taking u_A as positive, u_B must be -10.239 m s^{-1}. So now continue the solution by writing the momentum equation and the equation of equal approach and separation velocities (which you can find in Frame 12 if you have forgotten).

23

Momentum: $\qquad\qquad m_A u_A + m_B u_B = m_A v_A + m_B v_B$
Substituting: $\qquad 150 \times 6.145 + 100(-10.239) = 150 v_A + 100 v_B$
Simplifying (dividing throughout by 50):

$$3 \times 6.145 - 2 \times 10.239 = 3 v_A + 2 v_B$$

$$\therefore \qquad 3 v_A + 2 v_B = -2.043 \qquad\qquad (1)$$

For perfectly elastic collision: $\quad u_A - u_B = -(v_A - v_B)$

$$\therefore \qquad v_A - v_B = u_B - u_A$$

$$= -10.239 - 6.145$$

$$= -16.384 \qquad\qquad (2)$$

Since the equation requires the value of v_B, we eliminate v_A from the two equations. From equation (2):

$$v_A = v_B - 16.384$$

Substituting in equation (1):

$$3(v_B - 16.384) + 2 v_B = -2.043$$

$$\therefore \qquad 5 v_B = -2.043 + 49.152$$

$$= 47.109$$

$$\therefore \qquad v_B = 9.422 \text{ m s}^{-1}$$

The positive sign indicates that B rebounds up the slope.
  A simple energy equation gives us the additional height gained after rebound:

$$mgh = \tfrac{1}{2} m v_B^2$$

$$\therefore \qquad h = (9.422)^2 / 2g = 4.525 \text{ m}$$

The corresponding distance along the slope is $4.525 / \sin 20° = 13.23$ m.
  Adding this distance to x gives the final distance from the foot of the slope.
Distance from bottom $= 13.23 + 4.373 = \textbf{17.603 m.}$

24

In programme 7, Frames 47 and 48, we made a calculation of a ship being moved by a tug. This was deliberately simplified. The problem is really one of momentum, and we shall make a more accurate analysis here. We shall re-state the problem, somewhat differently.

Example. A tug of mass 45 tonnes is connected to a vessel of mass 80 tonnes by a tow-rope of length 80.65 m. The rope stiffness is determined from a tensile test on a 1-metre length, when it is found that a force of 1 kN causes an extension of 0.62 mm. Initially, the vessel is stationary, and the tug is moving away at 2.5 m s^{-1}. Calculate the common speed of tug and vessel when the tow-rope is at maximum stretch, and determine the corresponding tension in the rope.

The common speed is calculated simply from an equation of conservation of linear momentum. Calling the common velocity v:

$$m_A u_A + m_B u_B = (m_A + m_B)v$$

$$\therefore \qquad 45\,000 \times 2.5 + 80\,000 \times 0 = 125\,000\, v$$

$$\therefore \qquad v = \textbf{0.9 m s}^{-1}$$

We calculate the tension in the rope by equating the loss of kinetic energy to the gain of strain energy.

$$\text{Loss of } E_{\text{kin}} = \tfrac{1}{2} \times 45\,000 \times (2.5)^2 - \tfrac{1}{2}(45\,000 + 80\,000)(0.9)^2 = 90\,000 \text{ J}$$

The stiffness k of the rope (force per metre extension) is given by:

$$k = \frac{1000}{(0.62 \times 10^{-3}) \times 80.65} = 20 \text{ kN per metre}$$

$$E_{\text{str}} = \tfrac{1}{2}kx^2$$

$$\therefore \qquad 90\,000 = \tfrac{1}{2} \times 20\,000\, x^2$$

$$\therefore \qquad x = 3 \text{ m}$$

$$\therefore \qquad \text{load} = 3 \times 20\,000 = \textbf{60 kN}$$

The length was calculated previously on the basis of a maximum safe load of 75 kN, with a corresponding stretch of 3.75 m. It was mentioned that this was a pessimistic conclusion, based on the assumption that all the kinetic energy of the tug would be converted to strain energy in the rope.

The problem is still over-simplified. We have assumed that the tug is 'coasting', that is, it is not actually pulling the vessel. In practice, it would be pulling, but this calculation of maximum tension is probably close to what it would actually be, and certainly much closer than the figure of 75 kN in the earlier calculation.

25

PROBLEMS

1. Two vehicles are on a straight horizontal frictionless track. Vehicle A has a mass of 180 kg and is moving towards B at 2 m s^{-1}. Vehicle B has a mass of 120 kg and is moving towards A at 1.5 m s^{-1}. Calculate the speeds of the vehicles after they have collided (a) if the vehicles remain locked together after collision; (b) if the collision is perfectly elastic; (c) if 20% of the kinetic energy before collisions is lost in collision. [*Ans. (a) Both 0.6 m s^{-1}; (b) $v_A = 0.8$ m s^{-1}, $v_B = 2.7$ m s^{-1}; (c) $v_A = 0.633$ m s^{-1}, $v_B = 2.45$ m s^{-1}.*]

2. Three trucks, A, B and C, are located on a smooth horizontal rail in that order. The masses are, A, 50 kg, B, 150 kg, and C, 100 kg. Initially, B and C are stationary and A is moving towards them at 4 m s^{-1}. Assuming all collisions to be perfectly elastic, calculate the final speeds of all three trucks after all collisions have taken place. [*Ans. $v_A = -2$ m s^{-1}; $v_B = +0.4$ m s^{-1}; $v_C = +2.4$ m s^{-1}. Only two collisions.*]

3. Three bodies, A, B and C, are located in that order on a smooth horizontal rail. The masses are respectively 100 kg, 200 kg and 150 kg. Initially, A moves towards B at 6 m s^{-1} and C also moves towards B at 3 m s^{-1}. B is initially stationary. Assuming that A collides with B before C does, calculate the speeds of all three bodies after all collisions have ceased. Assume all collisions to be perfectly elastic. [*Ans. A and B, 2 m s^{-1}; C, 5 m s^{-1} in opposite direction. Two collisions only.*]

26

Now we must examine the concept of momentum as it relates to a rotating body. The general Equation of Motion for a body in pure rotation (see Programme 1, Frame 111) is:

$$\Sigma(M) = I\alpha$$

which can be written:

$$\Sigma(M) = I\frac{\omega_2 - \omega_1}{t} = \frac{I\omega_2 - I\omega_1}{t}$$

and this expression is analogous to that in Programme 1, Frame 116, where we defined linear momentum. The quantity ($I\omega$) we now define as **angular momentum**, and we continue the analogy by stating:

Moment, or Torque = rate of change of angular momentum

27

All the statements and conclusions in this programme in Frames 3 and 4 can be exactly paralleled for angular momentum. Angular momentum of a body cannot be changed except by the action of a torque or moment. The same applies to a system of rotating bodies; only an *external* moment or torque can produce a change of angular momentum. An internal moment or torque may alter the angular momentum of components of a system, but the total angular momentum is not changed.

Again, an impulsive torque or moment acting on a component or a body may frequently absorb some kinetic energy of a system, and consequently, an energy equation should not be used to solve such a problem unless one is certain that there is indeed no loss of kinetic energy.

Although the expressions in the previous frame are analogous to the corresponding expressions relating to linear momentum, they are not identical, and the units are different. Determine for yourself the units of I, the moment of inertia, and ω, the angular velocity, and show that the units of the product $(I\omega/t)$ are those of moment, M.

28

$$[I] = ML^2; \qquad [\omega] = T^{-1}; \qquad [I\omega/t] = ML^2T^{-2}$$

Moment = force × length = mass × acceleration × length
$$\therefore \qquad [M] = M \times L/T^2 \times L = ML^2T^{-2}$$

Solve this simple example.

Example. A flywheel has a moment of inertia of 2.6 kg m². It rotates at a speed of 640 revolutions per minute. A retarding torque of magnitude 12 N m acts on the wheel for six seconds. Calculate the speed at the end of that time.

You can, of course, use the general Equation of Motion $(\Sigma(M) = I\alpha)$, find the retardation, and use a kinematic equation. But since we are investigating angular momentum, use instead the equation in Frame 26. Your answer should be 375.8 rev/min.

29

Transposing the equation of Frame 26:

$$\text{Change of angular momentum} = Mt = 12 \times 6 = 72$$
$$\text{Initial angular momentum} = I\omega_1 = 2.6(640 \times 2\pi/60) = 174.3$$
$$\therefore \quad \text{final angular momentum} = 174.3 - 72 = 102.3$$
$$\therefore \quad I\omega_2 = 102.3$$
$$\therefore \quad \omega_2 = 102.3/2.6 = 39.35 \text{ rad s}^{-1}$$
$$= (39.35) \times 60/2\pi) \text{ rev/min} = \textbf{375.8 rev/min}$$

30

Now imagine two rotors, having moments of inertia of I_A and I_B, rotating at different speeds about the same axis, and arranged so that they can be connected by a pair of friction-plates, or 'clutch'.

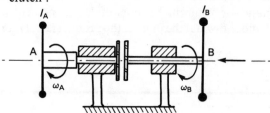

Initially, the rotor speeds are ω_{A1} and ω_{B1}. If one rotor is then moved axially, the friction plates come together, and the speeds will change, and both plates will eventually rotate at the same speed. If you think about this, you will see that it is exactly analogous to two bodies colliding when moving at different speeds, with the reservation that there is in this case no equivalent to rebounding; both bodies remain together after 'collision'.

If A were turning faster than B, the right-hand rotor would be accelerated, while the left-hand one would be retarded. This friction torque need not be constant; the essential point is, that *at any instant*, the two rotors are subjected to the *same* torque, but in *opposite directions*. Moreover, the torque acts for the same period of time on each rotor. We can call the impulse of this torque $\int(M \, dt)$. If we assume this torque positive on the one rotor, it must be negative on the other. Thus we can write two momentum equations:

$$+ \int(M \, dt) = I_B(\omega_{B2} - \omega_{B1}); \qquad - \int(M \, dt) = I_A(\omega_{A2} - \omega_{A1})$$

(arbitrarily calling the torque on B positive). Eliminating $\int(M \, dt)$ gives:

$$I_B(\omega_{B2} - \omega_{B1}) = -I_A(\omega_{A2} - \omega_{A1})$$

which gives:

$$I_A\omega_{A1} + I_B\omega_{B1} = I_A\omega_{A2} + I_B\omega_{B2}$$

which is seen to be an equation of **Conservation of Angular Momentum**.

Example. In the system shown in the figure in Frame 30, I_A is 12 kg m^2 and I_B is 20 kg m^2. The initial speed of A is 600 rev/min clockwise (looking from the left). Calculate the common speed of the two shafts after being coupled, if the initial speed of shaft B is (a) 300 rev/min clockwise; (b) zero; (c) 360 rev/min anti-clockwise. In all cases, calculate the loss of kinetic energy to the system.

The solution to part (a) follows; you should be able to complete the remaining parts unaided.

Part (a) Calling the final common speed ω, the general equation can be written:

$$I_A \omega_{A1} + I_B \omega_{B1} = (I_A + I_B)\omega$$

Writing $\omega = N \times 2\pi/60$, where N is in rev/min, $2\pi/60$ cancels throughout:

$$\therefore \qquad I_A N_{A1} + I_B N_{B1} = (I_A + I_B)N$$

Substituting values:

$$12 \times 600 + 20 \times 300 = 32 \times N$$

$$\therefore \qquad N = +\textbf{412.5 rev/min}, \text{ i.e. clockwise}$$

The energy loss is determined by subtracting the final kinetic energy from the initial.

$$\text{Loss of } E_{\text{kin}} = \tfrac{1}{2} \times 12(600 + 2\pi/60)^2 + \tfrac{1}{2} \times 20(300 \times 2\pi/60)$$

$$- \tfrac{1}{2}(12 + 20)(412.5 \times 2\pi/60)^2$$

$$= \tfrac{1}{2}(2\pi/60)^2 \{12 \times 600^2 + 20 \times 300^2 - 32 \times 412.5^2\}$$

$$= \textbf{3701 J}$$

The anwers to (b) and (c) are: part (b): **225 rev/min, clockwise; 14.8 kJ**
part (c): **zero; 37.9 kJ**

The calculations are similar, but note that in part (c), N_{B1} will be *negative*. Avoid the mistake of 'cancelling' $(2\pi/60)^2$ in the energy calculations; although the conversion factor cancels in the angular momentum equation, it does not in the calculation of energy.

In this problem, the loss of kinetic energy is more obvious than in the case of two translating bodies colliding. When the wheels are brought into contact, work is done against friction at the friction plates, and this work must reduce the kinetic energy of the system. In part (c), you can see that *all* the kinetic energy is lost.

32

At this point, we shall summarise what we have established so far.

Change of linear momentum of a body occurs only by the action of a force.

When a force acts between two parts of a system of bodies, the total momentum of the system is unchanged, although the momentum of each of the bodies may change.

Thus, change of linear momentum of a body or of a system of bodies requires the action of an *external* force.

Change of angular momentum of a body occurs only by the action of a moment or torque.

When a moment or torque acts between two parts of a system of rotating bodies, the total angular momentum of the system is unchanged, although the angular momentum of each of the bodies may change.

Thus, change of angular momentum of a body or of a system of rotating bodies requires the action of an *external* moment or torque.

33

Now have a look at this situation:

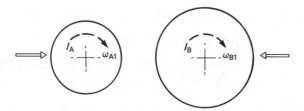

Two wheels of moments of inertia I_A and I_B rotate side by side in the same plane, close together, with initial speeds ω_{A1}, and ω_{B1}. The wheels are then brought together so that they contact at their rims, and are held together until there is no further slip at the rims. We require the final speeds of the two wheels.

We have assumed that both wheels are initially turning clockwise. We may also assume that the rim-speed of A is greater than that of B. (It doesn't actually matter whether it is greater or smaller.) When the wheels are held together, each wheel will be subjected to a tangential rim-force at the contact-point, which will be the same force on both, but opposite in direction. Have a try at drawing the free-body diagrams for the two wheels under these conditions.

34

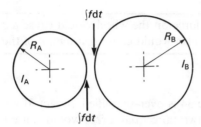

As with the two wheels of Frame 30, the contact-force at the rims need not be a constant force, and it is shown as an impulse $\int(f\,dt)$. If the rim-speed of A is greater than that of B, the forces will be in the directions shown. As the diagram clearly shows, the moments of the rim-forces are different for the two wheels.

Now, if we adopt a sign convention, for example, clockwise is positive, write down the moment of the rim-force for each wheel about the wheel centre.

35

> For wheel A: moment $= -\int(f\,dt) \times R_A$
>
> For wheel B: moment $= -\int(f\,dt) \times R_B$

and I hope you were not caught out by the fact that *both* these moments are negative: each force exerts an anti-clockwise moment about the wheel centre.

We can now write a 'change of momentum' equation for each wheel:

$$-\int(f\,dt) \times R_A = I_A(\omega_{A2} - \omega_{A1})$$
$$-\int(f\,dt) \times R_B = I_B(\omega_{B2} - \omega_{B1})$$

Eliminating $\int(f\,dt)$ from the pair of equations results in:

$$(I_A/R_A)(\omega_{A2} - \omega_{A1}) = (I_B/R_B)(\omega_{B2} - \omega_{B1})$$

The important feature of this equation is, that *it is not an equation of conservation of angular momentum*. Look carefully at the diagrams above, and try to explain why the principle of Conservation of Angular Momentum does not apply in this case. To help you a little, concentrate your attention on the free-body diagram of just one of the wheels.

36

> A tangential force on the wheel would cause a change of angular velocity, and also would cause *translation* of the wheel

The diagram in Frame 34 is over-simplified, in fact. If you brought two such wheels together in space, the two tangential forces would cause the *pair of wheels* to rotate. With the directions of forces assumed, the left-hand wheel would move upwards and the right-hand downwards; thus, the assembly would rotate clockwise. So, although the only force shown is an internal force, we have not taken into account the additional angular momentum resulting from this rotation.

If you mount the two wheels in a rigid framework so that the pair could not rotate bodily, the rim friction forces would cause an induced reaction force at each shaft between shaft and framework. Thus, you can stop the bodily rotation only by introducing a pair of *external forces*.

37

Example. Referring to the diagram in Frame 33, I_A is 12 kg m^2, I_B is 18 kg m^2. The rim radius of A is 0.1 m, and that of B is 0.12 m. Before contact, A is turning at 350 rev/min clockwise and B at 200 rev/min, also clockwise. Calculate the final speeds of the two wheels if they are brought into rim contact, after all relative slip has ceased. Calculate also the loss of kinetic energy to the system. Assume both wheels to be in a rigid mounting.

In addition to the equation derived in Frame 35, you need a 'compatibility' equation which connects the two final speeds, by virtue of the fact that the rim-speeds of the two wheels must be the same, after slipping was ceased. But take care of your signs when writing this equation! As was the case in the working in Frame 31, you can cancel the conversion from radians per second to revolutions per minute, so you can begin with the equation from Frame 35 in this form:

$$(I_A/R_A)(N_{A2} - N_{A1}) = (I_B/R_B)(N_{B2} - N_{B1})$$

and your compatibility equation can similarly be written in terms of N rather than ω.

Substituting values:

$$(12/0.1)(N_{A2} - 350) = (18/0.12)(N_{B2} - 200)$$
$$\therefore \quad N_{A2} - 350 = 1.25(N_{B2} - 200) \quad\quad\quad (1)$$

After rim-slip has ceased, the rim-speeds of both wheels must be the same, but they must *rotate in opposite directions.*

$$\therefore \quad (2\pi/60)N_{A2}R_A = -(2\pi/60)N_{B2}R_B$$
$$\therefore \quad N_{B2} = -N_{A2}(0.1/0.12) \quad\quad\quad (2)$$

Substitute in equation (1):

$$N_{A2} - 350 = 1.25(-N_{A2}(0.1/0.12) - 200)$$
$$\therefore \quad N_{A2} - 350 = -1.04167\,N_{A2} - 250$$
$$\therefore \quad N_{A2}(1 + 1.04167) = 100$$
$$\therefore \quad N_{A2} = +\textbf{48.98 rev/min}$$
$$\therefore \quad N_{B2} = -\textbf{40.82 rev/min} \quad\quad \text{(from equation (2))}$$

$$\text{Initial } E_{kin} = \Sigma(\tfrac{1}{2}I\omega^2)$$
$$= \tfrac{1}{2} \times 12(2\pi/60)^2(350)^2 + \tfrac{1}{2} \times 18(2\pi/60)^2(200)^2$$
$$= \tfrac{1}{2}(2\pi/60)^2\{12 \times (350)^2 + 18 \times (200)^2\}$$
$$= 12\,008 \text{ J}$$
$$\text{Final } E_{kin} = \tfrac{1}{2} \times 12(2\pi/60)^2(48.98)^2 + \tfrac{1}{2} \times 18(2\pi/60)^2(40.82)^2$$
$$= \tfrac{1}{2}(2\pi/60)^2\{12 \times (48.98)^2 + 18 \times (40.82)^2\}$$
$$= 322 \text{ J}$$
$$\therefore \quad \text{loss} = 12\,008 - 322$$
$$= \textbf{11\,686 J}$$

If you think you need practice, repeat these calculations, this time taking the initial speed of A as previously, and the initial speed of B as 200 rev/min anti-clockwise, instead of clockwise (i.e. N_{B1} is -200 rev/min). The calculations are not given, but your answers should be **293.9 rev/min clockwise** and **244.9 rev/min anti-clockwise** for the speeds of A and B, and **405 J** for the loss of kinetic energy.

The calculation for energy loss may sometimes act as a check on the calculation of the speeds. If the final kinetic energy is more than the initial value, it is time to go back and find out where you made a mistake!

39

We may use the same procedure when a translating body is coupled to a rotating one.

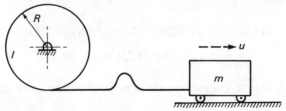

Example. A truck of mass $m = 650$ kg moves at a speed $u = 4$ m s^{-1} along a straight horizontal track. It is coupled by a rope, initially slack, to a drum of moment of inertia $I = 150$ kg m^2 and radius $R = 1.4$ m, initially at rest. Calculate the final speeds of drum and truck after the rope has tightened, and determine the loss of kinetic energy to the system.

We assume an impulse $\int f \, dt$ in the rope. This will reduce the velocity of the truck, and exert an anti-clockwise impulse moment on the drum. Calling left-to-right positive for the truck commits us to a compatible sign convention for the drum of anti-clockwise positive. The equations are:

$$- \int (f \, dt) = mv - mu$$

$$+ \int (f \, dt) \times R = I(\omega_2 - \omega_1)$$

Eliminating the impulse gives the single equation:

$$- m(v - u) = (I/R)(\omega_2 - \omega_1)$$

Substituting values:

$$- 650(v - 4) = (150/1.4)(\omega_2 - 0)$$

Compatibility: peripheral speed of drum = speed of truck:

$$\therefore \quad \omega_2 R = v$$

$$\therefore \quad 650(4 - v) = (150/1.4)(v/1.4)$$

$$\therefore \quad 2600 - 650v = 76.53v$$

$$\therefore \quad v(76.53 + 650) = 2600$$

$$\therefore \quad v = 2600/726.53 = \textbf{3.579 m s}^{-1}$$

$$\therefore \quad \omega_2 = 3.579/1.4 = \textbf{2.556 rad s}^{-1}$$

$$\text{Loss of } E_{\text{kin}} = \tfrac{1}{2}mu^2 - (\tfrac{1}{2}mv^2 + \tfrac{1}{2}I\omega_2^2)$$

$$= \tfrac{1}{2} \times 650(4)^2 - \tfrac{1}{2} \times 650(3.579)^2 - \tfrac{1}{2} \times 150(2.556)^2 = \textbf{547 J}$$

Now you solve this problem, given that the wheel, instead of being initially at rest, has a speed of 20 rev/min clockwise. The solution is not given, but your answers should be, $v = 3.27$ m s^{-1}, $\omega_2 = 2.336$ rad s^{-1}, loss of $E_{\text{kin}} = 1644$ J.

40

Our next example shows the importance of the vector nature of momentum.

Example. A gun has a mass of 2650 kg and fires a shell of mass 225 kg with a muzzle velocity of 640 m s^{-1}. The barrel is aimed upwards at an angle of 40° to the horizontal, and the gun rests on a smooth horizontal surface and is unrestrained. Determine the true velocity of the shell, and its angle of flight, as it leaves the barrel.

When a shell is fired from a gun, the propelling force is an *internal* force, acting forwards on the shell and backwards on the gun. If the gun were completely unrestrained, a simple equation of conservation of momentum would allow the recoil velocity to be determined. If the gun were aimed horizontally, we could do this. But the fact that the gun is elevated means that firing the shell will result in an impulsive reaction force between gun and ground, and this is an *external* force. If, however, the ground is smooth, this impulsive reaction can only be vertical, and hence, *there can be no change of horizontal momentum*, because there is no external horizontal force. A smooth surface exerts a reaction perpendicular to the surface only; there is no friction component.

The next point to realise is, that the shell fight will be at a steeper angle than the barrel elevation angle of 40°. Because the gun is recoiling backwards, the shell velocity relative to earth will be the sum of the muzzle velocity of 640 m s^{-1} and the gun recoil velocity. This should recall the work of Programme 2. Denoting gun, shell and earth by the letters g, s and e, sketch the velocity diagram relating the three velocities.

41

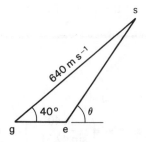

gs is the shell velocity relative to the gun, and therefore will have the value 640 m s^{-1} and will be at an elevation of 40°. The vector eg shows the gun to be recoiling backwards, as, of course, it must do.

One length of side and one angle only is not sufficient to solve a triangle. We must find another relationship. We can obtain this from an equation of linear momentum. Recalling the remark in the previous frame that there is no change of horizontal momentum, write this equation.

42

> Horizontal momentum before firing $= 0$. After firing:
>
> horizontal momentum of gun (to left) = horizontal momentum of shell (to right)
>
> $\therefore$ eg $\times$ 2650 = (es $\times$ 225) cos θ

This gives: eg/es $= 0.0849$ cos θ

Recalling that the external angle of a triangle is the sum of the two opposite angles:

$$\text{angle at s} = (\theta - 40°)$$

Using the Sine formula:

$$\text{eg/es} = \sin(\theta - 40°)/\sin 40° = 0.0849 \cos \theta$$

Expanding and re-arranging:

$$\frac{\sin \theta \cos 40° - \cos \theta \sin 40°}{\cos \theta \sin 40°} = 0.0849$$

$$\therefore \quad \frac{\tan \theta}{\tan 40°} - 1 = 0.0849$$

$$\therefore \quad \theta = \tan^{-1}(1.0849 \tan 40°) = \mathbf{42.31°}$$

Now we have all the angles, the Sine formula enables you to show that the required velocity of the shell, es, is **611.1 m s^{-1}**, but the working follows in Frame 43. Although it is not asked for, also calculate the value of the recoil velocity, eg.

43

$$\frac{640}{\sin(180° - \theta)} = \frac{\text{es}}{\sin 40°}$$

$$\therefore \quad \text{es} = 640\left(\frac{\sin 40°}{\sin 42.31°}\right) = \mathbf{611.1 \ m \ s^{-1}}$$

$$\frac{640}{\sin 42.31°} = \frac{\text{eg}}{\sin 2.31°}$$

$$\therefore \quad \text{eg} = 640\left(\frac{\sin 2.31°}{\sin 42.31°}\right) = \mathbf{38.32 \ m \ s^{-1}}$$

For additional practice in this type of problem, you will find another example in Frame 55 at the end of the programme.

44

The methods used so far in this programme are inadequate to deal with the problem of an impulsive blow on a body which does not rotate about a clearly-defined centre. Suppose, for example, that a wheel rolls along a horizontal surface, and then strikes a step, which gives an impulsive blow to the wheel. We need to expand our understanding of angular momentum in order to deal with this situation.

The diagram following represents a body having a mass centre at G, and rotating about a centre O with angular velocity ω.

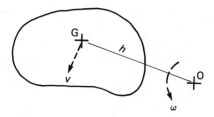

Angular momentum, H, is given by:

$$H = I_0 \omega$$

where suffix $_0$ denotes the moment of inertia of the body with respect to an axis through O. The Parallel Axis theorem gives us:

$$I_0 + I_G + mh^2$$

where h is the perpendicular distance from G to O.

$$\therefore \quad H = I_G \omega + mh^2 \omega$$

The linear velocity v of the mass centre G is given by:

$$v = \omega h$$

Substituting for (ωh) in the expression for H then gives:

$$H = I_G \omega + mvh$$

and the second term is seen to be the product of linear momentum and perpendicular distance h. The term is therefore appropriately called **moment of momentum**. In fact, moment of momentum is an alternative name for angular momentum. But this idea of multiplying linear momentum by a moment arm enables us to deal with the kind of situation mentioned at the beginning of this frame.

45

Let us look at the problem of a cylinder, rolling along a level surface, and then striking a step. The diagrams show (a) the wheel immediately before striking, and (b) immediately after.

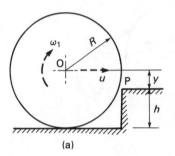

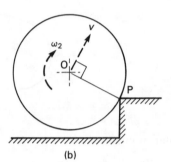

(a)   (b)

The collision of the cylinder with the step causes an impulsive blow on the cylinder, causing a change of momentum. Recalling that:

$$\text{impulsive moment} = \text{change of angular momentum}$$

then, if we consider the total moment with respect to the contact-point, then there will be no change, because *the impulse will have no moment about its own point of contact*.

In (a), before contact, the linear velocity u of the mass centre will be horizontal, as shown. After striking, the cylinder will roll about the step corner, and the velocity v must therefore be perpendicular to the radius to the corner. We must assume that the cylinder does not rebound or slip.

So we require an equation of conservation of moment of momentum with respect to the point P. Both before and after striking, the total moment of momentum will be the sum of the angular momentum due to turning of the cylinder, and the moment about P of the linear momentum of translation. Have a shot at writing this equation. Moment of momentum is, as we would expect, a vector, and thus, direction is important, but in this example, all components of the moment of momentum are positive.

Refer to diagram (a), Frame 45. The moment of linear momentum mu about the point P is $mu \times y = mu(R - h)$. In (b), the moment of linear momentum is mvR, since the velocity of the cylinder centre must be at right-angles to the radius OP. The resulting angular momentum equation is thus:

$$I\omega_1 + mu(R - h) = I\omega_2 + mvR$$

The two linear and angular velocities can be kinematically related:

$$u = \omega_1 R; \qquad v = \omega_2 R$$

Example. A uniform solid cylinder of mass 5 kg and radius 40 mm rolls along a horizontal plane without slip at 2 m s^{-1}. It strikes a step of height 10 mm without slip or rebound. Calculate (a) the linear velocity of the cylinder centre immediately after striking the step; (b) its velocity after mounting the step.

You need first to recall that the moment of inertia of a uniform solid cylinder about its axis of rotation is ... ?

Moment of inertia of uniform solid cylinder $= \frac{1}{2}mR^2$

Substituting this, and substituting for u and v in the moment of momentum equation gives an opportunity for cancelling m and R:

$$(\tfrac{1}{2}mR^2)\omega_1 + m\omega_1 R(R - h) = (\tfrac{1}{2}mR^2)\omega_2 + m\omega_2 R^2$$

$$\therefore \quad \omega_1(\tfrac{1}{2}R + R - h) = \omega_2(\tfrac{1}{2}R + R)$$

$$\therefore \quad \omega_1(1\tfrac{1}{2}R - h) = \omega_2 \times 1\tfrac{1}{2}R$$

$$\omega_1 = u/R = 2/0.04 = 50 \text{ rad s}^{-1}$$

$$\therefore \quad \omega_2 = 50\left(\frac{(1\tfrac{1}{2} \times 40 - 10)(10^{-3})}{1\tfrac{1}{2} \times 40 \times 10^{-3}}\right) = 41.67 \text{ rad s}^{-1}$$

$$\therefore \quad v = \omega_2 R = 41.67 \times 0.04 = \mathbf{1.667 \text{ m s}^{-1}}$$

The remainder of the solution requires an energy equation. See if you can arrive at the final answer yourself before reading on. This answer is 1.627 m s^{-1}.

48

Before climbing step, total $E_{kin} = \frac{1}{2}I\omega_2^2 + \frac{1}{2}mv^2$

$$\frac{1}{2}I\omega_2^2 = \frac{1}{2}(\frac{1}{2}mR^2)\omega_2^2 = \frac{1}{4} \times 5(0.04)^2(41.67)^2 = \quad 3.473 \text{ J}$$

$$\frac{1}{2}mv^2 = \frac{1}{2} \times 5(1.667)^2 = \quad 6.944 \text{ J}$$

$$\therefore \quad E_{kin}\text{ (total)} = 10.417 \text{ J}$$

$$E_{pot} = mgh = 5g \times 0.01 = \quad 0.491 \text{ J}$$

$$\therefore \quad \text{final } E_{kin} = 10.417 - 0.491 = \quad 9.926 \text{ J}$$

Calling velocities at top of step ω_3 and w:

$$\frac{1}{2}I\omega_3^2 + \frac{1}{2}mw^2 = 9.926$$

$$\omega_3 = w/R = w/0.04 = 25w$$

$$\therefore \quad \frac{1}{2}(\frac{1}{2} \times 5(0.04)^2)(25w)^2 + \frac{1}{2} \times 5w^2 = 9.926$$

$$\therefore \quad w^2(1.25 + 2.5) = 9.926$$

$$\therefore \quad w^2 = 2.647$$

$$\therefore \quad w = \textbf{1.627 m s}^{-1}$$

Now, using the same principle as in Frame 46, try this next example yourself. It isn't difficult.

Example. A uniform solid cylinder rolling with angular velocity ω along a plane surface strikes a vertical rigid wall. Show that the impulsive blow causes the cylinder to begin to roll up the wall with initial angular velocity $\frac{1}{3}\omega$. Assume no rebound or slip on collision.

Here is the diagram to help you. The impact point is P; the two figures show the cylinder, (a) immediately before impact, and (b) immediately after.

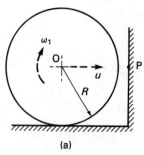

(a)

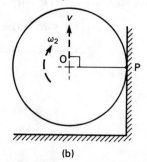

(b)

Remember: the principle to observe is, that the total moment of momentum with respect to the point of impact must be unchanged by impact, because the moment of the impact force about this point must be zero.

Moment of momentum equation with respect to P:

$$I\omega_1 + mu \times 0 = I\omega_2 + mv \times R$$

Compatibility: for no slip:

$$u = \omega_1 R; \qquad v = \omega_2 R$$

Substituting for v, and also $I = \frac{1}{2}mR^2$:

$$(\tfrac{1}{2}mR^2)\omega_1 = (\tfrac{1}{2}mR^2)\omega_2 + mR(\omega_2 R)$$

$$\therefore \quad \omega_1(\tfrac{1}{2}mR^2) = \omega_2(\tfrac{1}{2}mR^2 + mR^2)$$

$$\therefore \quad \boldsymbol{\omega_1 = 3\omega_2}$$

Now try this next one. The method is the same, and the diagram should help you.

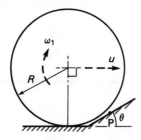 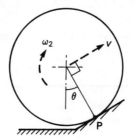

Example. A uniform solid cylinder rolling without slip along a horizontal plane with angular speed ω_1 suddenly contacts a plane inclined at angle θ as shown. Calculate the angular speed ω_2 immediately after impact. Hence determine the value of θ which would bring the cylinder immediately to rest.

Taking moment of momentum about contact-point P:

$$I\omega_1 + mu(R\cos\theta) = I\omega_2 + mvR$$

Substituting $u = \omega_1 R$, $v = \omega_2 R$, $I = \frac{1}{2}mR^2$:

$$\tfrac{1}{2}mR^2(\omega_1) + mR\cos\theta(\omega_1 R) = \tfrac{1}{2}mR^2(\omega_2) + mR(\omega_2 R)$$

$$\therefore \quad \omega_1(\tfrac{1}{2} + \cos\theta) = \omega_2(\tfrac{1}{2} + 1)$$

$$\therefore \quad \boldsymbol{\omega_2 = \omega(\tfrac{1}{3} + \tfrac{2}{3}\cos\theta)}$$

For $\omega_2 = 0$: $\qquad\qquad \theta = \cos^{-1}(-\tfrac{1}{2}) = \boldsymbol{120°}$

51

PROBLEMS

1. A solid uniform cylinder of radius 50 mm and mass 26 kg rolls along a flat surface at constant speed u when it strikes a step of height 25 mm. There is no slip or rebound at the impact.
   (a) Calculate the linear speed of the cylinder after it has mounted the step if $u = 1.2$ m s^{-1}.
   (b) Show that if $u = 0.858$ m s^{-1}, the cylinder will just come to rest at the top of the step.
   [*Ans. 0.559 m s^{-1}.*]
   Hint: solution will be exactly as in Frames 46 and 47.

2. A thin ring of outer radius 25 mm and negligible thickness rolls down a slope of 30° on to a horizontal surface. At the instant of touching the surface, the ring has a linear velocity of 2.4 m s^{-1}. Determine its linear velocity as it rolls along the horizontal surface. Assume no slip or bouncing as it changes direction. [*Ans. 2.239 m s^{-1}.*]
   Hints: analysis similar to that in Frame 50; prove that $v = \frac{1}{2}u(1 + \cos 30°)$. $I = mR^2$.

52

We can use the same method of approach for other bodies which strike fixed points.

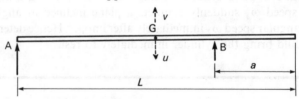

Example. A uniform rod of mass m and length L rests horizontally on two supports, one at the left-hand end A, and the other at B, distant a from the right-hand end. The right-hand end is raised a short distance and allowed to fall back on to the support. If, at the instant of striking, the angular velocity of the rod is ω_1, derive an expression for ω_2, the angular velocity immediately after striking.

The diagram shows u and v, the linear velocity of the rod centre G, before, and after striking the support at B. All that is required is a simple equation of conservation of moment of momentum with respect to the impact-point, which of course is B. The solution follows, but try and derive the equation yourself.

The situation, both before, and after the rod strikes the right-hand support, is represented by the diagrams below.

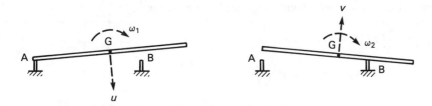

Just before the rod strikes the support at B, it has an angular velocity ω_1, and because it is turning about point A, the linear velocity u of the mass centre G is given by the compatibility equation:

$$u = \omega_1 \times \tfrac{1}{2}L \qquad (1)$$

Immediately after hitting the support at B, the rod lifts off the support at A; it is then turning about B as a pivot. The angular velocity is then ω_2. The linear velocity of the mass centre G is v. Because the rod is pivoting about B, the compatibility equation will now be:

$$v = \omega_2 \times (\tfrac{1}{2}L - a) \qquad (2)$$

As with the previous three examples, since the support at B exerts an impulsive blow on the rod, then the moment of momentum with respect to B must be unchanged by the blow, because the impulse has no moment about its point of impact. So we equate the total angular momentum both before and after the impact, taking B as the point for the moment of linear momentum. But notice in this example that before impact, whereas the angular momentum of the rod is clockwise, the moment of the linear momentum about B is anti-clockwise. After impact, angular momentum and moment of linear momentum are both clockwise.

So the required equation of moment of momentum with respect to B is:

$$I_G\omega_1 - mu(\tfrac{1}{2}L - a) = I_G\omega_2 + mv(\tfrac{1}{2}L - a)$$

Notice the negative sign for the moment of linear momentum before impact.

The rest of the problem consists of substituting for I_G and algebraic manipulation, to derive ω_2 in terms of ω_1. You should be able to complete this yourself, but the complete working is set out in the following frame.

54

Substituting for u and v from the compatibility equations, equations (1) and (2) from Frame 53, gives:

$$I_G\omega_1 - m(\omega_1 \times \tfrac{1}{2}L)(\tfrac{1}{2}L - a) = I_G\omega_2 + m(\omega_2(\tfrac{1}{2}L - a)(\tfrac{1}{2}L - a))$$

Substituting $I_G = \tfrac{1}{12}mL^2$, factorising, and cancelling m:

$$\omega_1(\tfrac{1}{12}L^2 - \tfrac{1}{2}L(\tfrac{1}{2}L - a)) = \omega_2(\tfrac{1}{12}L^2 + (\tfrac{1}{2}L - a)^2)$$

$$\therefore \qquad \omega_2 = \omega_1\left(\frac{\tfrac{1}{12}L^2 - \tfrac{1}{4}L^2 + \tfrac{1}{2}La}{\tfrac{1}{12}L^2 + (\tfrac{1}{2}L - a)^2}\right)$$

$$= \omega_1\left(\frac{\tfrac{1}{2}La - \tfrac{1}{6}L^2}{\tfrac{1}{12}L^2 + (\tfrac{1}{2}L - a)^2}\right) = \omega_1\left(\frac{6La - 2L^2}{L^2 + 12(\tfrac{1}{2}L - a)^2}\right)$$

and this expression could be used to determine the angular velocity for any given values of L and a.

Use this result to find the value of ω_2 for values of a of (a) $\tfrac{1}{2}L$; (b) $\tfrac{1}{3}L$.

55

(a) $a = \tfrac{1}{2}L$:

$$\omega_2 = \omega_1\left(\frac{6L(\tfrac{1}{2}L) - 2L^2}{L^2 + 12(\tfrac{1}{2}L - \tfrac{1}{2}L)^2}\right) = \omega_1\left(\frac{3 - 2}{1 + 0}\right) = \omega_1$$

(b) $a = \tfrac{1}{3}L$:

$$\omega_2 = \omega_1\left(\frac{6L(\tfrac{1}{3}L) - 2L^2}{L^2 + 12(\tfrac{1}{2}L - \tfrac{1}{3}L)^2}\right) = \omega_1\left(\frac{2 - 2}{1 + 12(\tfrac{1}{6})^2}\right) = 0$$

Notice that in determining the changes of velocities in such examples, we never take into account the constant forces acting, and this may cause you some anxiety, after the emphasis on the necessity of drawing free-body diagrams and writing equations of motion, in other programmes. But when dealing with impulsive forces, they are almost always of extremely short duration, and to simplify analysis, we assume in such cases that the changes of velocity occur instantaneously. The motions of bodies before impact, and after impact, are of course determined by the ordinary applications of Newton's Laws.

To complete this programme, Frame 56 consists of a couple of problems of this type, followed in Frame 57 by some problems covering the work of the whole programme.

PROBLEMS

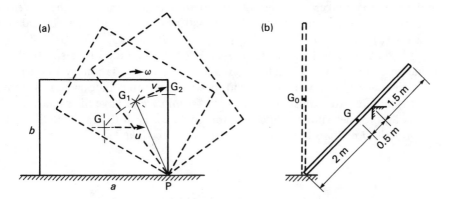

1. A uniform rectangular block of dimensions $a = 2$ m and $b = 1\frac{1}{2}$ m having a mass of 240 kg slides horizontally along a smooth floor at a speed of 4 m s^{-1} when the corner P strikes a fixed stop, causing the block to rotate about the corner, as shown in diagram (a) above. Calculate the angular velocity of this rotation, and the corresponding loss of kinetic energy due to the impact. Find at what speed the block would be required to slide in order that it should turn round through 90° after striking the block. The moment of inertia of such a block about a transverse axis through G is $\frac{1}{12} m(a^2 + b^2)$. [*Ans. 1.44 rad s^{-1}; 1401.6 J. 6.028 m s^{-1}.*]
   Hints: after collision, linear velocity of G will be perpendicular to line GP, and $v = \omega \times GP$. For last part, gain of $E_{pot} = $ loss of E_{kin}; G is raised by $(GP - \frac{1}{2}b)$ as shown dotted.

2. A ladder of length 4 m, standing vertically, falls from rest until it has turned through 45° when it strikes a fixed projection at a point $1\frac{1}{2}$ m from the upper end, as shown in diagram (b) above. Assuming there is no slip or rebound when it strikes, determine the maximum height to which the centre will rise after the collision. Assume the ladder to be a uniform thin bar. [*Ans. 0.0386 m.*]
   Hints: treat similarly to the example in Frame 52; use an energy equation to determine angular velocity before impact. Moment of linear momentum before impact is negative. Calculate loss of E_{kin}, and thus height to which centre G will be raised.

57

FURTHER PROBLEMS

1. Two steel balls, A and B, hang vertically from light strings 0.8 m long, so that they just touch. A has a mass of 1 kg and B a mass of $1\frac{1}{2}$ kg. A is pulled to one side until the string makes an angle of 60° to the vertical and it is then released. Determine the maximum angles the two strings make with the vertical after collision, (a) if $e = 1$; (b) if $e = 0.9$. [*Ans. (a) 11.48°, 47.15°. (b) 8.03°, 44.66°.*]

2. Three bodies, A, B and C, having masses of 2 kg, 4 kg and 3 kg respectively are in line on a smooth horizontal track. B and C are initially stationary and A moves to the right at 8 m s^{-1} and collides with B, which in turn collides with C. C moves to the right after this collision at 5 m s^{-1}. Assuming e to have the same value for both collisions, determine e, and also the final speeds of the three bodies. [*Ans. $e = 0.811$. A: 1.661 m s^{-1} to left; B: 1.080 m s^{-1} to right.*]

3.

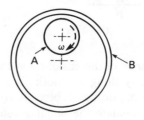

A wheel A of moment of inertia 2.4 kg m^2 and radius 0.08 m is brought into contact with the inner rim of a second wheel B of moment of inertia 11.5 kg m^2 and inner rim radius 0.23 m, as shown. Wheel B turns about a fixed axis, not shown. The initial speed of A is 45 rev/min clockwise. Calculate the final speeds of both wheels after all slip has ceased, if the initial speed of B is (a) zero; (b) 12 rev/min anti-clockwise. Calculate the energy loss in both cases. [*Ans. (a) 28.47 and 9.91 rev/min; 9.79 J. (b) 15.83 and 5.50 rev/min; 30.52 J.*]
Hint: refer to Frame 35, but note that impulse-moments will be of *opposite* signs, and final compatible speeds will be *same* sign.

4. A gun of mass 820 kg standing on smooth level ground fires a shell of mass 18 kg with a muzzle velocity of 900 m s^{-1}. If the shell is required to strike a stationary target which is at an elevation of 35° to the gun, calculate the required elevation of the gun barrel. Determine also the true velocity of the shell relative to earth. [*Ans. 34.42°; 886.9 m s^{-1}.*]
Hint: see Frame 40.

5.

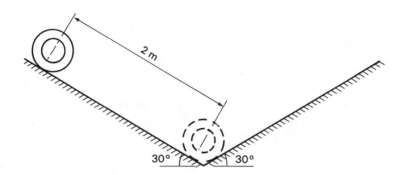

A cylinder has an outer radius of 25 mm and a radius of gyration of 20 mm. It is placed to roll down a plane inclined at 30°, up a similar plane, and back again. If it starts from rest 2 m above the lowest point, calculate how far it will climb up the same plane on return. [*Ans. 0.4669 m.*]

Hints: see Frame 49 *et seq.* Show that the approach velocity ω_1 and the retiring velocity ω_2 are related by $\omega_2 = \omega_1(k^2 + R^2 \cos 60°)/(k^2 + R^2)$. Thus calculate the velocity reduction factor, which operates twice. Energy reduction proportional to the square of the velocity ratio.

6.

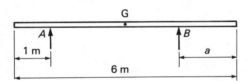

A uniform thin beam is 6 m long and has a mass of 400 kg. It rests horizontally on two supports, A, 1 m from the left-hand end, and B, distant *a* from the right-hand end, as shown. The right-hand end of the beam is raised a vertical height of 0.1 m and then released, the beam being allowed to drop back on to the support. It may be assumed that the beam does not bounce on the support at B.

(a) If *a* is 2 m, calculate the maximum amount that the left-hand end of the beam will be raised.

(b) Determine what value of *a* would be required in order that the beam would not lift off the support at A when dropped on to the support at B.

[*Ans. (a) 5.71 mm. (b) $1\frac{1}{2}$ m.*]

Hints: use the energy equation to calculate ω_1; G will be raised two-fifths of 0.1 m ($\omega_1 = 0.3348$ rad s^{-1}). Use the second energy equation after dropping to find height G is raised; left-hand end will be raised four times this amount.

Programme 9

COUPLED AND GEARED
SYSTEMS

1

The work in this programme is a follow-on from that of Programme 1 on Kinetics. Here, you will learn how to solve problems of kinetics when there is more than one body involved, particularly when the different bodies, or 'elements' have different accelerations. We looked at several problems in Programme 1 with two elements connected, but in each case, it was quite clear that all the elements had the same acceleration, as they were directly connected by a single string.

To begin with, remember that Newton's Second Law of Motion can be written very concisely in the form of two Equations of Motion, one for cases of linear acceleration, and the other for cases of angular acceleration. Write these equations down, together with the units in which each term must be stated.

2

Linear motion: $\Sigma(F) = ma$; Angular motion: $\Sigma(M) = I\alpha$

F (force)	expressed in **newtons** (N)
m (mass)	expressed in **kilograms** (kg)
a (linear acceleration)	expressed in **metres per second per second** (m s^{-2})
M (moment, or torque)	expressed in **newton metres** (N m)
I (moment of inertia)	expressed in **kilogram metres squared** (kg m^2)
α (angular acceleration)	expressed in **radians per second per second** (rad s^{-2})

Now, by way of revision of work that you should know by now, solve this simple example.

Example. Weights of mass 4 kg and 3 kg are connected by a light inextensible string which passes over a frictionless light pulley, so that the weights hang vertically. Determine the accelerations of the masses when they are released from rest.

Remember the technique: draw free-body diagrams for each body, showing all forces, and also acceleration. Don't forget also that the acceleration must have the same value for each mass, and that it must be upwards for one and downwards for the other. Write the equations for each mass, remembering always to take the direction of acceleration as positive. Eliminate *T*, the string tension, from the two equations.

3

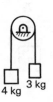
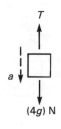

4 kg   3 kg

$(4g)$ N

$(3g)$ N

The equations of motion are:

$$4g - T = 4a$$
$$T - 3g = 3a$$

Adding:

$$g = 7a$$
$$\therefore \quad a = \textbf{1.401 m s}^{-2}$$

There is a short cut to such a simple problem as this, which you may know already. The total mass is $(4 + 3) = 7$ kg, and the nett force acting on the combined masses is the unbalance of weight which is the weight of 1 kg, i.e. 9.81 N. So we can write a single equation for the system:

$$9.81 = 7a$$

giving the same result. Much of the work of this programme will be concerned with writing a single equation for a system involving more than one body.

4

We shall take the previous example, with an added complication—the same two weights, but this time, connected to a compound pulley.

Example. Determine the accelerations of the two weights hanging from the compound pulley; m_1 is 4 kg, m_2 is 3 kg, R_1 is 40 mm, R_2 is 50 mm. The inertia of the pulley is negligible.

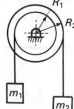

R_1

R_2

m_1

m_2

We now have two strings with different tensions, and two masses with different accelerations. To obtain sufficient equations, we must draw a free-body diagram of the pulley. See Frame 5.

5

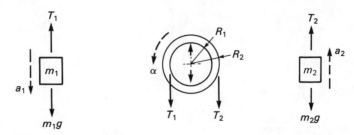

Here are the three free-body diagrams. Note the following points before we write the equations. First: although the three accelerations, a_1, a_2 and α are all different, they must be **compatible**. By this, we mean that if a_1 is downwards, as shown, then the angular acceleration of the pulley *must* be anti-clockwise. And this in turn means that the acceleration a_2 *must* be upwards. It does not matter if the direction a_1 is wrong; this would simply mean that we obtain a negative value in the calculation. The next point is, that they must also be compatible quantitatively, that is, we must write kinematic equations relating the accelerations. These equations are called **compatibility equations**. And finally, although the pulley has negligible inertia, we still have to write an equation of motion for it, in order to relate T_1 and T_2. In later examples, the inertia will not be negligible.

So begin by writing the equations of motion for m_1 and m_2. At this stage, work algebraically; leave the numbers out for the present.

6

$$\boxed{\begin{aligned} m_1 g - T_1 &= m_1 a_1 \qquad (1) \\ T_2 - m_2 g &= m_2 a_2 \qquad (2) \end{aligned}}$$

Now we write the equation of motion for the pulley. The general form of the equation is $\Sigma(M) = I\alpha$ because it is a rotating body. But because the inertia is negligible, $I = 0$, and the equation reduces to $\Sigma(M) = 0$, which is an equation of static equilibrium. So the required equation will be ... ?

7

$$T_1 R_1 - T_2 R_2 = 0 \qquad (3)$$

You should be able to write the kinematic equation of compatibility relating the three accelerations. You may need to look back at Programme 1, Frame 63 to refresh your memory.

8

$$a_1 = \alpha R_1 \qquad (4)$$
$$a_2 = \alpha R_2 \qquad (5)$$

Careless manipulation of five equations can land you in trouble. We reduce the last two to a single equation by eliminating α and substitute numbers:

$$\alpha = a_1/R_1 = a_2/R_2$$
$$\therefore \qquad a_2 = a_1(R_2/R_1) = a_1(50/40) = 1.25a_1$$

Now use the first two equations to substitute for T_1 and T_2 in equation (3):

$$R_1(m_1g - m_1a_1) - R_2(m_2a_2 + m_2g) = 0$$

We substitute numbers, expand and substitute for a_2.

$$40 \times 10^{-3}(4g - 4a_1) - 50 \times 10^{-3}(3 \times 1.25a_1 + 3g) = 0$$

Cancel 10^{-3} and collect the a_1 terms on the right-hand side:

$$160g - 150g = a_1(160 + 187.5)$$

$$\therefore \qquad a_1 = \frac{10 \times 9.81}{347.5} = \textbf{0.2823 m s}^{-2}; \qquad a_2 = 1.25a_1 = \textbf{0.3529 m s}^{-2}$$

9

PROBLEM

1.

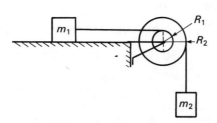

A block of mass $m_1 = 400$ kg rests on a horizontal surface. A cord attaches it to the smaller pulley of a compound pulley. A weight, m_2, of mass 90 kg hangs from the larger pulley. The pulley radii are, $R_1 = 0.2$ m, $R_2 = 1.0$ m. Calculate the accelerations of the two bodies (a) if the surface is smooth; (b) if the friction coefficient between block and surface is 0.1. Neglect the inertia of the pulley. [*Ans.* (*a*) 1.666 m s^{-2}, 8.329 m s^{-2}. (*b*) 1.518 m s^{-2}, 7.59 m s^{-2}.]

10

Now we shall introduce a further complication by assuming that the moment of inertia of the rotating element is not negligible. We shall assume the same data as the example of Frame 4 except that the pulley now has a moment of inertia of 0.02 kg m².

The free-body diagrams in Frame 5 will be the same, except that the pulley should be marked I. The equations will also be the same except for no. 3 in Frame 7. This will now read:

$$T_1 R_1 - T_2 R_2 = I\alpha \tag{3}$$

noting the importance of treating an anti-clockwise moment as positive, because that is the direction of the assumed acceleration. Substituting for T_1 and T_2 in equation (3) as we did before now gives:

$$R_1(m_1 g - m_1 a_1) - R_2(m_2 a_2 + m_2 g) = I\alpha$$

In this case, it is probably easier to use the compatibility equations to substitute for a_1 and a_2 in terms of α. It will also be instructive this time to retain algebraic symbols. So, expanding the equation, and substituting:

$$m_1 g R_1 - m_1 R_1(\alpha R_1) - m_2 R_2(\alpha R_2) - m_2 g R_2 = I\alpha$$

Collecting all terms with α on the right-hand side gives:

$$m_1 g R_1 - m_2 g R_2 = \alpha(I + m_1 R_1^2 + m_2 R_2^2)$$

and if this last equation is examined, it is seen to be a single equation, of the general form $\Sigma(M) = I\alpha$, the left-hand side being the nett or resultant moment on the pulley, and the bracketed terms on the right-hand side being the combined inertial effect of all three elements. We may indeed think of $m_1 R_1^2$ and $m_2 R_2^2$ as the effective or equivalent inertias of the masses m_1 and m_2. We shall meet this term 'equivalent inertia' again later.

Now substitute the given values.

$$9.81(10^{-3})(4 \times 40 - 3 \times 50) = \alpha(0.02 + 4(40 \times 10^{-3})^2 + 3(50 \times 10^{-3})^2)$$

$$\therefore \quad 0.0981 = \alpha(0.02 + 0.0064 + 0.0075)$$

$$\therefore \quad \alpha = \frac{0.0981}{0.0339} = \textbf{2.894 rad s}^{-2}$$

$$\therefore \quad a_1 = \alpha R_1 = 2.894 \times 40 \times 10^{-3} = \textbf{0.1158 m s}^{-2}$$

$$\text{and} \quad a_2 = \alpha R_2 = 2.894 \times 50 \times 10^{-3} = \textbf{0.1447 m s}^{-2}$$

These values for acceleration are less than the answers calculated in Frame 8. This is to be expected, as the same resultant force acts on a system which now includes another inertial element. You can check that making I zero in the equation derived above will result in the same answers for a_1 and a_2 as before.

11

Here is a procedure for solving problems of this kind.

1. Examine the system, and identify all inertial elements, i.e. masses, rotors, pulleys.
2. Examine the kinematics of the system, and write equations of compatibility, relating all accelerations.
3. When the direction of acceleration is not known, assume it for one element, but *ensure that directions of all others are compatible.*
4. Draw free-body diagrams for all elements. Distinguish arrow for acceleration from arrows for forces.
5. Write equations of motion ($\Sigma(F) = ma$, $\Sigma(M) = I\alpha$) for all elements, taking the assumed direction of acceleration as positive in every case.
6. Where necessary, write equations of equilibrium for elements in direction perpendicular to that of acceleration.
7. Check that you have as many equations as unknown terms. Then manipulate algebraically to find the unknown terms.

We shall go through one further example, to illustrate this procedure.

Example. Details of a simple inclined hoist are shown.

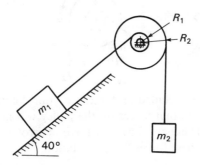

The load, m_1, 600 kg, is hauled up the inclined plane by means of a hanging weight of mass m_2, 140 kg, via a compound pulley which turns about a fixed axis, and has a moment of inertia of 95 kg m². The pulley radii are 0.45 m and 0.12 m. The coefficient of friction between load and plane is 0.15. How long will it take to haul the load up the plane a distance of 6 m starting from rest?

Check-point 1: we see there are three elements: load, weight and pulley.

Check-point 2: the kinematic equations are derived exactly as in the previous example. Write these down, and then check in the next frame before proceeding.

12

Calling the angular acceleration of the pulley α and the two linear accelerations a_1, a_2:

$$a_1 = \alpha R_1 = 0.12\alpha \tag{1}$$

$$a_2 = \alpha R_2 = 0.45\alpha \tag{2}$$

Check-point 3: the conditions of the example indicate that the acceleration of the load must be up the plane. So the angular acceleration of the pulley must be clockwise, and the acceleration of the hanging weight must be downwards.

Check-point 4: the three diagrams are drawn in Frame 13, but attempt them yourself first. There will be four forces acting on the load, there are also four forces acting on the pulley, but only two are relevant to the problem.

13

Here are the three diagrams.

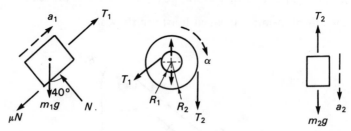

Check that you have included all forces on your diagrams; find where you were wrong, if you were. Note that forces on the pulley will include weight, and reaction at the pulley bearing. These are shown as a pair of arrows, but since the pulley rotates only, we do not need these forces for the solution.

Check-points 5 and 6: write the equations of motion, and also, the equation of equilibrium normal to the plane, for the load. Remember that the direction of acceleration is to be taken as positive.

14

Load:
$$T_1 - \mu N - m_1 g \sin 40° = m_1 a_1 \tag{3}$$

$$N = m_1 g \cos 40° \tag{4}$$

Pulley:
$$T_2 R_2 - T_1 R_1 = I\alpha \tag{5}$$

Weight:
$$m_2 g - T_2 = m_2 a_2 \tag{6}$$

15

Check-point 7: six equations. Unknown terms are: T_1, T_2, a_1, a_2, α, and N.

The algebraic manipulation follows the same form as in Frame 10: we may first use equations (3) and (6) to substitute for T_1 and T_2 in equation (5).

$$R_2(m_2g - m_2a_2) - R_1(m_1a_1 + m_1g\sin 40° + \mu N) = I\alpha$$

Now use equations (1) and (2) to express a_1 and a_2 in terms of α, and equation (4) to substitute for N, which reduces our six equations to one:

$$m_2gR_2 - m_2R_2(\alpha R_2) - m_1R_1(\alpha R_1) - m_1gR_1\sin 40° - \mu m_1gR_1\cos 40° = I\alpha$$

Transferring all terms in α to the right-hand side:

$$m_2gR_2 - m_1gR_1\sin 40° - \mu m_1gR_1\cos 40° = \alpha(I + m_1R_1^2 + m_2R_2^2)$$

Again, we have a single 'system' equation of motion, with the left-hand side constituting the resultant moment, and the right-hand side an effective, or 'equivalent' inertia of all three elements. There are checks to verify correct algebra, or to highlight mistakes. Firstly, a simple dimensional check. All terms on the left are seen to have dimensions of moment, i.e. force × distance, while all terms in the right-hand bracket are inertial terms (mass × length^2). Next, all inertial terms are positive; you cannot have negative mass or inertia. On the left-hand side, we have one positive and two negative terms. This agrees with the data provided: the weight of m_2 is the positive driving force, while the weight component of m_1, and the friction term, are both retarding effects.

Substituting values:

$$9.81(140 \times 0.45 - 600\sin 40° \times 0.12 - 0.15 \times 600\cos 40° \times 0.12)$$

$$= \alpha(95 + 600(0.12)^2 + 140(0.45)^2)$$

$$\therefore \quad 9.81(63 - 46.28 - 8.27) = \alpha(95 + 8.64 + 28.35)$$

$$\therefore \quad \alpha = \frac{9.81 \times 8.45}{131.99} = 0.628 \text{ rad s}^{-2}$$

From equation (1): $a_1 = 0.12 \times 0.628 = 0.0754 \text{ m s}^{-2}$

The solution is completed in the following frame, but you can complete it yourself first. A simple kinematic equation is all that is required. You can no doubt recall this, and substitute the values, but if you can't look up the four equations in Programme 1, Frame 48. You now have acceleration, distance (6 m) and initial velocity (zero—starts from rest) and you require time.

16

$$x = v_0 t + \tfrac{1}{2} at^2$$

$$\therefore \quad 6 = 0 + \tfrac{1}{2} \times 0.0754 t^2$$

$$\therefore \quad t = \sqrt{(12/0.0754)} = \mathbf{12.62 \ s}$$

A few problems follow.

17

PROBLEMS

1. A simple lift, or elevator, comprises a loaded cage of mass 750 kg, and a counter-weight of the same mass, connected by a cable which passes round a pulley of radius 1.1 m and moment of inertia 260 kg m^2. Cage and counter-weight hang freely. Calculate the torque required at the pulley axis to raise the cage with an upward acceleration of 0.5 m s^{-2}. Neglect friction forces. [*Ans. 943.2 N m.*]

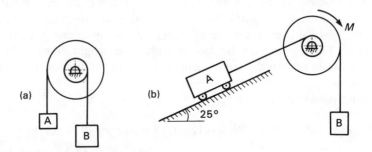

2. In diagram (a) above, bodies A and B, respectively 20 kg and 65 kg, hang from a compound pulley of moment of inertia $I = 2.6$ kg m^2 which turns about a fixed axis, the pulley radii being 0.082 m and 0.24 m. Calculate the accelerations of A and B. What clockwise torque M would be required about the pulley axis to raise A with an acceleration of 0.5 m s^{-2}? [*Ans. 0.298 m s^{-2}, 0.102 m s^{-2}. 3.528 N m.*]

3. In diagram (b) above, a load A of mass 1200 kg is hauled up a 25° slope by a torque M on a compound pulley of moment of inertia 240 kg m^2 and radii 0.25 m and 1.2 m. Neglecting friction forces, calculate the value of M to haul A 10 m from rest in 15 s if the hanging weight B has a mass of (a) zero; (b) 100 kg. [*Ans. (a) 1355.8 N m; (b) 229.8 N m.*]

18

A pulley system is a device consisting of ropes or cables, and wheels, so arranged that when a force or torque is applied at one point, motion is produced at another. An example is a pulley system used for raising or lowering loads, such as is found in almost every engineering workshop or building site, where the pulley system forms part of a crane. The functions of a pulley system are:

1. To 'magnify' force; that is, by means of applying a relatively small force to a pulley system, to produce a much greater force.
2. To change the direction of a force.

The second of these is not of importance in this text. An example is the simple pulley system used by builders raising small loads such as buckets of sand to the top of a building. A wheel is fixed to the top of the building, and a rope tied to the bucket, the rope passing round the wheel. The advantages are, that the load can be raised by pulling downwards, instead of pulling upwards, and that the load can also be raised by someone at ground level. There is no 'mechanical advantage', that is, the operator has to apply a force equal to the weight of the load. We shall define 'mechanical advantage' shortly.

When pulley systems are used for the first function listed above, we use the following terms.

The force applied to the system is called the **Effort**.

The force to be overcome (e.g. the weight of a load to be lifted) is called the **Load**.

Clearly, the advantage of a pulley system used in this way is that the load is much greater than the effort. A mechanic can raise the very heavy engine from a car merely by pulling on a rope with a force much less than the weight of the engine. For this reason, the ratio of load to effort is called the **Mechanical Advantage**.

$$\text{Mechanical Advantage} = \frac{\text{Load}}{\text{Effort}}$$

Mechanical advantage in a pulley system is achieved simply by arranging that the effort moves very much further than the load. To raise the car engine of the above example a few centimetres, the mechanic may need to pull several metres of rope through the pulley. The ratio of the distance moved by the effort to the corresponding distance moved by the load is called the **Velocity Ratio**.

$$\text{Velocity ratio} = \frac{\text{distance moved by effort}}{\text{distance moved by load}}$$

19

We can apply the principle of energy to a pulley system. If we assume that the work put in during an operation is equal to the work done at the output, then, if we call the effort F, and the load W, we may write:

$$F \times \text{distance moved by effort} = W \times \text{distance moved by load}$$

$$\therefore \quad \frac{\text{distance moved by effort}}{\text{distance moved by load}} = \frac{W}{F}$$

But the ratio W/F has been defined in Frame 18 as Mechanical Advantage

$$\therefore \quad \text{velocity ratio} = \text{mechanical advantage}.$$

This is assuming that the work that goes in is the same as the work that comes out, i.e. no loss. You should know by now that this can never be achieved. Every device involves some loss due to friction. This cannot affect the velocity ratio. On a pulley with velocity ratio 6, moving the load 1 m will always require the effort to move 6 m (apart from such negligible effects as stretching of the ropes). The energy loss is manifested by having to apply an effort which is greater than one-sixth of the load. So the mechanical advantage will be less than 6. In real devices, the mechanical advantage is always less than the velocity ratio. The ratio of the two is called the **efficiency** of the device.

$$\text{efficiency}, \eta \text{ (Greek eta)} = \frac{\text{mechanical advantage}}{\text{velocity ratio}}$$

and clearly, the efficiency must always be less than 1, although it is frequently expressed as a percentage. An efficiency of 85% means that $\eta = 0.85$. Efficiency of a pulley system can vary considerably. The efficiency of the pulley system of an industrial crane might be as high as 0.85 or 0.9, but that of a pulley used by a mechanic to lift a car engine, where ropes are replaced by chains running over specially-designed wheels, could be 0.4 or less.

Pulley systems can sometimes be used with a velocity ratio of less than 1, with the result that the effort is greater than the load. This is done where a relatively small motion is desired to produce a relatively large one, and the load is very small. An example is the system used to draw curtains. Pulling the cord a certain distance causes the curtains to move twice or three times as far. All the examples in this programme will involve pulley systems with a velocity ratio greater than 1.

Pulley systems are used on cranes and hoists. The commonest form is the **multi-sheave block**, consisting of a pair of blocks, each with several pulley wheels, one block usually fixed, and the other attached to the load, a single rope being passed alternately from fixed to moving block. The figure below shows two examples, (a) and (b). The pulley wheels are all the same size and turn about the same axis but for clarity, to illustrate the rope run, they are shown separated and different sizes.

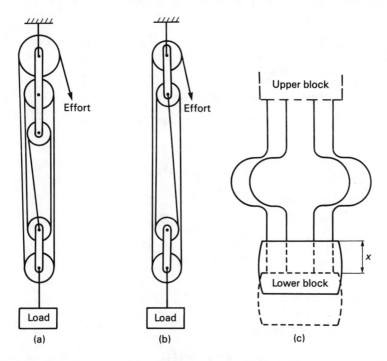

The determination of the velocity ratio of a pulley system can sometimes be a matter of some difficulty, but with the multi-sheave block, there is a very simple rule.

velocity ratio = number of ropes supporting the lower block

You can understand why this is so by imagining that, instead of pulling the effort-rope to raise the load a certain distance, you raise the load first, then haul in the 'slack' rope. This is shown at (c) above, for a system with four ropes supporting the hanging block. If you raise the load a height x, then each single rope attached to the lower block will have a bight of slack rope of length x. It is then clear that the total slack is the distance x multiplied by the number of supporting ropes.

State the velocity ratios of the two systems shown at (a) and (b) above.

21

> For (a): velocity ratio = 5
> For (b): velocity ratio = 4

It can be seen that the ratio of displacements of the input and output of a pulley system must be the same as the ratio of velocities (since the two motions occupy the same time); hence the name Velocity Ratio. The two accelerations also have the same ratio. This enables compatibility equations to be written for dynamic systems involving pulleys.

Example. A pulley system with a velocity ratio of 6 carries a load of 1200 kg. Calculate the effort required to raise the load 2 m from rest in 3 seconds with constant acceleration. Neglect any friction loss.

We calculate the required acceleration of the load.

$$x = v_0 t + \tfrac{1}{2}at^2$$
$$\therefore \quad 2 = 0 + \tfrac{1}{2}a(3)^2$$
$$\therefore \quad a = 0.4444 \text{ m s}^{-2}$$

Here is the free-body diagram of the load:

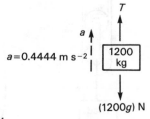

The equation of motion will be:

$$T - 1200g = 1200 \times 0.4444$$
$$\therefore \quad T = 1200(0.4444 + 9.81) = 12\,305 \text{ N}$$

and since there is no friction loss, we divide this by the velocity ratio for the required force.

$$\text{force required} = 12\,305/6 = \textbf{2051 N}$$

We shall add a complication.

Example. What mass must be applied to the effort-rope to raise the same load with the same acceleration?

The *force* required at the effort must be as before. So, draw a free-body diagram for the unknown mass *m*. Remember: the acceleration will be different.

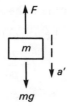

The equation of motion will be:

$$mg - F = ma'$$

$$a' = 0.4444 \times 6 \qquad \text{(see Frame 21)}$$

$$\therefore \quad m(9.81 - 0.4444 \times 6) = F = 2051 \text{ N}$$

$$\therefore \quad m = 2051/7.144 = \textbf{287.1 kg}$$

The same force applied at two different points in a pulley system will produce different accelerations, as the next example will show.

Example. A pulley system of velocity ratio 5 carries a mass of 100 kg on the load-rope and a mass of 20 kg on the effort-rope. Calculate the acceleration of the 20 kg mass if a force of 50 N is applied to it. Calculate the acceleration of the 100 kg mass if the same force is applied to it. Neglect any friction effects.

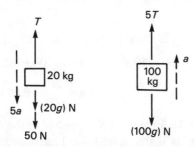

The two free-body diagrams are shown. We know that the accelerations will be in the ratio 5:1. And if the rope tension in the effort-rope is T, the tension in the load-rope must be $(5T)$. The diagrams are drawn accordingly. This enables us to write the two equations of motion:

effort: $$50 + 20g - T = 20(5a) \qquad (1)$$

load: $$5T - 100g = 100a \qquad (2)$$

Finish the problem by substituting for T in equation (2).

24

$$5(50 + 20g - 100a) - 100g = 100a$$

Expanding, and collecting a-terms on the right-hand side:

$$250 + 100g - 100g = a(100 + 500)$$

$$\therefore \quad a = \frac{250}{600} = 0.4167 \text{ m s}^{-2}$$

$$\therefore \quad \text{effort acceleration} = 5a = \mathbf{2.0833 \text{ m s}^{-2}}$$

The free-body diagrams for the second part will be:

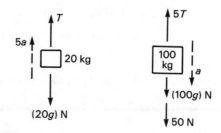

Write the two equations, and complete the solution yourself.

25

The equations: effort: $\qquad T = 20g = 20(5a)$ $\qquad\qquad$ (1)

$\qquad\qquad$ load: $\quad 50 + 100g - 5T = 100a$ $\qquad\qquad$ (2)

and substituting:

$$50 + 100g - 5(100a + 20g) = 100a$$

$$\therefore \quad 50 + 100g - 100g = a(100 + 500)$$

$$\therefore \quad a = \frac{50}{600} = \mathbf{0.0833 \text{ m s}^{-2}}$$

These answers show that if a force of 50 N is applied to the mass of 20 kg, the resulting acceleration is the same as if the same force had been applied to a total mass of 24 kg (you can check this yourself). But when the same force is applied to the 100 kg mass, the acceleration is the same as if the force had acted on a total mass of 600 kg. So we see that when the force is applied to the high-speed end of the system, the retarding effect of the larger mass is very much reduced. It acts like a mass of 4 kg. But when the force acts on the low-speed side, the retarding effect of the smaller mass is greatly increased. It behaves like a mass of 500 kg. The values of 4 kg and 500 kg are called the **equivalent masses** of the 20 kg and 100 kg masses respectively. The value of an equivalent mass is not constant, but as we shall see, depends on which part of the system one considers, i.e. at which part of the system the force is applied.

We shall use the terms 'equivalent inertia' and 'equivalent mass' later, when we look at the dynamics of gearboxes and wheeled vehicles.

Now look at this simple pulley system of velocity ratio 2.

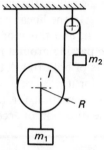

Suppose that now, we assume that the mass of the pulley-wheel supporting the load is not negligible, and that its moment of inertia is also not negligible. An example will illustrate this.

Example. In the diagram, the load m_1 has a mass of 68 kg, and the weight m_2 is 42 kg. The large moving pulley has a mass of 12 kg, a radius of 0.24 m and a moment of inertia of 0.85 kg m^2. Determine the acceleration of the load, neglecting friction and assuming no rope slip on the large pulley. The smaller fixed pulley-wheel has negligible inertia.

We begin, as always, by drawing the free-body diagrams.

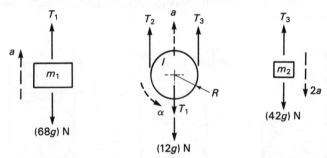

The diagrams for the two masses need little explanation. We know the system is a two-to-one pulley system, so that the acceleration of the 42 kg mass must be $(2a)$. This acceleration must be downwards because the weight is more than half the combined weight of load and pulley. Force T_1 is the tension in the rope connecting the load to the moving pulley.

Examining forces on the pulley, we have the weight and the downward tension force T_1. Forces T_2 and T_3 are the tension forces in the pulley-rope. In many earlier examples, when a rope or string passes round a pulley, the string force has been assumed to be constant throughout the length of the string. Why cannot we assume this to be so now?

27

> The pulley-rope tension cannot be constant because the pulley inertia is *not negligible* in this example.

Because the rope does not slip on the pulley, the pulley must turn, and with an angular acceleration which is compatible with the linear accelerations. Therefore, there must be a resultant moment acting on it, and this moment can be provided only by the difference of tensions in the rope passing around it.

Also, the pulley motion consists of both translation and rotation, so that we shall require two equations of motion for it.

So now, write four equations of motion for the three elements of the system. Remember, as always, to take the direction of acceleration as positive.

28

For load $(\Sigma(F) = ma)$:	$T_1 - 68g = 68a$	(1)
For weight $(\Sigma(F) = ma)$:	$42g - T_3 = 42(2a) = 84a$	(2)
For pulley $(\Sigma(F) = ma)$:	$T_2 + T_3 - T_1 - 12g = 12a$	(3)
For pulley $(\Sigma(M) = I\alpha)$:	$T_3 R - T_2 R = I\alpha = 0.85\alpha$	(4)

We see that we have five 'unknowns'—the three tension forces, a, and α. A further equation is needed. This is the kinematic equation of compatibility linking a and α. We can obtain this by first obtaining an equation of compatibility of displacement, knowing that the same equation will apply to velocity and acceleration (see Frame 21). Study these three diagrams.

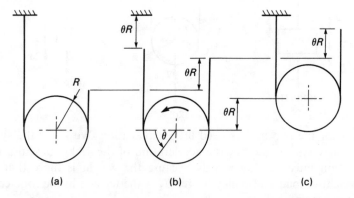

(a)   (b)   (c)

What actually happens is, that the right-hand rope is pulled up, resulting in the pulley being both raised and turned. If we take the motions separately, we can see what happens. Diagram (a) shows the pulley, radius R, with the upper end of the left-hand rope attached to the fixed point. Now imagine the pulley to be turned anti-clockwise an angle θ, but about a fixed centre. Diagram (b) shows what must happen.

If the rope does not slip on the pulley, then the upper left-hand end of the rope must be pulled down by the amount the rope is wound on to the pulley, which is θR. This is shown in diagram (b). To restore the rope-end to its fixed point, the pulley itself must be raised by this amount. Thus, for the pulley:

$$x = \theta R$$

and the equivalent equation of compatibility of acceleration is:

$$a = \alpha R$$

(The diagram incidentally makes it clear that the displacement of the right-hand end of the rope must be $2\theta R$, because the turning of the pulley at (b) raises the right-hand end by (θR), and raising the whole pulley as at (c) raises the end a further amount (θR). This confirms that the velocity ratio of the system is 2.)

So we have our fifth equation:

$$a = \alpha R = 0.24\alpha \tag{5}$$

We begin reducing our equations by substituting for α in equation (4). Re-writing this equation:

$$T_3 - T_2 = 0.85(a/R^2) = 0.85a/(0.24)^2 = 14.757a \tag{6}$$

Use equations (1) and (2) to substitute for T_1 and T_3 in equation (3):

$$T_2 + (42g - 84a) - (68a + 68g) - 12g = 12a$$

Simplifying this gives:

$$T_2 - 38g = 164a \tag{7}$$

Use equation (2) again to eliminate T_3 from equation (6):

$$(42g - 84a) - T_2 = 14.757a \tag{8}$$

Adding equations (7) and (8) eliminates T_2:

$$42g - 84a - T_2 + T_2 - 38g = 164a + 14.757a$$

$$\therefore \quad 4g = 262.757a$$

$$\therefore \quad a = \mathbf{0.1493 \ m \ s^{-2}}$$

This example shows that when bodies move and turn, the kinetic analysis can be quite complex. Sometimes, a simpler solution can be obtained by using an energy equation. An example is a vehicle with large wheels, when the inertial effect of the wheels themselves is not negligible. This will be examined in Frame 31. Some problems on pulleys follow.

PROBLEMS

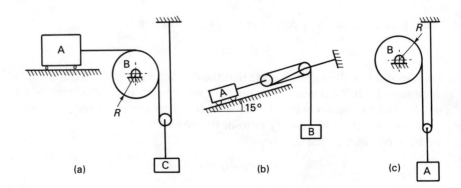

(a) (b) (c)

1. In diagram (a) above, the block A rests on a horizontal surface. A cord attached to it passes round pulley B of radius R, which turns about a fixed axis. The cord passes round a small pulley of negligible mass and inertia and is attached to a fixed point. A body C hangs from the small pulley. The mass of A is 60 kg, R is 0.3 m, the moment of inertia of B is 4.5 kg m^2. Calculate the mass of C so that A accelerates left to right across the surface at 1 m s^{-2}. Neglect friction. [*Ans. 23.63 kg.*]
   Hint: since acceleration of A is given, find all accelerations numerically. Then analyse A, B and C in turn, calculating intermediate forces as you go.
2. In diagram (b) above, load A is hauled up a slope of 15° by means of a pulley system of velocity ratio 8:1 by a weight B. The mass of A is 850 kg, and that of B, 30 kg. Calculate the upward acceleration of the load. Neglect friction throughout. [*Ans. 0.0708 m s^{-2}.*]
3. In diagram (c) above, the figure shows a simple form of fire-escape. Load A hangs from a pulley of negligible mass and inertia, and a rope round the pulley is fixed at one end and wound round a large wheel B of radius R and moment of inertia I. Given the load is 100 kg and is required to descend 8 m, calculate the required value for I if the load must not be travelling at more than 1 m s^{-1} when it reaches the lowest point, assuming it starts from rest. The radius R is 0.1 m. Neglect friction throughout. [*Ans. 38.99 kg m^2.*]
   Hint: use kinematic equation to calculate acceleration. For wheel, $\alpha = 2a/R$.

31

The kinetic analysis of a wheeled vehicle, taking into account the inertia of the wheels, is best accomplished by considering the energy of such a system. A truck of total mass m with a number of wheels, of total moment of inertia I, and rolling radius R, rolls along a surface. The kinetic energy will comprise energy of translation ($\frac{1}{2}mv^2$) and energy of rotation of the wheels ($\frac{1}{2}I\omega^2$). If the wheels roll without slip, the simple kinematic equation:

$$v = \omega R$$

may be written. Thus, the total energy of the system is given by:

$$E_{kin} = \tfrac{1}{2}mv^2 + \tfrac{1}{2}I\omega^2 = \tfrac{1}{2}mv^2 + \tfrac{1}{2}I(v/R)^2 = \tfrac{1}{2}v^2(m + I/R^2)$$

The bracketed term is seen to be the effective mass of the system, or the **equivalent mass**. By using this expression, in place of m, the actual mass of the truck, we allow for the inertia of the wheels. Remember that m, the truck mass, is the *total* mass of the truck, including the mass of the wheels themselves. This is because the wheels move translationally, in addition to turning.

If the wheels were of varying size and inertia, we would modify this expression:

$$\text{Equivalent mass} = m + \Sigma(I/R^2)$$

Here is an example to illustrate the use of the concept of equivalent mass.

Example. A wagon of total mass 1100 kg has four wheels, each of rolling radius 0.36 m, and moment of inertia 28 kg m^2. It stands on a slope of $7\frac{1}{2}°$. A force of 1450 N pulls it up the slope, starting from rest. How long will it take to move 6 m up the slope, and what will its speed be then? If the force is then removed, how long will it take to return to its starting-point? Neglect all friction forces.

Begin by calculating the equivalent mass of the wagon, using the formula above; this is straightforward. Then attempt to draw the free-body diagram. Be careful when evaluating the weight.

32

> Equivalent mass, $m_E = m + \Sigma(I/R^2) = 1100 + (4 \times 28)/(0.36)^2$
>
> $\therefore \qquad m_E = 1100 + 864.2$
>
> $\qquad\qquad = 1964.2$ kg

The free-body diagram is drawn in Frame 33.

33

Here is the free-body diagram.

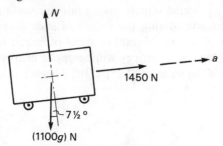

The weight of the wagon is $(1100g)$ N, not $(1964.2g)$ N. This is why you were told to be careful. The equivalent mass is an indication of the body's resistance to an accelerating force. But the weight is not affected by the inertia of the wheels.

Complete the first part of the problem. Write the equation of motion, calculate the acceleration, and use kinematic equations to determine the time and velocity after 6 m. The working is completed in the next frame; you should obtain an answer of 0.0211 m s^{-2} for the acceleration, a time of 23.85 seconds, and a final speed of 0.5032 m s^{-1}.

34

$$\Sigma(F) = ma: \qquad 1450 - 1100g \sin 7\tfrac{1}{2}° = 1964.2a$$

$$\therefore \qquad a = \frac{1450 - 1408.5}{1964.2} = \mathbf{0.0211 \ m \ s^{-2}}$$

$$x = v_0 t + \tfrac{1}{2}at^2$$

$$\therefore \qquad 6 = 0 + \tfrac{1}{2}(0.0211)t^2$$

$$\therefore \qquad t = \sqrt{(12/0.0211)} = \mathbf{23.85 \ s}$$

$$v^2 = v_0^2 + 2ac$$

$$= 0 + 2 \times 0.0211 \times 6$$

$$\therefore \qquad v = \mathbf{0.5032 \ m \ s^{-1}}$$

The upward force is now removed. We now have to calculate the new acceleration, which will, of course, be down the slope. The free-body diagram will be like the first one, except that the force of 1450 N is now removed. We need not re-draw the diagram for such a simple adjustment. Write the new equation of motion, and calculate the new acceleration, which you should find is 0.7171 m s^{-2}. Don't bother to calculate how far up the plane the wagon travels before coming to rest; this is not asked for. Use the appropriate kinematic equation (the one relating v_0, a, x and t), paying due regard to sign, and calling motion positive up the plane.

Your answer should be 4.8522 s. The solution is completed in Frame 35.

Completing the solution: the new equation of motion is:

$$1100g \sin 7\tfrac{1}{2}° = 1964.2a$$

$$\therefore \quad a = \frac{1408.5}{1964.2} = 0.7171 \text{ m s}^{-2} \text{ down plane}$$

Now taking direction up plane as positive:

$$x = -6 \text{ m}; \quad v_0 = +0.5032 \text{ m s}^{-1}; \quad a = -0.7171 \text{ m s}^{-2}; \quad t \text{ is required.}$$

Substituting in the kinematic equation $x = v_0 t + \tfrac{1}{2}at^2$:

$$-6 = 0.5032t + \tfrac{1}{2}(-0.7171)t^2$$

Carry all terms to left-hand side and divide throughout by coefficient of t^2:

$$t^2 - 1.4034t - 16.734 = 0$$

$$\therefore \quad t = \frac{1.4034 \pm \sqrt{\{(1.4034)^2 - 4(-16.734)\}}}{2}$$

$$= 0.7017 \pm \tfrac{1}{2}\sqrt{(1.9695 + 66.936)}$$

$$\therefore \quad t = \textbf{4.8522 s}$$

The alternative negative answer is not relevant to the question.

36

A single wheel can be treated in the same way.

Example

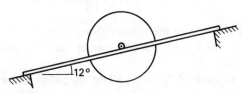

A small metal cylinder is mounted on a central spindle 4 mm diameter. The spindle rests horizontally, on a pair of rails inclined at 12° as shown. When released from rest it rolls down the rails a distance of 100 mm in 7 seconds. The mass of wheel and spindle is 0.3 kg. Neglecting any resistance to motion, and assuming the spindle rolls without slip and on the rails, calculate the moment of inertia of wheel and spindle.

First calculate the linear acceleration using a kinematic equation. You should get 0.00408 m s^{-2}. Check in the following frame.

$$x = v_0 t + \tfrac{1}{2} a t^2$$

$$\therefore \quad 0.1 = 0 + \tfrac{1}{2} a (7)^2$$

$$\therefore \quad a = 0.2/49 = 0.00408 \text{ m s}^{-2}$$

The free-body diagram is simple:

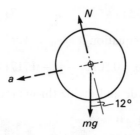

We write the equation, noting that because the body is rolling in addition to moving down the rails, we call the mass m_E, the equivalent mass, which will be greater than the true mass of 0.3 kg.

$$\Sigma(F) = ma: \quad mg \sin 12° = m_E a$$

$$\therefore \quad m_E = \frac{0.3g \sin 12°}{0.00408} = 149.97 \text{ kg}$$

Recall (Frame 31) that $m_E = m + \Sigma(I/R^2)$ where R is the rolling radius.
Substituting: $\qquad 149.97 = 0.3 + I/(2 \times 10^{-3})^2$

$$\therefore \quad I = 149.67 \times (0.002)^2 = \mathbf{0.0006 \text{ kg m}^2}$$

Looking at the substitution of the figures above, it is seen that the effective mass of the rolling wheel (149.67 kg) is so much greater than the actual mass of 0.3 kg that the latter is negligible.

In drawing the free-body diagram, a slight simplification was made. Just as, with a wheeled vehicle, we can dispense with drawing the free-body diagrams of the wheels themselves, so in this case, we do not need to draw the details of the forces acting on the spindle; the concept of equivalent mass allows us to simplify the analysis. The true kinetic analysis of a rolling wheel or disc is examined in Programme 6. For the present, it is enough to note that in order for the disc to roll, a friction force must exist between rail and spindle, and it is this force which has been excluded from the diagram.

Frame 38 comprises some more problems on the topic of rolling wheels.

38

PROBLEMS

1. A truck has a total mass of 1740 kg. It has six wheels; four are 0.8 m diameter, each 95 kg, with a radius of gyration of 0.32 m; the other two are 1.2 m diameter, each 150 kg, and radius of gyration 0.42 m. Calculate the force required to accelerate the truck to a speed of 5 m s^{-1} in a distance of 12 m, along a straight level track. Assume that there is no frictional resistance, and that the wheels roll without slip. [*Ans. 2219 N.*]

   Hint: see Frame 31 for the equivalent mass of various wheels. Calculate equivalent mass, m_E (2130.2 kg). (Recall $I = mk^2$ where $k =$ radius of gyration.) Then $\Sigma(F) = m_E a$.

2. A wheeled vehicle has a mass, including the wheels, of 1300 kg. A force of 3.5 kN is required to haul it up a slope of 15° from rest a distance of 6 metres in 9.6 seconds. If it is then released from rest on the slope, how long would it take to roll back down again, the same distance? Assume no frictional resistance to motion, and that the wheels roll without slip. [*Ans. 2.359 s.*]

   Hints: calculate the acceleration using a kinematic equation, and treat as in Frame 34, to evaluate m_E, the equivalent mass. You should get $m_E = 1530.5$ kg. Then use this to determine the acceleration down the slope.

3. A uniform solid cylinder is made of steel of density 7800 kg m^{-3}. It has a length of 40 mm and diameter 35 mm. It is mounted on a central spindle of diameter 6 mm. It is arranged with the spindle resting horizontally on a pair of rails sloping at 10°. How long will it take for the disc to roll 1 metre down the rails? Neglect any frictional resistance to motion, and assume that the spindle rolls without slip along the rails. Neglect the inertia of the spindle itself. [*Ans. 4.598 s.*]

   Hints: see Frame 36. The moment of inertia of a solid uniform disc is $\frac{1}{2}mR^2$. So determine I. Equivalent mass $m_E = I/r^2$ where r is the spindle radius, not the disc radius ($m_E = 5.4078$ kg).

4. A car wheel of mass 6.5 kg, diameter 0.75 m and radius of gyration 0.28 m is given a rotating speed of 5 revolutions per second. It is then placed at the bottom of a 30° slope. How far up the slope will it travel before coming to rest? Assume no slip at any time between wheel and slope, and neglect any frictional resistance. [*Ans. 22.037 m.*]

   Hints: calculate I, and hence m_E (10.124 kg). Write equation of motion; weight component down the slope is the only retarding force. Note that the problem could be solved alternatively using an energy equation.

39

A gearbox is a mechanical device for changing the speed of a rotating shaft. There are many types, but the commonest form consists of a number of meshing toothed wheels on parallel shafts.

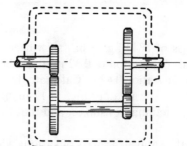

A gearbox is necessary in a car because a petrol-engine operates efficiently only at a much higher speed than the wheels rotate. Also the load varies considerably. For example, when a car starts, the wheels need to move extremely slowly, and require a high torque to move them, whereas when running fast, the torque needed is comparatively small. Also, if the car ascends a steep hill, again a higher torque is required at the driving wheels.

Think of some more examples of machines where a gearbox is needed.

40

An electrically-driven crane. Colliery winding-gear. A car lifting-jack.

Of course there are many others. In the first two of these, again, the need is to link a high-speed driver—an electric motor—to a low-speed load—the crane load or the mine cage. In the third, the speed is not relevant. As with pulley systems, as the speed reduces, the force, or torque, is increased.

The following diagram shows a pair of gear-wheels 'in mesh', i.e. running together without relative slip.

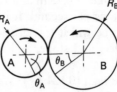

If A turns through an angle θ_A, the corresponding movement at the rim must be $R_A \theta_A$, and this rim movement must be the same for the mating wheel.

$$\therefore \qquad R_A \theta_A = R_B \theta_B$$

The displacement ratio $\theta_A / \theta_B = R_B / R_A$. This ratio G is called the gear ratio.

As with pulley systems, this ratio, G, applies to displacement, velocity and acceleration:

$$\therefore \quad G = \frac{\theta_A}{\theta_B} = \frac{\omega_A}{\omega_B} = \frac{\alpha_A}{\alpha_B}$$

We now assume a torque M to act on the shaft of wheel A. As a consequence, the system will accelerate, and we require the corresponding acceleration of wheel A. We draw the free-body diagrams for both the wheels. The applied torque will cause a tangential force F between the wheels at the rim, at the point of contact. This force will act equally on both wheels but in opposite directions.

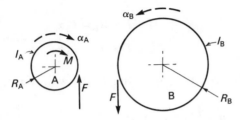

The equations of motion will be:

$$M - F \times R_A = I_A \alpha_A$$

$$F \times R_B = I_B \alpha_B$$

Substituting for F in the first, and also replacing α_B by α_A / G

$$M - R_A \left(\frac{I_B \alpha_A}{R_B G} \right) = I_A \alpha_A$$

$$\therefore \quad M = \alpha_A \left(I_A + \frac{I_B R_A}{G R_B} \right) = \alpha_A \left(I_A + \frac{I_B}{G^2} \right)$$

and we finish with a single system equation of the general form $\Sigma(M) = I\alpha$, the terms in the brackets both having dimensions of moment of inertia (G, the gear ratio, is a number, and dimensionless). We call the sum of the terms in the bracket, the **equivalent inertia of the system, referred to shaft A.** The system responds to a torque at this point exactly as though it were a single inertia of this value. In the pulley system of Frame 23, we had a similar result with masses; the effect of a 100 kg mass was the same as that of a 4 kg mass at another point, and we used the term 'equivalent mass'.

Now repeat the analysis of this system, but this time, with a torque M applied to wheel B instead of wheel A, and in terms of α_B instead of α_A. This is done in the following frame, but you should be able to find the answer yourself, as the working is exactly similar throughout. Have a guess at the answer before you start.

42

Here are the relevant free-body diagrams.

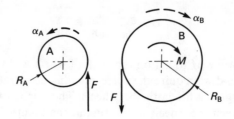

The equations now are:

$$M - F \times R_B = I_B \alpha_B$$

$$F \times R_A = I_A \alpha_A$$

Eliminating F as before, and substituting for α_A with $(G\alpha_B)$:

$$M - R_B\left(\frac{I_A \alpha_A}{R_A}\right) = I_B \alpha_B$$

$$\therefore \quad M = I_B \alpha_B + I_A(G\alpha_B)G = \alpha_B(I_B + G^2 I_A)$$

43

From the results obtained in the previous frame, we see that the effect of an inertia on a low-speed side of a gearbox is very much reduced when a torque is applied to the high-speed side. Also, the effect of an inertia on the high-speed side of a gearbox is very much enhanced, or increased, when a torque is applied to the low-speed side. Car drivers will know the pronounced retarding effect that results when the engine is engaged in 'low' gear as the car descends a steep hill. But if you want to start the engine by pushing the car, you will find it almost impossible to move the car in 'low' gear; you have to engage a 'higher' gear. (The words are in quote-marks, because 'low' gear to a driver means a high gear to an engineer, that is, a high ratio of engine speed to wheel speed.)

For the remainder of this programme, we shall consider a gearbox simply as a closed box, with input and output shafts, and the gear ratio, G, will always be the ratio of the high speed to the low speed; that is, G will always be a number greater than 1. Normally, the inertial effect of the moving wheels in the box is considered negligible: if this is not so, allowance is made by including an equivalent inertia on either the high-speed or low-speed shafts. The example in the following frame will illustrate this.

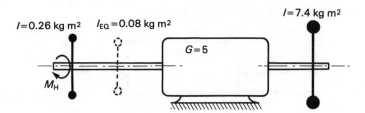

Example. A gearbox having a ratio of 5 has wheels of moment of inertia 0.26 kg m^2 and 7.4 kg m^2 attached to the high-speed and low-speed shafts respectively. The inertial effect of the box itself is equivalent to an added inertia of 0.08 kg m^2 on the high-speed shaft. Calculate the torque M_H required on the high-speed shaft to bring the low-speed shaft up to 250 rev/min in 10 seconds. If this torque is removed, calculate the braking torque required on the low-speed shaft to bring it to rest in 5 seconds.

Initially, the torque acts on the high-speed shaft, so we require the equivalent inertia of the system referred to this shaft. For the second part, the torque is on the low-speed shaft, and we shall want the equivalent inertia referred there.

So begin by calculating the two values of equivalent inertia, I_H and I_L. Just substitute the values in the two expressions of Frames 41 and 42. Then calculate the two angular accelerations. The second (the retardation) will be twice the first because the same change of speed takes half the time.

45

$$I_H = 0.26 + 0.08 + (7.4/(5)^2) = 0.636 \text{ kg m}^2$$

$$I_L = 7.4 + (0.26 + 0.08)(5)^2 = 15.9 \text{ kg m}^2$$

Kinematic equation: $\qquad\qquad \omega_2 = \omega_1 + \alpha t$

$$\omega_2 = 2\pi \times N/60 = 2\pi \times 250/60 = 26.18 \text{ rad s}^{-1}$$

$\therefore \qquad 26.18 = 0 + \alpha \times 10$

$\therefore \qquad \alpha = 2.618 \text{ rad s}^{-2} \qquad$ for the low-speed shaft

The high-speed shaft acceleration will be 5 times this.

$$M_H = I_H \alpha_H = 0.636(2.618 \times 5) = \textbf{8.325 N m}$$

For the second part, α_L will be (2.618×2) rad s^{-2}

$$M_L = I_L \alpha_L = 15.9(2.618 \times 2) = \textbf{83.25 N m}$$

46

There must be some energy loss in a gearbox. As with a pulley system, we take this into account by defining the **efficiency** of the box.

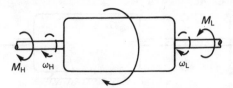

A schematic diagram of a gearbox is shown. Note the direction of M_L, the torque on the low-speed side. If the output shaft transmits a clockwise torque to the load, then the reaction torque on the box must be anti-clockwise, as shown. Assuming first that no energy loss occurs, the work done at the high-speed input and the low-speed output shafts per second must be equal. Thus:

$$M_H \omega_H = M_L \omega_L$$

$$\therefore \quad M_L/M_H = \omega_H/\omega_L = G$$

So the torque is multiplied by the gear ratio as the speed is reduced by the same factor.

If we now assume some energy loss in the box, efficiency, η, is defined:

$$\eta = \frac{\text{work done at output per second}}{\text{work done at input per second}} = \frac{M_L \omega_L}{M_H \omega_H}$$

$$\therefore \quad M_L = \eta\left(\frac{\omega_H}{\omega_L}\right) M_H = G\eta M_H$$

So the output torque is reduced by a factor of η from the theoretical value. This assumes, incidentally, that the input to the gearbox is the high-speed shaft, which is by far the most frequent case.

47

We shall now work through an example involving a gearbox with other components.

Example. A hoist comprises a drum of diameter 1.4 m and moment of inertia 34 kg m^2. A load of mass 65 kg hangs from the drum, which is driven by a motor through a reduction gearbox of ratio 124:1 and efficiency 0.9. The moving parts of the gearbox are equivalent to an inertia of 0.025 kg m^2 on the high-speed (input) shaft. The driving motor has a constant output torque of 13.5 N m. Calculate the upward acceleration of the load.

A schematic diagram of the arrangement is given in Frame 48, along with the associated free-body diagrams. With this problem, it is simpler to complete all calculations numerically as far as possible.

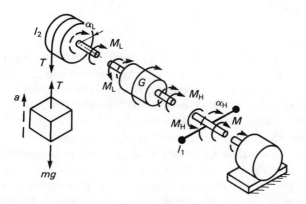

A clear diagram is essential to avoid errors. The motor output torque is shown as M. The inertia corresponding to the gearbox moving parts is the rotor I_1. M_H is the input torque to the gearbox, and M_L the output torque. The drum inertia is I_2. The load acceleration is a, the drum acceleration is α_L and the motor acceleration is α_H.

We calculate all accelerations in terms of a, the required acceleration.

$$\alpha_L = a/R = a/0.7 = 1.429a$$
$$\alpha_H = G\alpha L = 124 \times 1.429a = 177.2a$$

We may now write the equations of motion, starting with the inertia I_1, because we are given the value of motor torque M.

$$M - M_H = I_1\alpha_H$$
$$\therefore \quad M_H = M - I_1\alpha_H = 13.5 - 0.025 \times 177.2a = 13.5 - 4.43a$$

We use this expression for M_H to write the equation for the gearbox.

$$M_L = M_H \times G \times \eta = 124 \times 0.9(13.5 - 4.43a) = 1506.6 - 494.4a$$

This enables the equation for the drum to be written:

$$M_L - TR = I_2\alpha_L$$
$$\therefore \quad T \times 0.7 = M_L - I_2\alpha_L = 1506.6 - 494a - 34 \times 1.429a = 1506.6 - 542.59a$$
$$\therefore \quad T = 2152.3 - 775.1a$$

And finally, the linear equation of motion for the hanging load:

$$T - mg = ma$$
$$\therefore \quad 65a = 2152.3 - 775.1a - 65 \times 9.81$$
$$\therefore \quad 840.1a = 2152.3 - 637.7 = 1514.6$$
$$\therefore \quad a = \textbf{1.8028 m s}^{-2}$$

Some remarks concerning this solution follow in the next frame.

49

Mistakes are easily made with this sort of problem, and it is worth spending a little time discussing the procedures. You cannot be sure of a correct solution unless some time is spent on careful and correct diagrams. Beginning with the load, the linear acceleration is stated as being upwards. It follows that the rope tension, T, must be greater than the load weight, mg. An upward rope tension on the load must mean a downward rope tension on the drum (a rope, in any case, can only pull; it cannot push). Further, an upward acceleration of the load is compatible with clockwise drum acceleration, as drawn. Thus, the drum driving torque, M_L, must be clockwise, and opposite to the rope torque, $T \times R$ (R being the drum radius), which of course tends to retard the drum. Since the gearbox drives the drum with clockwise torque M_L, the gearbox itself is subject to an equal and opposite torque on the output shaft: this is Newton's Third Law applied to rotation. To make this clearer, when a machine applies a torque to a load, the machine itself suffers an equal and opposite reaction torque. Picture what happens when a hand-held drill seizes up when drilling a hole: the drill is wrenched round in the opposite direction to its rotation.

The diagram of the gearbox is not a free-body diagram, in that we do not need the equation of motion, but only an input–output equation. The free-body diagram of the small inertia on the high-speed input shaft again shows the equal and opposite reaction torque to the gearbox input torque M_H. And the motor output torque M must exceed this by an amount sufficient to accelerate this inertia.

Although this problem may appear complex, the working is relatively simple because each equation is developed, and used to substitute straight way in the next equation, obviating the necessity of solving a number of simultaneous equations. Working is simpler and clearer by substituting numbers and performing calculations where possible. But it could be solved algebraically. If you prefer this kind of solution, you should be able to show for yourself, by working sequentially as we did in Frame 48, that the load acceleration, a, can be obtained from the equation:

$$\frac{MG\eta}{R} - mg = a\left(m + \frac{I_2}{R^2} + \frac{I_1 G^2 \eta}{R^2} \right)$$

where the terms are those used in the diagram, and the solution. Substituting the appropriate values will give the same answer for a. It is seen once more that the equation has the general form $\Sigma(F) = ma$, with the three bracketed terms on the right-hand side representing an equivalent mass for all the system elements.

So far, we have considered torque and acceleration at the same point of a gearbox. We shall now consider the relation between the torque *at the input*, and the acceleration *at the output* of the gearbox. We shall use the expressions derived earlier to work through the following example.

Example. Rotors of moments of inertia 0.84 kg m^2 and 8.2 kg m^2 are attached to the high-speed and low-speed shafts of a gearbox of ratio G. The inertia of the gearbox moving parts is negligible, and the efficiency is 1. A torque of 5 N m acts on the rotor on the high-speed shaft. Calculate the angular acceleration of the low-speed shaft, for values of G of 2, 3, 4 and 5.

Using the expression from Frame 41:

$$M = \alpha_A(I_A + I_B/G^2)$$
$$\therefore \quad 5 = \alpha_A(0.84 + 8.2/G^2) \tag{1}$$

For $G = 2$:

$$5 = \alpha_A \times 2.89$$
$$\therefore \quad \alpha_A = 1.7301 \text{ rad s}^{-2}$$
$$\therefore \quad \alpha_B = \alpha_A/G = 0.8651 \text{ rad s}^{-2}$$

Now you complete the solution, calculating values of α_B, the low-speed acceleration, exactly as we have done here.

51

Including the result above, you should have the following:

$$\text{For } G = 2: \alpha_B = 0.8651 \text{ rad s}^{-2}$$
$$\text{For } G = 3: \alpha_B = 0.9517 \text{ rad s}^{-2}$$
$$\text{For } G = 4: \alpha_B = 0.9242 \text{ rad s}^{-2}$$
$$\text{For } G = 5: \alpha_B = 0.8561 \text{ rad s}^{-2}$$

and we have the interesting result that as G is increased, the low-speed shaft acceleration also increases up to a value of $G = 3$, after which it then begins to fall. This suggests that there is a possible value of G for which the low-speed shaft acceleration would be a maximum, and this is so. To find this 'optimum' value for G, arrange equation (1) in Frame 50 to give α_B in terms of G, and then differentiate with respect to G.

52

Here is the working.

From Frame 50:
$$5 = \alpha_A(0.84 + 8.2/G^2)$$

$$\therefore \quad \alpha_A = \frac{5}{0.84 + 8.2/G^2}$$

$$\alpha_B = \frac{\alpha_A}{G} = \frac{5}{G(0.84 + 8.2/G^2)} = \frac{5G}{0.84G^2 + 8.2}$$

Now differentiate. We use the 'quotient' formula: $d(u/v) = (v\,du - u\,dv)/v^2$:

$$\frac{d(\alpha_B)}{d(G)} = \frac{(0.84G^2 + 8.2)(5) - (5G)(2 \times 0.84G + 0)}{(0.84G^2 + 8.2)^2} = 0 \quad \text{for a maximum}$$

This is made simpler when we remember that for the expression to be zero, the top line must be zero. Expanding, and putting equal to 0, therefore:

$$4.2G^2 + 41 - 8.4G^2 = 0$$

giving:
$$4.2G^2 = 41$$

$$\therefore \quad G = \sqrt{(9.762)} = \mathbf{3.124}$$

and if we substitute this value for G in the expression for α_B:

$$\alpha_{Bmax} = \frac{5 \times 3.124}{0.84(3.124)^2 + 8.2} = \mathbf{0.9526}$$

This is higher than any of the four values calculated in Frame 51.

53

Optimum gear ratio for a maximum acceleration is an important feature of geared systems. Car drivers know that high acceleration, as for example, when overtaking, is often best achieved by changing to a lower gear.

Look at the example in Frame 47 again. Substitute the given values in the system equation which was given at the end of Frame 49, except for G; just leave this as G. This will give an equation relating G and a, the acceleration of the load. You should be able to reduce the equation to the following form:

$$a = \frac{17.36G - 637.7}{134.4 + 0.0459G^2}$$

and you can differentiate with respect to G, using the quotient formula as before. This is done in the following frame, but try it yourself first.

Begin by substituting the values given in Frame 47.

$$\frac{13.5G \times 0.9}{0.7} - 65 \times 9.81 = a\left(65 + \frac{34}{(0.7)^2} + \frac{G^2 \times 0.025 \times 0.9}{(0/7)^2}\right)$$

Completing the separate calculations gives:

$$17.36G - 637.7 = a(65 + 69.4 + 0.0459G^2)$$

$$\therefore \quad a = \frac{17.36G - 637.7}{134.4 + 0.0459G^2}$$

We use the quotient formula to differentiate.

$$\frac{(134.4 + 0.0459G^2)(17.36) - (17.36G - 637.7)(2 \times 0.0459G)}{(134.4 + 0.0459G^2)^2} = 0 \quad \text{for maximum } a$$

Again, some simplification is effected by equating just the top line to 0.

Multiplying out at the same time:

$$2333.2 + 0.7968G^2 - 1.5936G^2 + 58.54G = 0$$

This simplifies further to:

$$0.7968G^2 - 58.54G - 2333.2 = 0$$

Dividing all terms by the coefficient of G^2:

$$G^2 - 73.47G - 2928.2 = 0$$

Solving the quadratic:

$$G = \frac{+73.47 \pm \sqrt{\{(73.47)^2 - 4(-2928.2)\}}}{2} = 36.74 \pm \tfrac{1}{2}\sqrt{(5397.8 + 11\,713)}$$

$$= 36.74 \pm 65.40$$

$$= \mathbf{102.1}$$

The alternative negative solution has no practical significance.

Here is a brief summary of gearboxes.

1. For a gearbox of ratio G ($G > 1$) and efficiency η, with a torque input M on the high-speed shaft, the output torque on the low-speed shaft will be $M \times G\eta$.
2. For a gearbox of ratio G ($G > 1$) and efficiency η, with a torque input M on the low-speed shaft, the output torque on the high-speed shaft will be $(M/G)\eta$.
3. When a load is driven by a constant torque through a gearbox of ratio G, with inertias on input and output shafts, the load acceleration varies with G. There is an optimum value of G for maximum load acceleration.

56

PROBLEMS

1. A gearbox having an efficiency η has rotating elements of moments of inertia I_H and I_L attached to the high-speed and low-speed shafts respectively.

   (a) Show that a torque M applied to the high-speed shaft results in an acceleration αH given by the equation:

   $$M = \alpha_H(I_H + I_L/G^2\eta)$$

   (b) Show that a torque M applied to the low-speed shaft results in an acceleration α_L given by the equation:

   $$M = \alpha_L(I_L + I_H G^2/\eta)$$

   Hint: draw free-body diagrams of the rotors. See Frame 46 to allow for loss of energy in the box.

2. A gearbox has a gear ratio of G, and an efficiency of η. It carries rotating elements of moments of inertia I_H and I_L on the high-speed and low-speed shafts respectively. A torque M acts on the rotor on the high-speed shaft. Show that the maximum acceleration of the low-speed shaft would occur for a value of

   $$G = \sqrt{(I_L/\eta I_H)}$$

3.

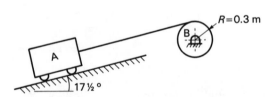

A truck A of mass 820 kg is hauled up a slope of $17\frac{1}{2}°$ by a rope wound round a drum B of radius 0.3 m and moment of inertia 66 kg m². The drum is driven by the output shaft of a gearbox (not shown) having a gear ratio of 56:1 and efficiency 0.85. The inertia of the gearbox rotating parts is equivalent to a rotor of moment of inertia 0.009 kg m² on the high-speed (input) shaft of the box. The input shaft is driven by an electric motor having a constant output torque of 16 N m. Calculate the acceleration of the truck up the slope. [*Ans. 0.0658 m s⁻².*]
Hint: treat generally as the solution in Frame 48.

57

We have mentioned the car as an example of a geared system. The engine drives the high-speed input shaft to the gearbox, through a clutch, which is a device for disconnecting the drive from the engine when changing the gearbox ratio. Also, a flywheel is attached to the high-speed engine shaft. The low-speed gearbox output shaft passes to a second gearbox—the differential, the output shaft of this being the actual driving-wheel axle. Torque on this axle drives the wheel, which in turn causes the tangential friction force between road and wheel which constitutes the actual driving force of the vehicle; this is called the **tractive force**. The motion of the car itself may be subjected to resistance due to the air, and, if it is moving up a slope, a component of its weight.

Here is a schematic diagram of the system.

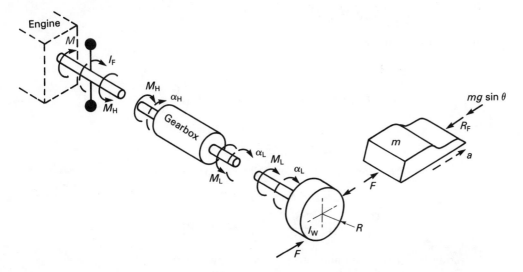

The diagram is a simplified version of the actual system. The differential gearbox is not included, and the gear ratio G is assumed to be the total ratio of the two boxes, that is, the ratio engine speed:wheel speed. Only one wheel is shown; the inertia I_ω is the moment of inertia of all four wheels. Usually, only two wheels drive the car, the remaining two being driven by the car. But this does not invalidate the analysis. The body of the car itself, shown as mass m, includes the mass of the wheels; this point was made clear in Frame 31. The car is subjected to a resisting force, shown as R_F, due to air resistance, and also, it is assumed that it is being driven up a slope, so that the component of weight, $mg \sin \theta$, also acts against the motion. The engine torque is shown as M; the input torque to the gearbox is M_H, and the output torque to the wheels is M_L.

In Frame 58, we shall derive a single system equation relating engine torque M to car acceleration, a.

58

Firstly, all accelerations are calculated in terms of the car acceleration, a.

$$\alpha_L = \frac{a}{R}; \qquad \alpha_H = G\alpha_L = \frac{Ga}{R}$$

We write the equation of motion for the flywheel I_F:

$$M - M_H = I_F \alpha_H = I_F \left(\frac{Ga}{R} \right)$$

$$\therefore \quad M_H = M - I_F \left(\frac{Ga}{R} \right)$$

For the gearbox:

$$M_L = M_H G\eta = MG\eta - I_F \left(\frac{G^2 \eta a}{R} \right)$$

The equation of motion for the wheel:

$$M_L - F \times R = I_\omega \alpha_L$$

$$\therefore \quad FR = M_L - I_\omega \left(\frac{a}{R} \right) = MG\eta - I_F \left(\frac{G^2 \eta a}{R} \right) - I_\omega \left(\frac{a}{R} \right)$$

$$\therefore \quad F = \frac{MG\eta}{R} - I_F \frac{G^2 \eta a}{R^2} - I_\omega \frac{a}{R^2}$$

The equation of motion for the vehicle ($\Sigma(F) = ma$) will be:

$$F - R_F - mg \sin\theta = ma$$

$$\therefore \quad \frac{MG\eta}{R} - I_F \left(\frac{G^2 \eta a}{R^2} \right) - I_\omega \left(\frac{a}{R^2} \right) - R_F - mg \sin\theta = ma$$

Collecting all terms containing a on the right-hand side:

$$\frac{MG\eta}{R} - mg \sin\theta - R_F = a \left(m + \frac{I_\omega}{R^2} + \frac{I_F G^2 \eta}{R^2} \right)$$

This is the single system equation of motion. The left-hand side is the nett driving force on the vehicle, the first term being the effective driving force on the car due to the engine torque, the second and third terms being the resisting forces resisting motion. Hence the negative signs. In the event of the car moving down the slope, the $mg \sin\theta$ term would be positive. On the right-hand side, in the bracket, we have the now familiar expression for the equivalent masses of the component parts of the system: the mass of the car itself, the effective mass of wheels, and the effective mass of the flywheel, in turn.

Although the result of this calculation is of interest, the work is laborious, and in a numerical example, the wiser procedure is to work arithmetically as far as possible, as in Frame 47. An example follows.

Example. A vehicle has a total mass, including wheels of 1145 kg. The wheels have a total inertia of 9.12 kg m^2 and the radius is 0.36 m. The rotating parts of the engine and gearbox correspond to a moment of inertia of 0.48 kg m^2 on the engine shaft. The overall gear ratio engine speed to wheel speed is 7.3. There is a frictional resisting torque on the engine shaft of 25 N m, and a frictional resisting torque on the wheels of 15 N m total. Motion of the vehicle is resisted by a wind force of 450 N. Calculate the engine torque required to drive the vehicle up a slope of $\sin^{-1}\frac{1}{8}$ with a forward acceleration of 1.75 m s^{-2}.

The formula derived in Frame 58 incorporates a gearbox efficiency, η. In this example, losses are given in terms of friction torques on the engine shaft and the gearbox output shaft. So the formula will not apply here.

We begin, this time, at the 'road' end of the system instead of the engine, as previously, because this time, the acceleration of the vehicle is given, and we are asked to find the engine torque. So begin by drawing a free-body diagram of the vehicle, and write the equation of motion. Show the vehicle tractive force (the tangential friction force between wheels and road) as F. Since all required data are given, F can be determined, and you should obtain a value for F of 3858 N. Complete the working as far as you can before checking in the next frame.

60

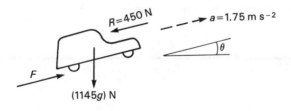

The equation ($\Sigma(F) = ma$):

$$F - 450 - 1145g\,\sin\theta = 1145a$$

$$\therefore \quad F = 1145 \times 1.75 + 450 + 1145 \times 9.81 \times \tfrac{1}{8} = 3858 \text{ N}$$

You can now draw a symbolic free-body diagram of the wheel as in the diagram in Frame 57. Because the equation of motion of the vehicle includes the wheel mass, we may treat the wheel as a purely rotating body. So draw the diagram and write the equation. The angular acceleration α is calculated from the linear acceleration of the vehicle. Show the driving torque on the axle as M_ω. You can then solve the equation and determine M_ω. You should get a value of 1433 N m.

61

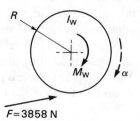

$$F = 3858 \text{ N}$$

Note that the tractive force, G, though directed forwards on the vehicle, exerts a retarding effect on the wheel itself. This is equivalent to saying that the axle driving torque, M_ω, is required both to accelerate the vehicle forwards, and also to accelerate the wheels. The equation of motion is:

$$M_\omega - F \times R = I_\omega \alpha$$

$$\therefore \quad M_\omega = I_\omega \alpha + F \times R$$

$$= 9.12(1.75/0.36) + 3858 \times 0.36 = 1433 \text{ N m}$$

This brings us to the gearbox. We must now add the friction torque on the wheels to the above figure; this gives the gearbox output torque. From this, you can calculate the gearbox input torque. A diagram is not necessary for this. Because friction losses are given numerically, we may assume a gearbox efficiency of 1 for the calculation. You should find the gearbox input torque is 198.4 N m.

62

Calling gearbox input torque M_H (subscript $_H$ for 'high'):

$$M_H = \frac{M_\omega + 15}{G} = \frac{1433 + 15}{7.3} = 198.4 \text{ N m}$$

The final state is the free-body diagram, and the equation for the inertia on the engine output shaft. Call the engine output torque M. The angular acceleration of the inertia is calculated, as before, from the vehicle linear acceleration. The engine torque is positive, and the friction torque on the engine shaft and the gearbox input torque are of course negative. Your equation should give an answer of 240.4 N m for the required engine torque.

63

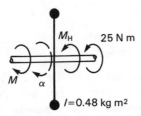

The equation $(\Sigma(M) = I\alpha)$ is:

$$M - 25 - 198.4 = I\alpha = 0.48(1.75/0.36 \times 7.3)$$
$$\therefore \quad M = 17.0 + 25 + 198.4$$
$$= \mathbf{240.4 \ N \ m}$$

64

Sometimes, gearboxes may be used in combination. Look at this arrangement.

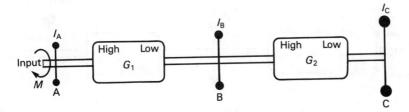

A torque M acts on the high-speed input shaft of the system. We want to find the corresponding acceleration of the rotor A on the input shaft.

If it is assumed that there is no loss in either gearbox, the answer is quite simply obtained, and indeed can be written straight down. To start you in the right direction, look back to Frame 41.

65

The system equation of motion is:

$$M = \alpha(I_A + I_B/G_1^2 + I_C/G_1^2 G_2^2)$$

This is how we obtain it. We deal first with the input and output to the second gearbox, and 'refer' I_C to the input shaft. Thus, I_C has an 'effective' moment of inertia of (I_C/G_2^2) when referred to the intermediate shaft. We may now forget the gearbox G_2. Box G_1 now has inertia I_A on the high-speed side and an equivalent inertia of $(I_B + I_C/G_2^2)$ on its low-speed side. 'Referring' this latter to the high-speed shaft by dividing again by the square of the ratio, the total referred inertia on the system input shaft is $(I_A + I_B/G_1^2 + I_C/G_1^2 G_2^2)$. A similar reasoning would show that the equivalent inertia of the system referred to the low-speed shaft would be $(I_A G_1^2 G_2^2 + I_B G_2^2 + I_C)$.

66

This next example shows how optimum gear ratio, which we examined in Frame 52, is affected by a two-stage gear reduction.

Example. Rotors having moments of inertia of 1, 12 and 100 kg m^2 are attached to the high-speed, intermediate-speed and low-speed shafts respectively of a two-stage reduction gear system, which consists of two reduction gearboxes, each of efficiency 0.9 and ratio G. A constant torque of 25 N m acts on the input (high-speed) end of the system. The low-speed shaft drives a load which has a constant resisting torque of 40 N m. Determine what value of G will result in maximum acceleration of the low-speed output shaft, and determine this maximum acceleration.

Writing the equation of motion for each rotor, and the equation for each gearbox, is preferable to attempting to determine equivalent inertias. Here is a diagram of the system.

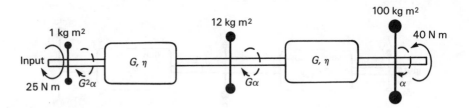

The kinematics have already been incorporated by indicating accelerations of α, $G\alpha$ and $G^2\alpha$ on the low-, intermediate- and high-speed shafts respectively.

The solution which follows uses an alternative, and somewhat simpler approach to previous solutions, which eliminates the necessity of drawing free-body diagrams for every component. It is clear that although 25 N m acts on the high-speed input shaft, 25 N m will not be the torque input to the first gearbox, because some of this torque will be used in accelerating the first rotor. We may call this part the 'inertia torque' of that rotor. Thus:

$$\text{input to first gearbox} = 25 - (1 \times G^2\alpha) \text{ N m}$$

$$\therefore \quad \text{gearbox output torque} = 0.9G(25 - G^2\alpha) = 22.5G - 0.9G^3\alpha \text{ N m}$$

(recalling that gearbox output torque = G × input torque × efficiency). We continue in Frame 67, working through the system, subtracting inertia torque, and multiplying by a gearbox factor as appropriate. You should be able to write the input torque to the second box yourself. Do so, and check your attempt in the following frame.

input torque to second gearbox $= 22.5G - 0.9G^3\alpha - (12 \times G\alpha)$

(Again, we just subtract the torque required to accelerate the second inertia.)

$\therefore$ 2nd gearbox output torque $= 0.9G(22.5G - 0.9G^3\alpha - 12G\alpha)$ N m
$= 20.25G^2 - 0.81G^4\alpha - 10.8G^2\alpha$ N m

And finally, the torque of 40 N m available to drive the load must be this output torque less the inertia torque of the last rotor

$\therefore$ $40 = 20.25G^2 - 0.81G^4\alpha - 10.8G^2\alpha - (100 \times \alpha)$

This is the equation of motion for the whole system. Arrange with all the α terms on the left-hand side:

$$\alpha(100 + 10.8G^2 + 0.81G^4) = 20.25G^2 - 40$$

The bracketed terms on the left-hand side are the equivalent inertias, referred to the output shaft. By dividing throughout by this bracket, we get α in terms of G.

$$\alpha = \frac{20.25G^2 - 40}{100 + 10.8G^2 + 0.81G^4}$$

We now have to differentiate α with respect to G. Although this looks formidable, we shall see that it is not too difficult.

68

We use the quotient formula for differentiating:

$$d(u/v) = \frac{v\,d(u) - u\,d(v)}{v^2}$$

But remembering that because we are seeking a maximum for α, we shall equate the expression to zero, remember that for the whole expression to be zero, the top line must be zero. Hence:

$$v\,d(u) - u\,d(v) = 0$$

Although we shall still finish with an expression involving G^4, the calculation is more tedious than difficult. Attempt to derive the expression yourself first, before checking in Frame 69.

69

$$(100 + 10.8G^2 + 0.81G^4)(2G \times 20.25) - (20.25G^2 - 40)(10.8 \times 2G + 0.81 \times 4G^3) = 0$$

Simplify by dividing throughout by G. Then multiply out all the brackets:

$$4050 + 437.4G^2 + 32.805G^4 - 437.4G^2 - 65.61G^4 + 864 + 129.6G^2 = 0$$

$$\therefore \quad 32.805G^4 - 129.6G^2 - 4914 = 0$$

and what appeared to be a fourth-power equation in G is now seen to be a fairly simple quadratic in G^2. We simplify further by dividing all terms by 32.805:

$$G^4 - 3.951G^2 - 149.8 = 0$$

Solve this yourself; you will find that G^2 is 14.37. The negative value is not relevant to the problem. Thus, $G = \sqrt{(14.37)} = \textbf{3.791}$. Also, substitute in the expression for α in Frame 67 to obtain the required maximum value for α which you should find, works out at **0.5941 rad s^{-2}**.

70

PROBLEMS

1. A car has a mass of 1075 kg. It has four wheels of diameter 0.75 m and inertia 1.75 kg m^2. The overall gear ratio engine speed to wheel speed is 6.2:1. The engine rotating parts have an effective inertia of 0.32 kg m^2. The engine delivers a constant torque of 165 N m. There are friction torques of 30 N m on the engine shaft and 25 N m total on the wheels. Find the acceleration of the car along a straight level road, assuming a resistance due to the air of 400 N. [*Ans. 1.456 m s^{-2}.*]
   Hint: solve generally as in Frame 58.
2. A car has a total mass of 1050 kg. The wheels are 0.67 m diameter and have a total moment of inertia of 8.5 kg m^2. The rotating engine parts are equivalent to a moment of inertia of 0.34 kg m^2 on the high-speed input shaft to the gearbox. The transmission efficiency is 0.9. The engine delivers a constant torque of 85 N m. If resistance due to air is 350 N, show that the acceleration of the car up a slope of $\sin^{-1} 0.1$ can be calculated from:

$$a = \frac{G - 6.043}{4.93 + 0.0119G^2}$$

Find the value of G for the highest acceleration, and find this acceleration. [*Ans. 27.24. 1.54 m s^{-2}.*]
   Hint: use formula from Frame 58.

Programme 10

SIMPLE VIBRATION

1

This programme is concerned with the analysis of some simple vibrating systems. They will all be examples of what is called **Free Undamped Response**. This term will be explained later. This subject is important in many branches of engineering: mechanical systems vibrate, buildings and structures vibrate, and electrical circuits oscillate. ('Oscillation' is just another word for vibration.) You will deal more thoroughly with the subject later in your course. Moreover, vibration analysis forms an excellent discipline for the analysis of mechanical system generally. You should find that writing the correct equation of motion for a vibrating system will reinforce your understanding of other dynamics problems. The programme comes at the end of the book because it calls upon various principles established in earlier programmes. You will find that we shall make use of work done in Programmes 1, 5, 6, 7 and 9. Referring to Programme 5 in particular, be clear at the outset that vibration is a case of *variable* acceleration. So never be tempted in this programme to make use of the well-known kinematic equations of Programme 1, Frame 48.

2

You may have met the term 'mathematical model' in the past, and may not be clear about it. A mathematical model is a simplification of an object, or system of objects, the purpose of which is to leave off everything which is unimportant and not relevant to the main aim of the problem, which, in the case of vibration analysis, is to obtain an equation of motion. We have used mathematical models quite a lot in this book, without using the name. The configuration diagrams of Programmes 2 and 3 are mathematical models of link-mechanisms, because we draw a link just as a straight line. And in Programme 9, we make a model when we draw a winding drum just as a simple circle. Vibration analysis is a good subject for mathematical models; you have to be particularly careful to get your model right. Here is an illustration.

It is very probable that you learned at some point the derivation of the formula for the simple pendulum—the expression for the period. Can you recall the formula? Can you also recall what is meant by 'period'? And finally, do you remember, in deriving the formula, that you needed to make several 'assumptions'? As a small test of memory, try and write the formula—you may possibly have learned the expression for frequency, instead of period, but it doesn't matter. The point of importance is the assumptions made during the analysis. See if you can recall any of them. You will find four of the most important ones in the next frame.

3

> The formula is:
> $$\tau = 2\pi \sqrt{\left(\frac{L}{g}\right)}$$
>
> where τ (Greek tau) is the period (the time for one complete swing) in seconds, and L is the length of the pendulum.

Here are the four most important assumptions made in deriving the formula.

1. The pendulum 'bob' is very small and is assumed to be just a particle.
2. The string has no mass.
3. Any effects due to surrounding air are neglected.
4. The angle of swing is small.

Students tend to memorise such assumptions, because they might crop up in an examination question, but do not always appreciate their significance. Why not analyse a system as it is, without making assumptions?

One reason is that whatever you may imagine to be the power of mathematics in engineering science, in fact, it has very severe limitations. For example, the ordinary maths learned at school would be quite inadequate to analyse the simple pendulum accurately, if the angle of swing were not limited to, say, 10°, but was for example, 60°. Another reason is, that analysing a simple system, even though the result may be of very little practical use, is a stepping-stone to analysing more complex systems, the results of which could well be useful. Thus, although you analyse the simple pendulum, and then may not see any practical applications of it, you are well on the way to analysing the compound pendulum, the result of which is much more useful.

Analysis, then, consists of looking at a real system, and making a mathematical model of it, which means, simplifying it purely in order to have something that can be analysed with reasonable ease. The big question that this raises is, *is the result accurate*? If it is, then the procedure is vindicated; your mathematical model was a good one. If it isn't, the model was a poor one, and you must choose a more refined model. If your formula for the simple pendulum does not agree sufficiently closely with the swing of a clock pendulum, you must abandon the assumption that the mass of the pendulum is concentrated at a point; in other words, you must analyse a compound pendulum.

A last remark about models. A model which is good for one result may be quite inadequate for another. The simple pendulum formula will be found to predict the period, or frequency of a small weight on a long string with very high accuracy. But it is useless if you wish to predict how long it will take the pendulum to come to rest. For this purpose, you will need a more refined model, which assumes some friction or resisting force acting on the pendulum.

4

Below is a mathematical model for a body oscillating at the end of a spring. This is one of the simplest vibrating systems we can devise.

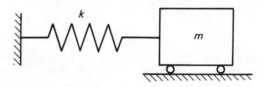

m denotes the mass of the vibrating body. The spring is shown as having a stiffness k. The stiffness of a spring is defined as the force to extend or compress it by 1 unit. It is measured in newtons per metre ($N\ m^{-1}$). Thus:

$$k = \frac{F}{x}$$

where x is the extension or compression. The body is shown resting on a horizontal surface with small symbolic rollers under it; this is a convention to indicate that there is assumed to be no friction between body and surface. The left-hand end of the spring is shown attached to a hatched vertical line. This convention is used to indicate an absolutely rigid and fixed point.

5

We make the following assumptions.

1. The body is infinitely rigid. The result of the analysis will be found accurate for, say a 2 kg weight on a spring, but may not be accurate for a thin flat steel bar held transversely on the end of a spring.
2. The spring has no mass. The result will probably be inaccurate for the case of a 1 kg weight on the end of a spring of mass 5 kg.
3. The spring anchorage is infinitely rigid—it will not move under any force.
4. There are no friction or air-resisting forces present.
5. The body is constrained to move only along a path coincident with the spring axis; it cannot move sideways or twist.

We shall find that the assumption of no friction or resistance is the one which is most difficult to reconcile with real systems. The result of this present analysis will indicate that our vibrating system will go on for ever. Real vibrating systems eventually die down, owing to resisting forces which we have assumed not to be there. These forces are called **damping** forces, and vibration analysis which includes them is called **damped vibration**. Analysis of damped vibration will not be undertaken in this book.

6

The diagram in Frame 4 shows the system components. Below, we show the dynamic system, and the free-body diagram of the vibrating body.

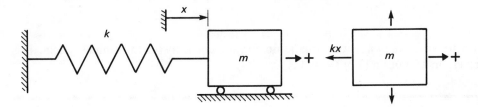

We show a ' + ' sign, indicating that all quantities left-to-right are to be considered positive. Because, by their nature, vibrating systems move in both directions, we always begin by adopting a sign convention. The convention is arbitrary: we could as easily have taken positive as right-to-left. We have also assumed the body to have a displacement x, relative to the position of static equilibrium, and x must be positive, as defined by the sign convention.

At this point, we must explain the term 'free response'. The 'response' of a system is the manner in which it behaves under certain conditions. A car is a good example of a vibrating system; it has a mass and is mounted on springs. You could cause the car to vibrate by pressing down on the body, and then releasing it; the car would vibrate up and down for a short time, and would then come to rest. This sort of response is called **free response**, because there is just an initial disturbance which is not repeated. But if you switched on the engine, the car would again vibrate but this time in a different manner; it would shake up and down a small amount in sympathy with the running engine. This is **forced response**; the vibration resulting from a *continuous disturbance*. In the example we are analysing, we are seeking the free response. We assume that the system has already been set vibrating—the body has been pulled to one side and released, for example—and we are examining it while it is vibrating.

The diagram above is therefore not a representation of a static situation. The body is oscillating backwards and forwards, and we are drawing it *at an instant* when it is displaced x to the right—we are 'freezing' the motion, so to speak. Students new to the subject often make the mistake of confusing this with a state of static equilibrium.

The free-body diagram is also shown. Because the body is a distance x to the right of the neutral position (when the spring is unstretched), the spring will be in tension, and the force in it will be (kx). The free-body diagram also shows the weight acting downwards, and the surface reaction force acting upwards. But since motion is constrained along an axial line, these two forces must be equal and opposite, and do not affect the vibratory motion.

7

We can now write the equation of motion. Recall Programme 5 here; the acceleration is not constant, and the equation of motion will be a differential equation in x and t. Throughout this programme, we shall adopt the 'dot' notation:

$$\dot{x} = \frac{dx}{dt}; \qquad \ddot{x} = \frac{d^2 x}{dt^2}$$

Try to write the differential equation of motion correctly for this simple system. The equation of motion $(\Sigma(f) = ma)$ is ...

8

$$\boxed{-(kx) = m\ddot{x}}$$

The negative sign is of paramount importance. The force (kx) is to the left, and therefore negative.

Throughout this programme, we shall always manipulate the equation so that the second differential term is on the left-hand side of the equation, and has a coefficient of 1. So, dividing by m and re-arranging:

$$\ddot{x} = -(k/m)x$$

and because both k and m are constants, the equation may be written even more simply as:

$$\ddot{x} = -Cx$$

where C is a constant which in this particular case has the value (k/m).

Before solving the equation, we shall examine some other simple systems. First, however, note what would have been the result of adopting a 'left is positive' sign convention. We should then have had to assume that the body was displaced a distance x to the *left* of the neutral position. This would have put the spring into compression, and the resulting force on the body would then have been (kx) to the *right*, in other words, negative. Thus, the equation of motion would have been exactly the same.

Now imagine that we have the same body, of mass m, attached to the same spring, of stiffness k, but this time, hanging vertically, instead of being horizontal. We must obtain the equation of motion when this system is set vibrating. Begin by drawing the dynamic system, and assuming a 'down is positive' convention. From there, try to draw the free-body diagram. Remember that the displacement x will be *from the position of static equilibrium*, not from the position when the spring is unstrained.

9

The dynamic diagram of the system, and the free-body diagram are shown.

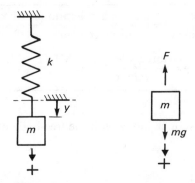

In the dynamic system, the position of static equilibrium is shown as a chain-line. In the free-body diagram, the spring-force is shown as F. When the system is stationary, in equilibrium, the force in the spring will be the weight of the body (mg). If the spring is then stretched an additional distance y, the spring force F will be:

$$F = mg + ky$$

So we write the equation of motion:

$$mg - F = ma = m\ddot{y}$$

$$\therefore \quad mg - (mg + ky) = m\ddot{y}$$

which simplifies to:

$$-ky = m\ddot{y}$$

$$\therefore \quad \ddot{y} = -(k/m)y = -Cy$$

which is, of course, exactly the same equation as we obtained for the first example, except in the trivial detail of using y for displacement instead of x.

10

Now we shall look at an example of torsional oscillation. Imagine a disc attached to one end of a steel rod, the other end of which is clamped in a vice. If the disc is given a twist and then released, it will begin to vibrate torsionally. The steel rod will behave as a torsional spring, and we may define torsional stiffness, k_t, in a similar way to spring stiffness defined in Frame 4.

$$k_t = M/\theta$$

where M is the torque, in newton metres, θ is the corresponding angle of twist, in radians, and k_t is the stiffness, in newton metres per radian.

The *dimensions* of torsional stiffness will not be the same as those of linear stiffness. What will the dimensions of each be?

$$[k] = \frac{\text{force}}{\text{displacement}} = \frac{\text{mass} \times \text{acceleration}}{\text{displacement}} = \frac{M \times L/T^2}{L} = MT^{-2}$$

$$[k_t] = \frac{\text{torque}}{\text{ang. displ.}} = \frac{\text{force} \times \text{length}}{\text{radians}} = \frac{ML/T^2 \times L}{—} = ML^2T^{-2}$$

The diagram shows the system, along with the free-body diagram of the disc.

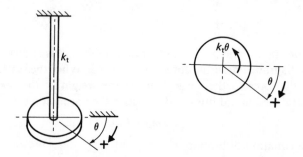

We have chosen a sign convention that 'clockwise is positive' when the disc is viewed from above. k_t defines the torsional stiffness of the rod, and I is the polar moment of inertia of the disc, that is, the moment of inertia about a vertical axis through the disc centre.

The assumptions we make are:

1. The disc is infinitely rigid.
2. The rod has negligible mass.
3. The rod anchorage is infinitely rigid.
4. There are no friction or air-resistance torques present.
5. The disc can twist only; it cannot move up or down or side-to-side.

And you will see that these assumptions are exact analogues of those in Frame 5.

At the instant of viewing, the disc is assumed to be displaced by an angle θ from the position of static equilibrium, in the positive direction.

The free-body diagram is a view looking vertically downwards on to the top of the disc. There will of course be the weight acting, and also a tension force in the rod balancing this, but these are not relevant to the oscillatory motion. The only relevant item is the torque in the rod arising out of the twist θ. Because the rod is twisted clockwise, it must exert an anti-clockwise torque on the disc.

The motion is rotational. The general equation of motion, $\Sigma(M) = I\alpha$, applies.

So, the equation of motion will be ...

12

$$-(k_t\theta) = I\alpha = I\ddot{\theta}$$
$$\therefore \qquad \ddot{\theta} = -(k_t/I)\theta = -C\theta$$

C is a constant, in this case (k_t/I). It is seen that mathematically, this second-order differential equation is the same as that in Frame 8.

At this point, we may state that *every* example of free undamped response will be found to have the same type of differential equation of motion. Let us recapitulate the meanings of the terms used.

Free response of a system means its behaviour once it has been set in motion and then allowed to continue moving under the action of its own internal forces only, and subject to no further external disturbance. Thus, if a weight hangs from a spring, we may pull the weight to extend the spring: this is the initial disturbance. We then release it; no further disturbance acts on the system; its motion is determined purely by the dynamics of the weight, the spring and the spring anchorage.

Damped response is the response of a system which is subjected to external or internal forces which cause the vibration to die down. An example is the resistance due to air or other fluid in which the system operates. Another example is hysteretic damping, arising out of the energy lost to the system due to the continual stressing of the material of the spring element. Sometimes, damping is deliberately introduced into a system, to ensure that vibration initiated by some external cause does not persist for inconveniently long periods. An illustration of this is a vehicle suspension system, which includes shock absorbers, the function of which is to cause vibrations to die away quickly, when the vehicle runs over some irregularity such as a stone, or a pot-hole in the road. A car speed indicator is damped mechanically, so that changes of speed do not cause it to oscillate too much, and thus make it ineffectual for its purpose.

It is clear that all real systems are damped, and that in consequence, the mathematical model of an undamped system is highly theoretical, although very useful.

Now try to draw the system diagram for a simple pendulum, and the free-body diagram. Here are three hints. Firstly, do not bother to limit the swing to a small angle. Secondly, treat the system as a rotational one, not translational. Thirdly, when drawing the free-body diagram, the 'body' should comprise the pendulum bob *together with the string*.

The complete analysis is found in Frame 13.

13

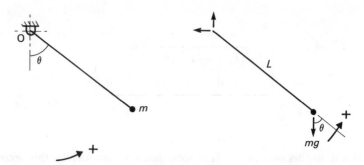

A sign-convention 'anti-clockwise is positive' has been chosen, and the pendulum is shown with an instantaneous anti-clockwise displacement θ. The assumptions made were set out in Frame 3. (Never mind the one about small angles for the present.) The right-hand diagram is the free-body diagram. Because we are treating the system as a rotational system, we include the string as well. The forces acting are thus, the weight (mg) acting vertically downwards, and a force exerted by the string anchorage on the string. We do not know this force, and have represented it by arrows showing unknown vertical and horizontal components.

The system is rotating about the point O. The equation $\Sigma(M) = I\alpha$ applies. Since the pivot force passes through O, its moment will be zero. Only the force (mg) is relevant. The moment of (mg) about O will be the moment of the component of (mg) perpendicular to the string; the component along the string will have no moment about O. So the equation of motion (paying due attention to the sign convention) is:

$$-(mg \sin \theta \times L) = I\alpha = I\ddot{\theta}$$

I is defined by $\Sigma(\delta mr^2)$. Since the only mass-element is m, and this is concentrated at radius L:

$$I = mL^2$$

Hence:

$$-(mg \sin \theta \times L) = mL^2 \ddot{\theta}$$

which can be simplified to:

$$\ddot{\theta} = -(g/L) \sin \theta$$

Now this equation is not of the expected form: it should be $\ddot{\theta} = -C\theta$. The presence of the $\sin \theta$ upsets this pattern. But we know that for small values of θ, we may say that $\sin \theta$ is approximately equal to angle θ in radians. With this condition now included, therefore, the equation becomes:

$$\ddot{\theta} = -(g/L)\theta = -C\theta$$

and the equation is seen now to have the same form as the earlier ones.

14

A compound pendulum is a body which may not be considered as a single concentrated mass, swinging from a pivot.

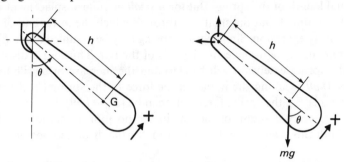

The analysis follows the same lines as that of the simple pendulum. The equation $\Sigma(M) = I\alpha$ applies. The free-body diagram shows only the weight (mg) to be relevant. Point G is the mass centre of the body, and it is a distance h from the pivot O. We call the moment of inertia of the pendulum with respect to a transverse axis through the pivot O, I_o. The equation of motion is:

$$-(mg \sin \theta \times h) = I_o \alpha = I_o \ddot{\theta}$$

and if we stipulate again that angle θ be small, this can be simplified to:

$$\ddot{\theta} = -(mgh/I_o)\theta = -C\theta$$

Now look at the system shown in Frame 15.

15

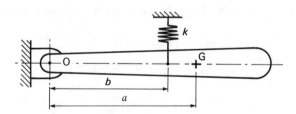

Example. A bar is pivoted at a point O to a rigid mounting. The mass centre of the bar is G, a distance a from O. The moment of inertia of the bar about a transverse axis through O is I_o. The bar is held in the horizontal position by a spring of stiffness k, attached to a rigid mounting, so that the spring axis is vertical. The bar is given an initial small displacement and then released. Derive the differential equation of motion.

Here are some points to get you going. Assume 'clockwise is positive'. Assume a **small** angular displacement θ from the neutral horizontal position. Calculate the *additional* spring force resulting from this displacement.

16

Accurate determination of the extension of the spring when the bar moves would need the actual length of the spring. But for a *small* angular displacement of the bar, then it may be assumed that the small arc through which the lower end of the spring moves is the spring extension. Similarly, the spring may be assumed to remain vertical, and its axis remain at right-angles to the axis of the bar. Thus, for a displacement θ of the bar, the spring extension will be $(b\theta)$ and the increase of tensile force in the spring will be $(kb\theta)$. Calling the initial tensile force in the spring (in the position of static equilibrium) F_0, the spring force will then be $(F_0 + kb\theta)$. Determination of F_0 requires the free-body diagram of the bar in the position of static equilibrium, i.e. when $\theta = 0$. Both this diagram and the diagram for the displaced position are shown here.

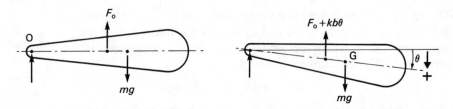

Both diagrams include unknown forces at the pivot O, but for moment equations about O, these forces are not required. For static equilibrium, taking moments of forces about O:

$$F_0 b = mga$$

and for the dynamic free-body diagram, again taking moments about O:

$$mga - (F_0 + kb\theta)b = I_0 \alpha = I_0 \ddot{\theta}$$

$$\therefore \quad mga - F_0 b - kb^2 \theta = I_0 \ddot{\theta}$$

and since $F_0 b = mga$:

$$-kb^2 \theta = I_0 \ddot{\theta}$$

giving

$$\ddot{\theta} = -(kb^2/I_0)\theta = -C\theta$$

The equation is once more of the expected form.

In Programme 6, Frame 10 we stressed the importance of always writing a moment equilibrium equation about the mass centre only when analysing the dynamics of a rigid body. But it is quite correct to write a *dynamic* equation $(\Sigma(M) = I\alpha)$ with respect to other points.

17

PROBLEMS

1.

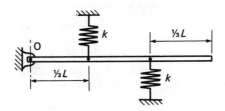

A thin uniform bar of mass m and length L is pivoted at one end so that it can turn in a horizontal plane. Two springs, each of stiffness k, are attached at the two third-length points as shown, so that the spring axes are perpendicular to the bar. Show that for small angular oscillations, the equation of motion will be:

$$\ddot{\theta} = -(\tfrac{5}{3}k/m)\theta$$

Hints: I_o for the bar is $\tfrac{1}{3}mL^2$. The bar moves in a horizontal plane, so weight does not affect the motion.

2.

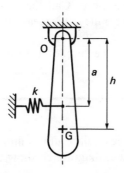

An irregular bar is supported on a pivot at O. A coiled spring of stiffness k is attached to the bar at a distance a from the pivot, the other end of the spring being secured to a fixed mounting. The spring axis is perpendicular to the axis of the bar. The mass centre of the bar, G, is distant h from the pivot. In static equilibrium, the bar hangs vertically. If the bar is displaced a small amount from the vertical and released, show that the equation of the resulting vibratory motion is:

$$\ddot{\theta} = -\theta\left(\frac{mgh + ka^2}{I_o}\right)$$

where I_o is the moment of inertia of the bar with respect to a transverse axis through the pivot and m is the mass of the bar.

Hints: use the methods of Frames 15 and 16.

18

Sometimes, the 'mass-element' might comprise two parts. Look at this.

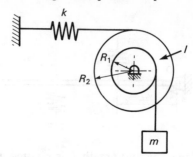

The compound pulley turns about a fixed axis. A light string connects the spring to the larger radius of the compound pulley. A weight hangs vertically by a second string from the smaller pulley. It is clearly a vibrating system; if the weight is pulled down (or raised up) a small amount and released, the system will vibrate.

Begin the analysis by assuming a 'clockwise-positive' convention. Assume the pulley to have a *small* angular clockwise displacement θ. Calculation of the initial spring force is simple; an equilibrium diagram is probably unnecessary. Separate free-body diagrams will be required for weight and pulley. You will need an equation of compatibility for the two accelerations. Call the string tension force T. Remember that if clockwise is positive for the pulley, this means that downwards must be positive for the weight.

This analysis is similar to several examples in Programme 9. The one in Frame 10 is typical.

19

If we consider the system in static equilibrium, calling the spring tension force F_0, it should not be necessary to draw a diagram to show that:

$$F_0 \times R_2 = mg \times R_1$$

Rotation of the pulley through a small angle θ will extend the spring by an amount (θR_2). The spring force will thus be $(F_0 + k\theta R_2)$.

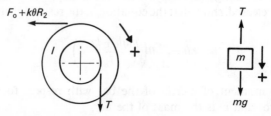

The figure shows the two free-body diagrams.

The equation of motion of the pulley ($\Sigma(M) = I\alpha$) is:

$$TR_1 - (F_0 + k\theta R_2)R_2 = I\alpha = I\ddot{\theta} \tag{1}$$

Calling the acceleration of the weight a, the equation of motion of the weight ($\Sigma(F) = ma$) will be:

$$mg - T = ma \tag{2}$$

The compatibility equation relating $\ddot{\theta}$ and a is:

$$a = \ddot{\theta}R_1 \tag{3}$$

Substituting for a in equation (2) and re-arranging:

$$T = mg - m\ddot{\theta}R_1$$

and substituting now for T in equation (1):

$$R_1(mg - m\ddot{\theta}R_1) - F_0 R_2 - k\theta R_2^2 = I\ddot{\theta}$$

$$\therefore \quad mgR_1 - mR_1^2\ddot{\theta} - F_0 R_2 - kR_2^2\theta = I\ddot{\theta}$$

The static-equilibrium equation of Frame 19 shows that the first and third terms cancel out.

$$\therefore \quad \ddot{\theta}(I + mR_1^2) = -\theta(kR_2^2)$$

$$\therefore \quad \ddot{\theta} = -\theta\left(\frac{kR_2^2}{I + mR_1^2}\right) = -C\theta$$

and it is seen that the general pattern of the equation is the same as in the earlier examples. The bottom line of the expression in brackets may be recognised as an 'equivalent inertia' of pulley and weight combined.

The equation may be expressed in terms of $\ddot{\theta}$ and θ, or in terms of the linear acceleration and displacement of the weight, $\ddot{y}$ and y, as a matter of convenience or choice. You could perhaps show for yourself that the equation above can be arranged to form the following:

$$\ddot{y} = -y\left(\frac{k(R_2/R_1)^2}{I/R_1^2 + m}\right) = -Cy$$

the constant C now, of course having a different value. In this equation, the bottom line of the constant now is the equivalent mass of the system, referred to the position of the hanging weight.

Seven different vibrating systems have been shown all to result in a second-order differential equation of the same form. The two problems in Frame 21 are left for you to analyse.

21

PROBLEMS

1.

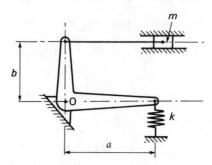

A right-angled crank pivots about a point O and can move only in a horizontal plane. A body of mass m is attached by a light rod, and is constrained to move in the frictionless guide. A spring of stiffness k is attached as shown. Show that for small oscillations of the system, the equation of motion is:

$$\ddot{\theta} = -\theta\left(\frac{ka^2}{I + mb^2}\right)$$

where I is the moment of inertia of the crank about an axis through the pivot-point.

2.

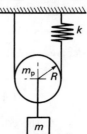

A light string passes from a fixed point round a pulley and is attached to one end of a spring of stiffness k. The other end of the spring is attached to a fixed point. A weight of mass m hangs from the pulley as shown. The pulley radius is R, its mass m_p and its moment of inertia about the central axis is I. The string does not slip on the pulley. Show that the equation of motion for a small pulley displacement θ is:

$$\ddot{\theta} = -\theta\left(\frac{4kR^2}{I + (m + m_p)R^2}\right)$$

Hints: assume small rotation θ of the pulley. The spring will stretch $(2\theta R)$ and pulley and weight will descend (θR). (See Programme 9, Frames 28 and 29.) Thus linear acceleration a of pulley and weight is $(\ddot{\theta} R)$. Two equations required for pulley: translation and rotation. The string forces on the two sides of the pulley will not be the same. In this example, ignore weight of hanging weight and pulley, and also initial static spring tension.

22

We now have to solve the differential equation. This means, finding some function of the variables which will satisfy the equation. So, if our equation involves a variable x and the second differential of x with respect to time, the solution to the equation will be another equation, relaxing x and t, and this second equation, the solution, can then be used to solve specific problems.

It is often possible to find more than one solution to a differential equation. Consider the equation:

$$\ddot{x} = 12t$$

If you write

$$x = 2t^3$$

and check by differentiating x twice, you will see that $x = 2t^3$ is a valid solution: in other words, it is a solution which will satisfy the equation. But this is not sufficient. If you had solved the equation by integrating twice, you would have included a constant of integration at each stage.

Differential equations of vibrating systems cannot be solved by direct integration. Therefore constants must be included in the solution—two constants, in the case of second-order equations. Such a solution is called the **general solution** of the equation. When solving problems of vibration, always begin with the general solution to the equation, and then evaluate the constants of integration from the data provided.

23

The solution of the equation:

$$\ddot{x} = -Cx$$

is:

$$x = A \, \sin(\sqrt{(C)}t + B)$$

and you can verify this for yourself by differentiating twice and proving that the original equation is satisfied. A and B are the two constants of integration we have specified as necessary for a general solution.

Another form of the solution is:

$$x = A \, \sin(\sqrt{(C)}t) + B \, \cos(\sqrt{(C)}t)$$

and yet another form is:

$$x = A \, e^{\sqrt{(C)}it} + B \, e^{-\sqrt{(C)}it}$$

although of course, the constants A and B would be different.

24

Of the three solutions in Frame 23, the first is the one we shall use. Knowing that the function represents the behaviour of a vibrating system, we should not be surprised to find that it is a sine function. If we are asked to sketch a graph of displacement against time for the vibrating body, our sketch would probably suggest a sine curve. You may, of course, provide yourself with some extra practice by solving some of the exercises and problems in this programme by using the second or third of these solutions.

There is a final adjustment to be made before starting some problems. The $(\sqrt{C})$ term can be avoided simply by adopting a squared term for our constant in the first place. So instead of calling the constant C, we shall call it ω^2. This is not mere perversity; we shall find later that there is a good reason for choosing the Greek letter ω (omega). For the present, this change implies firstly, that the differential equation of motion can always be expressed in the form:

$$\ddot{x} = -\omega^2 x$$

and secondly, that the general solution to this equation is:

$$x = A \sin(\omega t + B)$$

The equation, in the form above, probably reminds you of Simple Harmonic Motion, as indeed it should, as free undamped vibration is an example of Simple Harmonic Motion. We shall go a little more deeply into this when we discuss the interpretation of the general solution, in Frame 26.

Now, by referring back to Frames 8, 12, 13 and 14, obtain the general solutions to the equations of motion for:

(a) a weight of 4 kg on the end of a spring of stiffness 800 N m^{-1};
(b) a disc of moment of inertia 0.8 kg m^2 on the end of a torsional spring of stiffness 2.4 N m rad^{-1};
(c) a simple pendulum having a mass of 0.5 kg at the end of a string of length 1.8 m.
(d) a thin uniform steel rod of length 1.4 m and mass 2.2 kg, swinging in a vertical plane about an axis at one end. The moment of inertia of a thin uniform rod of mass m and length L about an axis through one end is $\frac{1}{3}mL^2$.

The general equation of motion is: $\ddot{x} = -\omega^2 x$

(a) For a mass m on the end of a spring of stiffness k, Frame 8 gave us the equation:

$$\ddot{x} = -(k/m)x$$

$$\therefore \quad \omega = \sqrt{(k/m)} = \sqrt{(800/4)} = 14.142 \ \text{s}^{-1}$$

So the solution is:

$$x = A \ \sin(14.142 \ t + B)$$

(b) For a disc of inertia I on the end of a torsional spring of stiffness k_t, Frame 12 gave:

$$\ddot{\theta} = -(k_t/I)\theta$$

$$\therefore \quad \omega = \sqrt{(k_t/I)} = \sqrt{(2.4/0/8)} = 1.732 \ \text{s}^{-1}$$

So the solution is:

$$\theta = A \ \sin(1.732 \ t + B)$$

(c) For the simple pendulum, from Frame 13:

$$\ddot{\theta} = -(g/L)\theta$$

$$\therefore \quad \omega = \sqrt{(9.81/1.8)} = 2.335 \ \text{s}^{-1}$$

and the solution therefore is:

$$\theta = A \ \sin(2.335 \ t + B)$$

(d) From Frame 14:

$$\omega = \sqrt{(mgh/I_o)}$$

h is the distance between mass centre, G and the pivot; in this case, $h = 0.7$ m because the mass centre is at the centre of the rod. $I_o = \frac{1}{3}mL^2$.

$$I_o = \frac{1}{3} \times 2.2 \times (1.4)^2 = 1.437 \ \text{kg m}^2$$

$$\therefore \quad \omega = \sqrt{((2.2 \times 9.81 \times 0.7)/1.437)} = 3.242 \ \text{s}^{-1}$$

and the solution is:

$$\theta = A \ \sin(3.242 \ t + B)$$

26

Recapitulating, a simple vibrating system of the types we have so far examined, has an equation of motion of the general form:

$$\ddot{x} = -\omega^2 x$$

which has the general solution

$$x = A \sin(\omega t + B)$$

where ω is a quantity determined by the system parameters (such as mass, spring stiffness, etc.) and A and B are integration constants, determined from specific conditions of displacement, velocity and acceleration at known times.

Here is a plot of the solution: a graph of x against t.

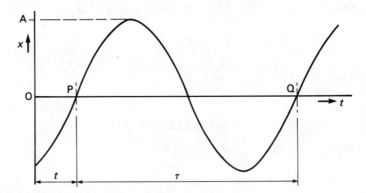

It is, as we might have expected, a sine curve, although the presence of the constant B means that the curve does not necessarily begin at the origin.

The time-increment τ shown on the graph is called the **period** of the motion, the time for one complete cycle of motion. We may determine τ as follows.

Calling the time t at point P, the time at Q must be $(t + \tau)$. At P and Q, $\sin(\omega t + B) = 0$. The argument of the function (i.e. the term in the brackets) must increase by 2π. So:

$$\omega t + B + 2\pi = \omega(t + \tau) + B$$

which gives

$$\tau = 2\pi/\omega$$

The reciprocal of period is called the **frequency**, n; this is the number of vibrations, or cycles in unit time.

$$n = 1/\tau = \omega/2\pi$$

The quantity ω itself is called the **circular frequency**. It is unfortunately sometimes abbreviated to frequency, particularly in advanced work.

The maximum value of x is clearly A; this is called the **amplitude** of the vibration.

Example. A weight of 1.5 kg hangs from a spring of stiffness 500 N m^{-1}. It is vibrating vertically, and at an instant ($t = 0$) the displacement is 20 mm downwards and the velocity 300 mm s^{-1} also downwards. Determine the period and amplitude of the motion, and calculate the least time before the displacement is zero.

We begin by writing the equation of motion. This is done exactly as in the first of the four exercises at the end of Frame 24. So refer to Frame 8.
  The equation is ... ?

$$\ddot{x} = -(k/m)x = -(500/1.5)x = -333.3x$$

The general form of the equation is $\ddot{x} = -\omega^2 x$.

$$\therefore \qquad \omega = \sqrt{(333.3)} = 18.26 \text{ s}^{-1}$$

(Notice the units of ω. Check yourself that the dimensions of $\sqrt{(k/m)}$ are T^{-1}.)
  Now we write the solution of the equation.

$$x = A \sin(18.26\, t + B)$$

The next part of the work—determining the two constants of integration—recalls Programme 5. The two required conditions are clearly stated in the question. But we shall require the velocity in order to substitute one of them. We find the velocity by differentiating x. Do this.

$$\dot{x} = 18.26A \cos(18.26\, t + B)$$

Substituting the first condition ($x = 20$ mm when $t = 0$) gives:

$$20 = A \sin(0 + B)$$

and substituting the second ($\dot{x} = 300$ mm s^{-1} when $t = 0$) gives:

$$+300 = 18.26A \cos(0 + B)$$

Velocity is positive, because it is downwards, as is displacement.
  Eliminate A and hence calculate B. You should find $B = 0.8831$ rad.

A cancels when we divide the equations.

$$\frac{20}{300} = \frac{\sin(B)}{18.26\,\cos(B)}$$

$$\therefore \quad \tan(B) = \frac{20 \times 18.26}{300} = 1.217$$

$$\therefore \quad B = 0.8831 \text{ rad}$$

Substituting this value in the expression for x:

$$20 = A\,\sin(0.8831)$$

$$\therefore \quad A = 20/0.7727 = 25.88 \text{ mm}$$

So the expression for displacement is finally:

$$x = (\mathbf{25.88\,\sin(18.26\,}t\mathbf{+0.8831)\ mm}$$

The required period is given by:

$$\tau = 2\pi/\omega = 2\pi/18.26 = \mathbf{0.3441 \ s}$$

The amplitude is A.

$$\text{amplitude} = \mathbf{25.88 \ mm}$$

To find the least time in which the displacement becomes zero, we equate x to 0.

$$0 = 25.88\,\sin(18.26t + 0.8831)$$

from which it is seen that the sine term must be zero. For t to have a positive value, the *least* value of $(18.26t + 0.8831)$ must therefore be π.

$$\therefore \quad 18.26t = \pi - 0.8831 = 2.2585$$

$$\therefore \quad t = \mathbf{0.1237 \ s}$$

A few reminders and remarks. Firstly, all angles are to be in **radians**, not degrees. Secondly, although you should normally work in metres, kilograms and seconds, one may be allowed an exception in this example. Substituting the values of displacement and velocity given, results simply in the expression for x being in millimetres, not metres. Similarly, if we write the final expression for $\dot{x}$, this must be in millimetres per second. Thus:

$$\dot{x} = (18.26 \times 25.88)\,\cos(18.26\,t + 0.8831)$$

$$= (\mathbf{472.57\,\cos(18.26\,}t\mathbf{+0.8831))\ mm\ s}^{-1}$$

If you plot the expression for x, you will find that the sine curve begins about half-way through the first half-cycle.

31

Example. A simple pendulum has a length of 2.5 m. The pendulum is drawn to one side, until the string makes an angle of 6° with the vertical. It is released from rest in this position. Determine (a) the time for the pendulum to reach the lowest point of swing; (b) the velocity at the lowest point of swing; (c) the period, and frequency.

Follow this procedure.

1. Determine ω. (Refer to Frames 13 and 24 if you have forgotten.)
2. Write the expression for displacement θ. (See Frame 23. For x read θ.)
3. Differentiate this to obtain the velocity.
4. Determine the two conditions to find constants A and B.
5. Substitute the conditions, and thus find A and B.
6. Write the complete expressions for displacement and velocity.
7. Substitute $\theta = 0$ in expression for displacement, and find t.
8. Substitute this value of t in expression for velocity.
9. For period and frequency, refer to Frame 26.

A brief solution follows.

32

1. $\omega = \sqrt{(g/L)} = \sqrt{(9.81/2.5)} = \mathbf{1.981 \ s^{-1}}$
2. $\theta = A \sin(1.981t + B)$
3. $\dot{\theta} = 1.981A \cos(1.981t + B)$
4. The conditions are: when $t = 0$, $\theta = 6° = 0.1047$ rad
$\qquad\qquad\qquad\quad$ when $t = 0$, $\dot{\theta} = 0$ (released from rest).
5. Substituting in displacement and velocity:

$$0.1047 = A \sin(B); \ 0 = 1.981A \cos(B)$$

Second expression shows that $B = \pi/2$.

$$\sin(\pi/2) = 1. \text{ Thus } A = 0.1047 \text{ rad} = 6°$$

6. $\theta = 0.1047 \sin(1.981t + \pi/2)$ rad
$\dot{\theta} = (0.1047 \times 1.981) \cos(1.981t + \pi/2)$ rad s^{-1}
7. $0 = 0.1047 \sin(1.981t + \pi/2)$
$\therefore \qquad 1.981t + \pi/2 = \pi$ (for least +ve value of t)
$\therefore \qquad\qquad t = \mathbf{0.793 \ s}$
8. $\dot{\theta}_{0.793} = (0.147 \times 1.981) \cos(1.981 \times 0.793 + \pi/2)$
$\qquad = (0.1047 \times 1.981) \times \cos(\pi)$
$\qquad = \mathbf{-0.2074 \ rad \ s^{-1}} = \mathbf{11.88 \ degrees \ s^{-1}}$
9. $\tau = 2\pi/\omega = \mathbf{3.172 \ s}. \ n = 1/\tau = \mathbf{0.315 \ cycles \ s^{-1}}$

33

This diagram, used to illustrate Simple Harmonic Motion, may be familiar.

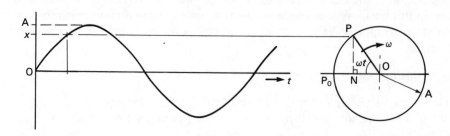

The circle on the right has a radius A which is rotating at an angular speed ω in a clockwise direction. Thus, if it starts in the position OP_0, in time t, it will rotate through an angle (ωt) radians to the position OP. Let x be the length of the perpendicular PN. From the right-angled triangle, it is seen that:

$$x = A \sin(\omega t)$$

This circle diagram illustrates the motion of a vibrating body, although for the sake of simplicity, it illustrates the function above instead of the more general function $x = A \sin(\omega t + B)$. Alongside the circle is the graph of x against t, which of course is a simple sine curve.

The diagram clearly illustrates the period of the motion. Since the radius rotates at a constant speed of ω, it will take a time of $(2\pi/\omega)$ seconds to traverse a full revolution of (2π) radians.

The diagram also explains why the constant (ω^2) was chosen when formulating the general equation of motion in Frame 24. ω is the symbol generally used to represent an angular velocity, which is what it does in this diagram. It is unfortunate that the term 'frequency' is used for ω, and for this reason, it is sometimes confused with the frequency, n: the number of cycles per second. The terms are of course not the same. The correct full name for ω is the **circular frequency**, although both n and ω have the same dimension of $[T^{-1}]$. Frequency, n, and circular frequency, ω, are related by the expression

$$\omega = 2\pi n$$

34

PROBLEM

1. Calculate the frequency, n, and the circular frequency, ω, for (a) a weight of mass 3 kg hanging from a spring of stiffness 96 N m^{-1}; (b) a simple pendulum of length 0.249 m; (c) a compound pendulum consisting of a thin uniform bar of length 1.9 m and mass 8.6 kg, swinging on a pivot at one end. [*Ans. (a) 0.90 Hz; (b) 1.00 Hz; (c) 0.443 Hz.*]

35

Here is a summary of the work in this programme so far.

1. All simple vibrating systems in free undamped response can be shown to conform to the equation of motion: $\ddot{x} = -\omega^2 x$ where x is the displacement (linear or angular) and (ω^2) is a constant determined by the system parameters (e.g. mass, spring stiffness).
2. The equation of motion has the general solution: $x = A\sin(\omega t + B)$ where A and B are constants of integration, determined by knowledge of specific values of displacement, velocity or acceleration at specific times.
3. Velocity $\dot{x}$ and acceleration $\ddot{x}$ are given by:

$$\dot{x} = A\omega\cos(\omega t + B)$$

$$\ddot{x} = -A\omega^2\sin(\omega t + B) = -\omega^2 x$$

4. The free response is a sinusoidal motion.
   Frequency, $n = \omega/2\pi$ cycles per second, or Hertz (Hz)
   Period, $\tau = 1/n = 2\pi/\omega$ seconds per cycle
   Amplitude, A, is the maximum displacement.

36

Here is a procedure for the solving of problems of vibration.

1. Adopt a sign convention.
2. Assume a small displacement of the mass-element in the positive direction.
3. Draw the free-body diagram of the mass-element.
4. Write the equation of motion ($\Sigma(F) = ma$ for linear motion, $\Sigma(M) = I\alpha$ for angular motion) having regard to the sign convention. When there is more than one mass-element, write equations for all, and compatibility equations for the accelerations, thus arriving at a single 'system' equation of motion.
5. Arrange the equation into the form:

$$\ddot{x} = -(\omega^2)x$$

6. Either evaluate (ω^2) from knowledge of the system parameters, or evaluate ω from knowledge of vibration frequency, and use the result to determine any unknown system parameters.
7. When specific values of displacement, velocity or acceleration are required for specific values of time, the constants of integration A and B must be determined by applying known conditions of motion and thus obtaining the particular expressions for x, $\dot{x}$ and $\ddot{x}$.

37

PROBLEMS

1. A loaded mine-cage has a total mass of 2800 kg. It is supported by a steel cable which is known to extend by 9 mm under a tensile load of 10 kN. Calculate the frequency of vertical vibration. Neglect the mass of the cable itself. [*Ans. 3.17 Hz.*]
   Hint: treat the cable as a 'spring'; calculate the stiffness from the extension data given.

2. A horizontal steel bar has one end clamped in a vice. From the free end, a weight hangs vertically, connected to the bar by a light string. The weight is observed to cause a static deflection at the end of the bar of 12.4 mm. Calculate the maximum amplitude of vertical vibration of the system such that the string should not go slack at any time. [*Ans. 12.4 mm.*]
   Hints: treat as a simple spring–mass system (Frame 9), calculating k from the static deflection due to weight. When vibrating, the maximum possible downward force on the mass will be (mg) (because the string cannot push downwards). Hence maximum acceleration of the mass will be (g).

3.

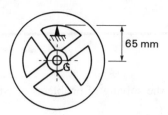

65 mm

A symmetrical wheel has a mass of 11.6 kg. It is swung on a knife-edge which is 65 mm from the wheel centre G, and caused to vibrate over a small amplitude. It takes 15.1 seconds to complete 20 swings. Determine the moment of inertia of the wheel about the central axis. [*Ans. 0.05779 kg m².*]
   Hint: Frame 14. Determine I_o and use the Parallel Axis theorem to find I_G.

4. A symmetrical disc is mounted axially on one end of a steel rod of length 0.9 m and diameter 6 mm. The other end of the rod is clamped in a vice, the rod being vertical, with the disc at the bottom. The disc has a moment of inertia about its central axis of 0.065 kg m². The disc is given a small angular displacement and released, causing it to execute torsional vibration. It is observed that 20 oscillations take 9.5 seconds. Calculate G, the Modulus of Rigidity of the steel rod. [*Ans. 80.45×10^9 N m⁻².*]
   Hints: use the formula $T/J = G\theta/L$ from stress analysis; torsional stiffness k_t is $T/\theta = GJ/L$. See Frames 11 and 12.

38

A unique feature of an undamped free-response system is that no energy is added to the system, once vibration is initiated, and no energy is taken from it, because there is no friction, or other resisting force. Such systems are called **conservative systems**. In a conservative system, the energy is continually changing from one sort to another, but the total energy remains constant. In a spring–mass system, energy is continually being changed from kinetic to strain energy and back again; in a pendulum, it is changing from kinetic to potential and back again. This fact enables us to arrive at the Equation of Motion in another way.

We shall re-examine the spring–mass system analysed in Frame 6. The diagram is repeated here for convenience, although this time, we show additionally, a positive velocity $\dot{x}$.

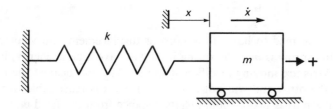

For the instant shown, the total energy E is the sum of the strain energy and the kinetic energy. Strain energy for a spring of stiffness k is $\frac{1}{2}kx^2$. (See Programme 7.)

$$\therefore \quad E = \tfrac{1}{2}kx^2 + \tfrac{1}{2}m(\dot{x})^2$$

and because this quantity is constant, if we differentiate it with respect to time, the answer must be zero:

$$\therefore \quad \tfrac{1}{2}k(2x)(\dot{x}) + \tfrac{1}{2}m(2\dot{x})(\ddot{x}) = 0$$

which simplifies to:

$$kx + m\ddot{x} = 0$$

or:

$$\ddot{x} = -(k/m)x$$

which is the equation of motion we obtained before.

There is no advantage in using this method in this particular case, but the principle of energy can be used with advantage to obtain a solution to problems which otherwise could be much more difficult to solve. In the analysis of the simple spring–mass system, it was assumed that the spring had no mass. This means that the expression for frequency would only be accurate if the mass of the spring was small in comparison with the mass m on the end of it. For a large massive spring carrying a relatively small mass, it would be inaccurate.

In the following frame, we shall see how the principle of Conservation of Energy may be used to take into account the mass of the spring itself.

39

The diagram illustrates a very large spring carrying a small mass.

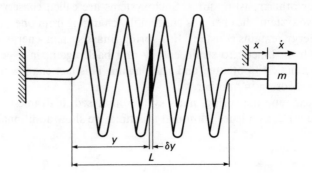

The mass m is assumed to have instantaneous displacement and velocity, x and $\dot{x}$. The mass of the spring is m_s. The spring itself will have kinetic energy; it is moving, but different parts are moving at different speeds. The end nearest the mass will be moving at $\dot{x}$; the other end will not move at all. So it is reasonable to assume that the velocity of a part is proportional to its distance from the fixed end. An element of the spring, of length δy is shown, a distance y from the end; the velocity at this point is $\dot{x}(y/L)$ where L is the length of the whole spring. The mass of the element, assuming the spring to be uniform along its length, will be $(m_s\delta y/L)$. The kinetic energy of the element, $\delta(\mathrm{KE})$, is therefore:

$$\delta(\mathrm{KE}) = \tfrac{1}{2}(m_s\delta y/L)(\dot{x}(y/L))^2$$

So the total kinetic energy of the whole system will be:

$$\mathrm{KE} = \tfrac{1}{2}m\dot{x}^2 + \Sigma(\tfrac{1}{2}(m_s\delta y/L)(\dot{x}(y/L))^2)$$

The summation is along the spring; for this purpose, all terms except y can be regarded as constant.

$$\therefore \quad \mathrm{KE} = \tfrac{1}{2}m\dot{x}^2 + \tfrac{1}{2}(m_s/L)(\dot{x}/L)^2\int_0^L (y^2\,\mathrm{d}y)$$

$$= \tfrac{1}{2}m\dot{x}^2 + \tfrac{1}{2}(m_s/L)(\dot{x}/L)^2[\tfrac{1}{3}y^3]_0^L$$

$$= \tfrac{1}{2}m\dot{x}^2 + \tfrac{1}{2}m_s\dot{x}^2/L^3(\tfrac{1}{3}L^3)$$

$$= \tfrac{1}{2}m\dot{x}^2 + \tfrac{1}{2}m_s\dot{x}^2(\tfrac{1}{3})$$

$$= \tfrac{1}{2}\dot{x}^2(m + \tfrac{1}{3}m_s)$$

which suggests that the mass of the spring may be taken into account in calculating frequency by adding one-third of it to the mass attached to it.

Example. A coiled spring has a stiffness of 250 N m^{-1} and its mass is 1.4 kg. A body of mass m is attached to one end of the spring, the other being attached to a rigid mounting. Calculate the frequency of vibration of the system, both allowing for, and neglecting the mass of the spring, when m is (a) 8 kg; (b) 0.2 kg. Calculate the percentage error in each case resulting from neglecting the spring mass.

In Frame 8 we showed that for a simple spring–mass system, $\omega = \sqrt{(k/m)}$. To allow for the spring mass we must now modify this formula to:

$$\omega = \sqrt{\{k/(m + \tfrac{1}{3}m_s)\}}$$

(a) Allowing for spring mass:

$$\omega = \sqrt{\{250/(8 + \tfrac{1}{3} \times 1.4)\}} = 5.433 \text{ s}^{-1}$$

$$\therefore \quad n = \omega/2\pi = \textbf{0.865 Hz}$$

Neglecting spring mass:

$$\omega = \sqrt{(250/8)} = 5.590 \text{ s}^{-1}$$

$$\therefore \quad n = 5.590/2\pi = \textbf{0.890 Hz}$$

$$\text{Error} = 0.890 - 0.865 = 0.025 \text{ Hz}$$

$$\text{Percentage error} = 100 \times 0.025/0.865 = \textbf{2.89\%}$$

(b) Allowing for spring mass:

$$\omega = \sqrt{\{250/(0.2 + \tfrac{1}{3} \times 1.4)\}} = 19.365 \text{ s}^{-1}$$

$$\therefore \quad n = 19.365/2\pi = \textbf{3.082 Hz}$$

Neglecting spring mass:

$$\omega = \sqrt{(250/0.2)} = 35.36 \text{ s}^{-1}$$

$$\therefore \quad n = 35.36/2\pi = \textbf{5.628 Hz}$$

$$\text{Error} = 5.628 - 3.082 = 2.546 \text{ Hz}$$

$$\text{Percentage error} = 100 \times 2.546/3.082 = \textbf{82.6\%}$$

The conclusion is that for a large mass on a small spring, one may safely ignore the spring mass in calculating the vibration frequency, but that for a small mass on a large spring, ignoring the spring mass would result in a very inaccurate estimate of frequency. The terms 'large' and 'small' in this context are of course relative, but if, for example, the error resulting from neglecting the spring mass is not to exceed 1%, you should be able to show for yourself that the mass of the spring should not be greater than 0.0603 times the mass attached to it. Or putting it the other way round, the mass should be at least 16.58 times the mass of the spring. For the example above, this would mean a mass of 23.22 kg. Check for yourself that this gives approximately a 1% error.

PROBLEMS

1. A machine has a mass of 25 000 kg. It is mounted on four springs, the load shared equally between them. Calculate the required spring stiffness if the natural frequency of vertical vibration is not to exceed 3 Hz. If the amplitude of vibration is 5 mm, calculate the maximum velocity and acceleration of the machine, and the maximum load on one spring. [*Ans. 2221 kN m^{-1}; 94.25 mm s^{-1}; 1.776 m s^{-2}; 72.42 kN.*] *Hint:* maximum force in spring = amplitude × stiffness + static weight.

2. A particle moves on a straight path with SHM with a frequency of 0.05 Hz. At a particular instant, it is 1 m to the right of the path centre, with a velocity of 0.5 m s^{-1} also to the right. Obtain the equation of motion of the particle. Calculate its amplitude, the least time for the particle to come to rest, and the least time for it to return to the path centre. [*Ans. x = 1.879 sin (0.3142t + 0.561); 1.879 m; 3.213 s; 8.213 s.*]

   Hint: see Frame 27 *et seq.*

3.

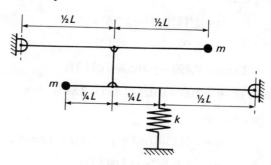

   Two rods of negligible mass each carrying a single concentrated mass m are connected by a third rod of negligible mass, as shown. A spring of stiffness k is connected to the lower rod. Show that the natural frequency of small oscillations of the system is given by:

$$n = \frac{1}{2\pi} \sqrt{\left(\frac{k}{13m}\right)}$$

   Hints: see Frame 18 *et seq.* Assume small displacement θ of lower rod and show that displacement of upper rod is $(1\frac{1}{2}\theta)$. Assume force F in the linking rod.

4. A mine-cage weighs 20 kN. It hands from a cable having a mass of 3.8 kg per metre. A test on a 1 metre length shows that a load of 1 kN produces a stretch of 0.032 mm. Determine the frequency of vertical vibration of the cage–cable system when 1700 m of cable support the cage: (a) neglecting the mass of the cable; (b) allowing for the cable mass. [*Ans. (a) 0.478 Hz; (b) 0.333 Hz.*]

INDEX